Medicine at Queen's

Medicine at Queen's 1854–1920

A Peculiarly Happy Relationship

A. A. TRAVILL

Faculty of Medicine,
Queen's University

The Hannah Institute
for the History of Medicine

© Faculty of Medicine, Queen's University
ISBN 0-88911-506-0

Printed on acid-free paper in Canada

Canadian Cataloguing in Publication Data

Travill, A.A.
Medicine at Queen's, 1854–1920
ISBN 0-88911-506-0
I. Queen's University (Kingston, Ont.). Faculty
of Medicine – History. I. Queen's University (Kingston,
Ont.). Faculty of Medicine. I. Title.
R749.Q42T73 1988   610'.7'1171372   C87-090211-3

To the deans of Queen's medical faculty,
to all those who have been proud to be
associated with the faculty over the years,
and to Sheila

Contents

Illustrations

Foreword

Anthony A. Travill was born and educated in England. After four years of aircrew service in the RAF 1943-47, he studied medicine at the London Hospital, University of London, where he qualified in 1954. After his internship, he undertook family practice in Coventry from 1955-57 and then emigrated to Canada, where after a year of residency training and a further year in family practice in Orillia, Ontario, Dr Travill decided on an academic career. Two years later, in 1961, he earned the M.Sc.(Med.) degree in the Department of Anatomy of Queen's University at Kingston and joined the faculty of Creighton University in Omaha as an assistant professor.

Dr Travill was soon recognized as a stimulating and scholarly teacher of anatomy. He was attracted back to the Department of Anatomy at Queen's in 1964 where he has remained until the present. From 1969 to 1978, he served as professor and head of the department.

Throughout his professional life Dr Travill has shown an informed interest in the history of medicine – an interest which has illuminated his teaching and led to his appointment as faculty historian. It was only natural then that he should have become absorbed in the rich historical heritage of Queen's Medical School – fitting and almost inevitable that he should have decided to chronicle it for his colleagues. And a fascinating chronicle it is, for the roots of Queen's Medicine are thoroughly intermingled with the roots of medicine in the struggling immigrant culture of pre-Confederation Upper Canada. The volume tells the story to 1920, showing medicine, Queen's University, and Canadian society all emerging into the modern era with the help of a memorable cast of characters.

The general reader will find much of interest in the volume. The Queen's medical graduate will find it a delight.

Kingston, Ontario,   D. Laurence Wilson
17 November 1987

Preface

Queen's University's medical school is over 130 years old. This book recounts the first half of its story: the foundation of the faculty and its first twelve years; its autonomous existence; the 26-year affiliation of the Royal College of Physicians and Surgeons of Kingston (the Royal) with Queen's University; the short-lived but highly successful experiment in women's medical education at the "Royal" and the Women's Medical College (the first founded in Canada); the "organic union" established between Queen's and the Royal in 1892; the development of the faculty during the first decade of the twentieth century; and finally, the faculty's contribution to the Great War and the problems which arose in the aftermath.

At each stage of its growth certain faculty guided the school's destiny, directing its internal organization and external relationship with the university and Kingston's hospitals – Kingston General Hospital, the Hotel Dieu and Kingston Psychiatric Hospital. Others, according to their talents, defined the curriculum, taught their subjects and maintained research programmes. All carried on their academic vocations while caring for the acute and chronically ill of Kingston. The contributions of faculty members and students to the full stature of Queen's University have been incorporated into this history because it was these men and women who ensured the longevity of Queen's medical school – its major success. In Principal Grant's own words, it was the faculty and students, who, over the years, ensured "a peculiarly happy relationship" with the university.

Acknowledgments

In 1979, Queen's celebrated the 125th anniversary of its medical school and to mark the occasion a short illustrated history was prepared.[1] Its publication led Dr Stuart Vandewater to suggest that I write a fuller account of our faculty's history. I accepted with some trepidation but now must thank him for the idea because of the pleasure it has given me over the last few years. Similarly I appreciate the support and encouragement received from Deans T.J. Boag and D. Laurence Wilson.

It would have been almost impossible to have done the necessary research and brought the work to publication without financial support. The Faculty of Medicine, Queen's University, acknowledges gratefully the financial support given this book by Associated Medical Services, Inc. and the Hannah Institute for the History of Medicine. I appreciate the courteous advice of Dr "Pat" Paterson, executive director of the Hannah Institute, as well as the help provided by Mrs Sheila Snelgrove in facilitating the book's publication.

Mrs Anne Macdermaid, chief archivist, and her colleagues at Queen's University Archives have not only provided most of the material for writing the story, but also, their courteous scholarship made "going to the archives" such a pleasurable experience. For their suffering uncomplainingly my pestering curiosity, I thank them sincerely.

This account of the faculty's history would have been markedly different without the persistent industry of Lynn Marks and Martha Bala. They often brought to light facts previously passed over by others. I would like to acknowledge with gratitude my debt to them for their commitment to the project. Mrs Eleanor Teepell and Mrs Carol Cattermole deciphered the original handwritten version and typed many drafts with skill and patience. For their sorely tried equanimity, I am deeply grateful.

While writing the earlier versions of this history I was fortunate to receive guidance and encouragement from Professor E.A. Walker. For his generous and patient advice I am particularly indebted, and sincerely thank him.

If the reader enjoys reliving the trials, tribulations and triumphs of Queen's Medical Faculty as much as I have in setting them down, I feel sure they will wish to join me in acknowledging our indebtedness to Dr Mary Baldwin's editorial skill. Through her ability to act concurrently as shepherd and sergeant major, she has kept me on the straight and narrow, enabling me to bring to the reader this story. To her I express my special thanks.

Finally, I wish to thank Philip Cercone, Susanne McAdam and Colleen Gray for their professional expertise which patiently guided the last laborious stages of this book's gestation.

Medicine at Queen's

CHAPTER ONE

Medicine in Upper Canada and Kingston before 1854

For the first hundred years after Count Frontenac landed at Cataraqui on the morning of 1 June 1673 and established a colonial settlement, the medical needs of the residents were served like any other frontier outpost. Military authorities supplied doctors if a sufficiently large garrison occupied Fort Frontenac (Kingston's original name) and when no doctors were available, a priest or trader attended the sick or wounded as best as possible.

After Canada became a British colony in 1763, the fort received two official surgeons. The United Empire Loyalists who fled from the rebellious American colonies brought to the eastern end of Lake Ontario's northern shore a degree of civic sophistication beyond that usually found close to a fortified trading post. The surrounding land was surveyed, apportioned, and granted for homesteading; the first township settled was called Kingston in 1788. It and other communities grew and established communications with Montreal and Quebec City. Commanding as it did the junction of Lake Ontario and the St Lawrence River, Kingston became the most significant forwarding port and municipality of the region and a strategic naval base and arsenal for the whole of Upper Canada.

By 1800 the population of Kingston had grown to about 1,000. Little is known of those who served the medical needs of the small community prior to the War of 1812 and the establishment of newspapers. Military hospitals had existed in or close to Kingston from the earliest days of the British settlement. The largest was located at the foot of what is now Brock Street, between Fort Frontenac to the north and the future Market Battery to the south. When no civilian doctors were available, the settlers successfully petitioned military authorities to allow them to take advantage of the garrison's hospital facilities. Permission was immediately granted for the treatment of both settlers and Indians by the resident medical officer.[1]

Between the end of the War of 1812 and the opening of the medical department of Queen's College in 1854, Kingston grew in size and population. Unfortunately, the decline in naval and military activity in the area was accompanied by a corresponding decrease in the military's direct contribution to the health-care of the Kingston population. The loss of this unofficial medical help was particularly grievous because of the almost continual flow into Upper Canada of emigrants from the more destitute parts of the British Isles – disbanded soldiers and sailors, stonemasons and other workers released on the completion of the Rideau Canal. To look after a population which grew from 2,000 at the end of the war to about 10,000 in 1850, a small but steady stream of medical men began to set up practice in Kingston.

Initially, most of them came to British North America as surgeons in His Majesty's Army or Navy. When discharged – on half pay, if they were lucky – these commissioned surgeons, surgeons' assistants or surgeons' mates often preferred the rugged life and opportunities in Upper Canada to the risks of trying to establish themselves in a medical community at home that was often less than appreciative of veterans returning from the American or Napoleonic wars. Kingston was particularly popular with many of these half-pay men because of the cordial manner in which the citizens treated them while they were stationed in the town.[2]

The cholera epidemics of 1832 and 1834 proved catastrophic for Kingston. During the early part of 1832 physicians in Upper Canada had hoped that the Asiatic cholera which had swept over Europe would not cross the Atlantic. Alas, on 8 June it reached Quebec City and on the eleventh, Montreal, "where it burst out like a volcano"; by the fifteenth two were dead in Prescott. Before the epidemic claimed its first victim in Kingston on 17 June, both municipal and military authorities had been spurred into feverish activity. Dr Thomas W. Robison, health officer, sent out orders that all garbage was to be carted away, pigs to be taken into the country and the whole town cleaned up. The military scrubbed and whitewashed its barracks and small hospitals. Married soldiers and their families were hastily evacuated from Kingston to a newly erected camp on Fort Henry hill and the barrack gates were shut.[3]

In town the first onslaught of the epidemic lasted two weeks. Business was suspended, ships were forbidden to enter the harbour, and the yellow quarantine flag flew on the waterfront close to the marketplace. The city united against the common enemy – in the

words of Surgeon Walter Henry of the 66th Regiment (the Berk-
shires), then stationed in Kingston: "the medical men and Clergy of
all persuasions vied with each other in the fearless discharge of their
respective dangerous duties; and the exertions of all classes were
judicious, manly and energetic: for the genuine English spirit shewed
itself, as usual, undaunted in the midst of peril, and rising above it."[4]

Dr James Sampson, Kingston's most renowned physician during
the first half of the nineteenth century, led the city's fight against the
cholera epidemic. Forty-two at this time, he was well on the way to
consolidating his reputation. Sampson spent his early years in his
father's vicarage in County Armagh, Northern Ireland. He matriculated at Trinity College, Dublin, and enrolled in medical classes at the
Middlesex Hospital in London. He also walked the wards of the York
Military Hospital in Chelsea. In 1811, at the age of twenty-two, he
was appointed general service hospital assistant. After a further six-
month military indoctrination, he was promoted to assistant surgeon
in the 85th Foot and posted to Canada. The following year he was
transferred to the Royal Newfoundland Fencibles.[5] While the regiment was stationed in Upper Canada, Sampson participated in the
attack on Sackett's Harbour at the height of the War of 1812. During
the summer of 1814 he played a significant role when the British sloop
Nancy was blown up in the Nottawasaga River near Penetanguishene,
and the subsequent capture of the American *Tigress* and *Scorpion* off
Fort Michilimackinac. On 31 August 1815, Dr Sampson was transferred to the 104th Foot stationed in Kingston. In 1817, his regiment
was disbanded and he was demobilized on half pay. Between the end
of the war and his demobilization, Dr Sampson married Eliza,
daughter of Chief Justice Winslow.[6]

For the first few years in civilian life Sampson practised as a
surgeon in the Niagara Peninsula. Here he became concerned about
unlicensed practitioners operating in the district. Through a friend he
approached the attorney general for information on how to collect
evidence to proceed against the quacks. This interest in maintaining
professional standards and his friendship with a senior military
colleague, Dr James Macaulay, probably brought him to the attention
of the lieutenant-governor, who, in 1822, appointed him to the newly
formed provincial medical board.

The financial rewards of a half-pay surgeon on the Niagara frontier
appear to have been too meagre for Dr Sampson's needs. Perhaps
remembering Kingston's affluence in 1815, he returned there with his
wife and child. For the first year or two his practice grew slowly.
Every young practitioner who has just opened his own practice
understands how Dr Sampson felt when he wrote: "If you saw the

affability which I put on with the riff-raff here, you would accuse me of familiarity with my inferiors. As for the 'first society' (who are not those by whom I most thrive), I cannot aspire to their patronage till I own a wharf or have ten shares in the Bank of Upper Canada."[7]

Soon, however, Kingston's upper classes began to appreciate him. In 1826, he was recalled to the colours on full pay active service as a staff surgeon. However, he was able to decline the order to report for duty because twelve of the most affluent families – the Tory establishment – in town banded together and covenanted to pay him £25 each per annum for life. The guaranteed annuity of £300 compensated for the retirement half pay he had forfeited by remaining in Kingston.

The assiduity with which he followed his profession quickly earned him a reputation as a skilled surgeon. His affability and availability for house calls, in town or the country, in good or bad weather, assured him a successful practice. During the short time that Kingston was the country's capital, Governors-General Sydenham, Bagot, and Metcalfe were his patients.

Sampson was a strong, tall, handsome man, described as "very clever, if abrupt, very kind, if very blunt," and as "personally responsible for establishing the tradition of medical excellence in Kingston."[8] His high standard of patient care set an example for all other medical men in town.

During the cholera epidemics, Surgeon Henry was impressed, as a fellow professional, with Dr Sampson's compassionate concern for his patients and his willingness to employ a regimen for choleric dehydration well in advance of routine British or European treatment (consisting of combinations of calomel (mercurous chloride), laudanum (opium) and castor oil). He wrote:

We had all heard wonderful accounts of the effects of transfusion of saline fluid into the veins, and Dr Sampson, the principal practitioner in Kingston, and a man of talent, was determined, as well as myself, to give it a fair trial ... We used it in twenty bad cases, but unsuccessfully in all though the first effect in every instance was the apparent restoration of the powers of life; and in one remarkable case of a poor emigrant from Yorkshire was protracted seven days by constant pumping. Here the man almost instantaneously recovered voice, strength, colour and appetite; and Sampson and myself, seeing this miraculous change, almost believed we had discovered the new elixir of life in the humble shape of salt and water.[9]

The part Dr Sampson played in the cholera epidemics in Kingston in the 1830s foreshadows his leadership in the fledgling medical school twenty years later, in both scientific and humanistic medicine.

Despondency succeeded the elation of the 1840s in Kingston. The city, no longer the colony's capital, had seen, by the end of the decade, if not precisely captains and kings, certainly governor-generals and civil servants come and go. Kingston's advantage as one of Her Majesty's dockyards was moribund. Moreover railways were by-passing the city and weakening its economic position as the Great Lakes's forwarding port. Fortunately, new settlers combined with those loyal citizens who remained through the desperate forties, combatted the last of the great epidemics to sweep across Upper Canada and strengthened its pioneer vigour. Typhus fever struck Kingston with the arrival of the first boatloads of Irish immigrants in the spring of 1847. Again all the medical and administrative apparatus of the city was harnessed. This time Drs Sampson and Robison received support from a team of fairly recently qualified doctors who had decided to settle in Kingston. Three of these men – Dr John Stewart, Dr John R. Dickson, and Dr Horatio Yates – joined Dr Sampson a few years later to found Kingston's medical school.

MEDICAL EDUCATION IN
UPPER CANADA

Following the Battle of the Plains of Abraham in 1759, the Treaty of Paris in 1763 formally ceded Quebec to Britain. In 1791, the province was divided into Upper and Lower Canada. Upper Canada was in time to become Ontario. Although sparsely populated, various laws to license the practice of medicine, first in Quebec, then Upper Canada, were considered in 1794, 1795, 1806, 1808, and 1815 until the establishment of the Medical Board of Upper Canada in 1818.[10] Apart from a few ill-educated quacks or charlatans, the majority of military or loyalist doctors in Upper Canada had entered the profession following a complete university medical education, by holding a military commission or by a combined apprenticeship with some attendance at a proprietary or university medical school. The conscientious master or "preceptor," under whom many received practical experience, required his apprentice to continue to improve his Latin, to keep the office clean and tidy, to wash bottles, and to run errands. Gradually he taught his "boy" to mix medicines, to compound pills and powders, and to lay on plasters. More experienced apprentices assisted at amputations: dosing the patient with laudanum and spirits before the operation, holding the limb during it, and bandaging the stump afterwards. They were also taught the techniques of

blistering, cupping, and bleeding. The apprentice attended his preceptor on his house calls or walked through the hospital wards as the
surgeon's "dresser" or the physician's clerk.

Because of the establishment of the Medical Board of Upper
Canada early in the colony's history, a full apprenticeship never
became a substitute for medical school in Canada to the same extent
that it did in pre-Revolutionary America. The Medical Board set
standards for medicine, surgery, midwifery, and Latin, making it
impossible for prospective doctors to choose apprenticeship as the
only means of entering the medical profession. The Medical Board
required young men wishing to practise medicine to provide, at the
examination, first, evidence of a good grounding in Latin, to ensure
understanding of the pharmacopeia and, second, certificates of attendance at a recognized medical school which attested that at least two
full sessions, usually October to April, had been spent in studying
anatomy, medicine, surgery and midwifery.[11] Before the foundation of
McGill's medical faculty in the Montreal General Hospital in 1824,
such experience could only be gained in Europe or the larger
American cities – Philadelphia, New York or Boston.

Because the Medical Board cut short apprenticeship as a major
component of medical education, it never became a source of abuse.
Only medical men in the larger Canadian communities, with both
medical and civic reputations – men such as Rolph and Duncombe in
the Talbot settlement, Widmer and Diehl in York or Sampson in
Kingston – were considered of sufficient stature to take apprentices.
This they did, not to enhance their incomes, but because they
recognized that this was the only way Upper Canada, in the short
run, could meet its needs from among its own people until the
establishment of bona fide medical schools.

Only Dr Sampson appears to have played a significant role as a
medical teacher in Kingston before the foundation of Queen's University in 1841. When he was appointed a member of the Medical Board
of Upper Canada in 1822, he already had a substantial reputation
from his work as a surgeon with the Royal Newfoundland Fencibles.
Since he was the sole Kingston man on the board of examiners, it was
not unnatural that the leading citizens should send their sons to him
as apprentices. A number of Kingston practitioners in the generation
before the establishment of Queen's Medical Department, including
Drs Robison and Horatio Yates, were, at one time or another,
apprentices of Dr Sampson.

Dr John Rolph and Dr Charles Duncombe made the first attempt to
establish a medical school in Upper Canada. During the summer of
1824 they suggested to Col Thomas Talbot, whose position as land

agent for the region between Lake Erie and the Thames River made him a powerful figure in the growing settlement, the idea of establishing a medical school at St Thomas. Notwithstanding the limited resources available in sparsely settled Upper Canada, Rolph and Duncombe at once enrolled twelve students in their school. It unfortunately operated for only two years – the doctors became involved in William Lyon Mackenzie's politics and lost Colonel Talbot's support.[12]

In Toronto, the energetic Rev. Dr John Strachan, leader of the Anglican party in Upper Canada, urged Sir Peregrine Maitland, the lieutenant governor, to establish a medical faculty in conjunction with the recently chartered King's College (1827). While this suggestion was being considered, Dr Rolph moved to York and, in 1832, again opened a private medical school. It met with immediate success, but it too was abandoned because of Dr Rolph's inability to keep out of politics – this time Mackenzie's rebellion of 1837 caused Dr Rolph's precipitous departure from Toronto (formerly York until 1834).

The president and council of King's College in 1837 proposed a practical organization for the university: six divisions or faculties, one, medical science, was itself to be further subdivided into six departments. This plan was never implemented because of the rebellion. However, during the short life of the Medical Board when it presumptuously assumed the title of the College of Physicians and Surgeons of Upper Canada, Toronto's leading physicians made another serious attempt to start a medical school at King's College. As before, it came to nothing, this time because Queen Victoria disallowed the college's charter in 1840 on the advice of her government in London and the Royal College of Surgeons of England which was jealous of its own authority to grant licences throughout the Queen's dominions.

Organized medical teaching began in September 1843, when the authorities of King's College set up another committee to form a tentative list of nominees for the various medical chairs and the salaries to be attached to them. The first year medical class consisted of two matriculated students who graduated M.D. in 1845. King's College medical department was showing a steady and substantial growth when it was unfortunately abolished by the Hincks Act of 1853, which limited public expenditure on higher education.[13]

While the King's College medical faculty was in its final planning stages during the early 1840s, Dr Rolph returned to Toronto after the general amnesty in 1843 and refounded his private school. From the beginning, because of the high quality of his lectures, it was a success: its reputation was soon recognized by McGill's medical faculty, which gave Rolph's students *ad eundem* standing for equivalent time spent studying under him. When the school was fully established, and the students were accepted as candidates by the Medical Board of Upper Canada, it changed its name to the Toronto School of Medicine. It continued to flourish as the most respectable of Upper Canada's proprietary schools until it became, in 1854, the Toronto Medical Department of Victoria University. In 1887 its faculty members became the nucleus of the restored medical faculty of the University of Toronto.

In 1850, Dr James Bovell and Dr E.M. Hodder founded another medical school in Toronto. They called it the Upper Canada School of Medicine. Both Bovell and Hodder were high churchmen and in the following year agreed for it to become the medical faculty of Bishop Strachan's newly chartered Trinity College. This school eventually became part of Toronto University's Faculty of Medicine in 1903 when the two parent universities amalgamated.

In Kingston, as early as 1834, Dr George Colls made one attempt to establish institutional medical education. Dr Colls was a surgeon in the Royal Navy who had served in the Kingston dockyards since 1816, retired and, after a brief attempt at private practice, decided to open a medical academy. The Kingston *Chronicle and Gazette* 22 July 1834, records his elaborate plans:

KINGSTON, UPPER CANADA, MEDICAL ACADEMY
Under the Auspices and Patronage of the Lieutenant-Governor, Sir John Colborne.
Mr. Colls, Surgeon, Royal Navy, will open an establishment on August 1st. His terms are as follows: With board and lodging, washing, etc., £100 per year; without board etc. £50.
The gentlemen will be taught with great care the duties incumbent upon them as professors of the general science, in every branch, theoretically and practically. Their morals will be carefully watched, and their religious duties will be impressively enforced upon them according to their tenets. They will be taught Anatomy, Surgery, Medicine, Midwifery, etc. Lectures will be given daily.
Mr. Colls will teach the following languages, with which he is well acquainted: French, Spanish, Portuguese, Italian and Dutch. These will be gratuitous. £.25 will be required in advance as an entrance fee, part of the annual payment.[14]

The concept was imaginative but stillborn. It would be twenty years before Kingston would have sufficient population or hospital facilities to support such a venture. Kingston's hospital facilities only became adequate enough to permit medical students to "walk the wards" when Drs Yates and Dickson, recognizing that radical changes were needed in the organization of the municipal hospital, encouraged John A. Macdonald, then Kingston's member of the legislative assembly, to add a paragraph to the Bill to Incorporate Kingston General Hospital (12 Victoria, C. 103, 1849).[15] This provision permitted medical students to attend the bedside of patients under supervision, thereby introducing the possibility of institutional clinical medical teaching to Kingston, and leading to the early fulfilment of the medical men's aspiration for a university medical school closely associated with a hospital, as in both Montreal and Toronto.

CHAPTER TWO

The Foundation of the University and Its Department of Medicine

John A. Macdonald and the Kingston doctors had to wait only a short while after the 1849 incorporation of the Kingston General Hospital before their hopes for a medical school became a reality. The city already had a university, which had been founded upon such liberal concepts that they had good reason to hope that their enthusiasm would be reciprocated by the trustees and professors.

From the early 1830s, the Presbyterians in Upper Canada felt that they should have a university in Kingston connected to the Synod of the Church of Scotland in Canada. After over a decade of discussion in Presbyterian communities across the province, eventually on a Wednesday evening, 18 December 1839, the Reverend John Machar called a meeting in St Andrew's Church in Kingston to discuss the foundation of a university that would not only train ministers for the Kirk, but also provide a general education like that offered in the universities of Scotland and England. Reverend Machar opened the meeting with a prayer and, as chairman, addressed the meeting on the holiness and wholesomeness of the task before them:

the establishment of a University in which, while one of its most important objects will be the training up of ministers of the Gospel to supply the long-crying destitution of this land, there will be given to our youth the fullest access to the cultivation of all the branches of a literary and scientific education.... Need I speak of its importance to the lawyer and to the physician? It is here that they will have an opportunity of making those acquirements and of forming those habits which will enable them to enter with the fullest advantage upon the study of their respective professions.[1]

The elegance and aptness of the speech led immediately to Major

Logie moving and John A. Macdonald Esq. seconding the following motion:

That this meeting deeply regrets the limited means afforded the youth of this country of acquiring a liberal education, founded on religious principles, and more especially the total want of an institution for educating and preparing young men for the Ministry in connection with the Church of Scotland.[2]

Fifty years later, during the anniversary celebrations of this occasion, Sir John A. Macdonald, then prime minister of the Dominion of Canada, vividly recalled the scene and his own predicament in St Andrew's Church that night:

I am happy to say that my recollection is perfect. (Applause.) . . . I was modest then – (laughter) – modest as those young friends of mine in the gallery, and when I arose to move the resolution that was placed in my hands, and although I had prepared an eloquent oration, I was in such a mortal fright that I did not say a single word. *Obstupui, steteruntque comae, vox faucibus haesit.* (Laughter.) I just placed the resolution in the chairman's hands and sat down. My silence was golden, and I was cheered more than if I had given a speech or had pluck enough to deliver it. It was an occasion of great pride to me to see the successful laying of the foundations of this University.[3]

After nearly two years of debating, resolving, petitioning, and making pilgrimages to the Church of Scotland in Edinburgh and the government in London, Queen's University was eventually established by royal charter on 16 October 1841. Paragraph four of the charter reflects the founders' desire for the new university to be empowered to offer instruction in "all the branches of a literary and scientific education":

And We do further Will, Ordain and Grant, that the said College shall be deemed and taken to be an University; and that the Students in the said College shall have liberty and faculty of taking the degrees of Bachelor, Master and Doctor in the several Arts and faculties at the appointed times.[4]

The university opened its doors on 7 March 1842, with two professors and fifteen students, the van of that splendid company to whom Queen's is Alma Mater. During its first ten years, Queen's was buffeted, weak, and undernourished, but the Kingston trustees kept careful watch over their slowly developing university. A frame house on Colborne Street provided sufficient accommodation for the first session. The next few years saw the college housed opposite St Andrew's Church on Princess Street at the corner of Clergy Street, and, in 1844, Queen's rented two stone houses on William Street. Here it remained until, in 1853, it moved to the spacious country villa of Archdeacon O'Kill Stuart on the outskirts of town. Called Summerhill, it was situated on high ground, overlooking the Kingston General Hospital and Lake Ontario. The trustees prudently sought advice from the medical practitioners as to the safety of its location, and when they pronounced it free from any noxious effluvia that might emanate from the hospital,[5] this property, with its surrounding six and one-half acres, became the heart of Queen's University in 1853 and remains so to the present.

While the trustees concerned themselves with the survival of the institution, the students pursued their studies in divinity and the arts with what appears to the twentieth-century mind to be commendable determination and fortitude. Little is known of the careers of most of the early graduates in arts. One, Sir James Alexander Grant, K.C.M.G., B.A. (Queens), M.D. (McGill), M.P., because Queen's lacked a medical school, went to McGill, which even then had a fine reputation for its medical education. He became a most successful Ottawa physician, president of the Medical Council of Canada, fellow of the Royal College of Physicians (London), and eventually consulting physician to Sir John A. Macdonald and royalty. The aspirations of nonclerical students such as James Grant strengthened the desire of Queen's trustees and professors and of the Kingston medical men to establish a school of medicine in conjunction with the university as soon as possible.

ESTABLISHMENT OF THE MEDICAL DEPARTMENT AT QUEEN'S

If Queen's College was to rise to its charter and become a full university and not degenerate into a simple Bible college with liberal arts appendages, it had to include law and medicine in its teaching programme. Montreal's McGill University had a thriving medical school. In Toronto, King's College was also beginning to educate physicians, and Rolph's school was acquiring a national reputation. To the legal and medical men of Kingston it became apparent that if lawyers and doctors were being trained in the Roman Catholic environment of Montreal and Quebec City to the east and in the Anglican ambience to the west, it would be only reasonable to educate Presbyterian professionals in their own established university.

Interest existed in establishing a medical school at Queen's even before it received its charter or opened its doors. The board of trustees considered at its 1841 summer general meeting a letter from Dr William Dunlop of Goderich in which he offered to deliver a course of lectures on medical jurisprudence; the board thanked Dr Dunlop for his "very liberal offer" and tabled the letter.[6] Prudence and a shortage of money inhibited any rash action that might have developed from the lawyers' or physicians' civic pride. However, the Kingston doctors and their supporters must have been encouraged to some extent by the following resolution, adopted by the board in May 1842:

To carry out more fully the designs of this Institution it is necessary to establish a Medical Faculty and that the Principal in his visit to Britain be requested to consult as far as opportunity will be afforded him with the most distinguished members of the Medical Professions in the United Kingdom as to the best measures of carrying this into effect and to state to persons of competent qualifications who might be suitably recommended to have the encouragement that Queen's College might prospectively hold out to them.[7]

Nothing materialized from the resolution despite Principal Thomas Liddell's presence in Edinburgh during the summer of 1842. No record exists of any attempt to meet Mr James Syme, the undoubted leader of the British medical profession, or any of the other eminent medical men then resident in Edinburgh.

For the next ten years no visible progress was made. But Queen's College survived and grew, and the doctors, stimulated by people like John A. Macdonald, continued to talk, plan and prepare the ground for a new Edinburgh University on the Old Ontario Strand. Further impetus came from the board of trustees in July 1853, when the Reverend Mr McGill moved "that this Board resolve as early as possible to open up the Faculties of Law and Medicine in this University and appoint the following committee – the Rev. Mr. McGill, the Rev. Dr. Machar, John Mowat and Hugh Allan, Esquires to consider the best method of doing it and take steps in the meantime to have lectures delivered next session in anatomy and physiology and in jurisprudence and colonial laws."[8] Except Mr Hugh Allan, the gentlemen named to the committee were all founders of Queen's. They were well-meaning and competent men, but for reasons unrecorded – a probable mixture of philosophical differences concerning the way the university should grow as well as financial constraints – the committee was unproductive. Fortunately, events did not wait for the committee members to reach a consensus and issue their report.

While the committee at Queen's was debating, the senior students attending the Upper Canada School of Medicine were unexpectedly informed that to graduate as M.D.s they would have to testify to their Anglican loyalty by signing the Thirty-nine Articles. Though he was a staunch high churchman, Dr Bovell advised those students who could not, in conscience, sign the Articles to transfer their allegiance out of his school.[9] Although McGill would probably have accepted his students, Bovell wrote on their behalf to the senate of Queen's University.

D.D. Calvin presumes in his history of Queen's that Dr Bovell's idea may have been an indirect consequence of the deliberation of Queen's own committee. Undoubtedly the Toronto academic community was aware of the committee's existence – the senate, early in 1854, had written to Robert Douglas, a graduate of Queen's who had gone on to study medicine at Trinity, explaining that Queen's was considering the feasibility of establishing a medical school. Early in 1854, the senate received Dr Bovell's letter enquiring into the possibility of his students being granted medical degrees by Queen's without penalty. He indicated that though they were all in their final year of medical school, none would become an apostate for a Toronto degree.[10] Looking back on this time fifty years later, one of these students, Dr W.L. Herriman, remarked, "I was born a Methodist, have lived a Methodist and am likely to die a Methodist. So I and others had to seek shelter elsewhere."[11]

The local doctors and their friend, John A. Macdonald, who had for some time been discussing the merits of establishing a medical school in Kingston, obviously got wind of the communications between Toronto and Kingston. Macdonald suggested that even though the iron was only lukewarm, the time was probably right to strike before the trustee's fiscal prudence overcame their desire to have a medical faculty in their university. On the suggestion of his friend, Dr Dickson, Macdonald invited all members of the medical profession in Kingston to attend a meeting in the front parlour of his new house on Brock Street. There were fifteen to twenty medical men practising in Kingston at that time, but only nine attended the meeting on the evening of 7 February 1854.

Two handwritten reports of the first meeting are still extant. The first, in the handwriting of Dr Orlando S. Strange, who acted as secretary, is dated 7 February 1854, and signed by Dr Strange and Dr Sampson, the chairman. The meeting's main business was reported as follows:

In compliance with the request of the Trustees of the University of Queen's College, a general meeting of the Medical Practitioners of Kingston was called for the 3rd (*sic*) inst. at the house of the Honble. J.A. Macdonald, and in consequence thereof the following persons assembled for the purpose of nominating such among the Profession as would appear the most likely to undertake with advantage the offices of Professors in the several branches of Medical and Surgical Science in the school of the University, where it is proposed by the Trustees to establish a Faculty

Dr. Sampson	Dr. Yates
Baker	Meagher
J. Stewart	R. Stewart
Dickson	Harvey

and Strange

It was agreed to submit respectfully to the consideration of the Trustees the names of the following Practitioners of this City with the particular Professorship which each of them is willing to undertake.

Dr. Sampson
Clinical Medicine and Surgery

Dr. J. Stewart
Anatomy and Physiology

Dr. Dickson
Principles and Practice of Surgery

Dr. Yates
Theory and Practice of Medicine

Dr. Meagher (deleted) Dr. Hayward
Obstetrics and Diseases of Women and Children

Dr. Strange
Chemistry, and *Materia Medica* (and Pharmacy – deleted)

Kingston, Feby. 7th/54
(signed) O.S. Strange   (signed) Jas. Sampson
        Secy   Chairman[13]

Following a lengthy discussion, the meeting was adjourned "for a fortnight, in order to allow time for more mature deliberation."[14]

The second document, dated 1 March 1862, written by Dr John Dickson eight years after the event, was testified to be a true account by John A. Macdonald. They thought they remembered "the late Dr. Sampson being called to the chair. Dr. Stewart was appointed Secretary to the meeting on the motion of Dr. Dickson."[15]

A second founding meeting was held a fortnight later. Dr. Dickson wrote the only surviving description. His account indicates that some of his colleagues had entertained second thoughts in the intervening two weeks - some nominees for professorships had shifted their positions, some, perhaps counting the cost or anticipating the uncomfortableness of a professorial chair, had withdrawn their support.

According to Dickson, all members of the profession in the city attended the second meeting. Again Dr Sampson chaired the meeting and this time Dr Stewart took a firm grip of the secretaryship. After a very full expression of opinion, it was resolved that "it is desirable to make an effort to establish a medical school here. To which resolution the only dissentient voice was that of Dr. Stewart."[16]

Dr Sampson, the dean of the profession in the city, stated that he was too old to start preparing a full course of lectures in medicine. In February 1854 he was sixty-five years old and had only seven more years to live. He expressed his willingness, however, to render every assistance in his power to the school. He was promptly recommended to the university trustees as the obvious choice as the president of the faculty. Dr Dickson was unanimously nominated professor of surgery and Dr Yates, professor of medicine. Dickson then nominated Dr Stewart, who, overruled, had acquiesced to the majority vote, and accepted the chair of anatomy. The motion carried; but at Stewart's request a motion to appoint Dr Harvey as demonstrator of anatomy was withdrawn as Stewart said that "he did not feel himself competent to teach Anatomy until he would apply himself for some time to its study and if the Faculty would allow him to be his own Demonstrator he would qualify himself more readily."[17] This uncharacteristically modest acceptance should perhaps be taken with a grain of salt. John Stewart, surgeon, no doubt felt himself the most competent person to hold the chair of surgery, where he would have lectured on what he knew and practised every day - at any rate Dickson, who had been nominated for it, was henceforth one of his *bêtes noires*.

While the medical men were determining their positions in the prospective faculty, the executive committee of the university board of trustees was also active. On 7 February, the board appointed the Reverend Professor Malcolm Smith, professor of classics, Professor James Williamson, professor of natural philosophy and mathematics, and Mr Angus Drummond to a committee to meet with the medical men to ascertain their views on the feasibility of establishing a medical school in connection with the university as soon as possible.[18] A deputation, consisting of Stewart, Dickson, and Strange, headed by Dr Sampson, explained their recommendations to the trustees' committee. By the beginning of March 1854, a tentative agreement had been reached, and in spite of the strong opposition of Dr Machar of Kingston, Vice-Principal George, and Judge Malloch of Brockville, the university board was able to write, with some satisfaction, to the Colonial Committee of the Church of Scotland that "it was taking steps for the establishment of a Medical College in connexion with Queen's College University, the want of which they believe to have operated injuriously on Classes of the College."[19]

THE BEGINNING OF THE BEGINNING

Students eager to learn and willing to pay were waiting to come to Kingston. Academically inclined doctors ready to teach without salaries were already in town. In an attempt to allay the fears of the trustees who opposed the opening of a medical school, the board authorized continued discussions with the doctors throughout the summer of 1854 which were productive enough to allow the special committee to make the following recommendation at the annual general meeting of the board of trustees on Wednesday 2 August:

That the Board should give power to the Executive Committee to appoint Lecturers in Medicine for the several Branches, such Lecturers until the circumstances of the University shall warrant the appointment of permanent Professors in that Faculty to constitute a Board of Examination on the report of which the Senatus Academicus may have the power of conferring Degrees upon the Students – It being provided that the Executive Committee shall have the superintendence of the Lecturers and the Emoluments of the Lecturers shall be derived solely from the Fees of the students in their respective classes and any funds which may hereafter be received for the special endowment of the School of Medicine. That the Board should authorize the Executive Committee to procure a separate building for the accommodation of the Medical Lecturers, containing two Lecture Rooms and an anatomical Room or Museum and to make the requisite disbursement for this purpose, with the addition of Fifty pounds Currency for the purchase of drawings and other illustrations of these lectures – such disbursement in all not to exceed the sum of Two hundred and fifty pounds currency.[20]

The lack of academic status and the very uncertain remuneration at first rather piqued the medical lecturers. On consideration, however, they realized that both could be improved in time by their own endeavours. The doctors, recognizing that the trustees would be more agreeable to granting professorships than permanent salaries, asked for the professorships. In an attempt to satisfy the doctors, the negotiating committee of the board wrote to all the trustees, asking for their approval to grant a professorship to each senior medical teacher in the faculty of medicine, indicating that the doctors would not consent to teach merely as lecturers:

They will not consent to act in the latter capacity, while gratuitously offering a large portion of their valuable time to the College, and the Committee are persuaded, that they may with perfect safety, and the greatest advantage to the interests of the Institution, be appointed Professors.[21]

Professor James Williamson who then, and on all subsequent occasions, worked assiduously on behalf of the medical faculty in the higher councils of the university, probably held this opinion most strongly. This time he was unsuccessful – during the first year of the school's operation the medical men remained as "mere" lecturers in the department of medicine of the University of Queen's College.

The trustees accepted the concept that the medical lecturers could retain, for their own purposes, "funds which may hereafter be received for the special endowment of the School of Medicine."[22] This policy did not seem imprudent in 1854. At that time the university's own income from all sources was only £2,083. The trustees were not confident that the Hinck's University Act of 1853 would provide funds for any institution of higher education other than the extravagant University of Toronto.[23] As far as the trustees were concerned, the medical men were welcome to all they could get. Had they realized this agreement was to turn into a major confrontation with the faculty within a few years, the trustees would not have been so complacent. Strangely, the board of trustees forgot that two of the most forceful of these doctors were Scotsmen without the inhibitions of the "cloth."

Whatever reservations the doubting Thomases may have had during the summer of 1854, the trustees living in Kingston and the local practitioners appointed as lecturers set to work to make the new venture a success. They added Dr Fife Fowler, newly arrived in the city, to the staff to teach *materia medica* in place of Dr Harvey, who had moved to the Bay of Quinte.

Fowler, born in Elgin, Morayshire on 21 August 1823, was the son of a dentist, who sent him to a grammar school in Aberdeen. From there he progressed to King's College before it became associated with

Marischal College as the University of Aberdeen under the principalship of Rev. Peter Colin Campbell, who had been the first professor at Queen's University, Kingston. For the next four years Fowler was apprenticed in medicine to Dr Pirie of Marischal and received his M.B. degree in 1843. Later he obtained the licenciate of the Royal College of Surgeons (Edinburgh) and the M.D. from Aberdeen. To defray the expenses of his education, he took an appointment for twenty months, between his third and fourth year of medical studies, as surgeon on a whaling ship off the coast of Greenland.[24]

After graduation, Fowler set up a general practice in the village of Aboyne on Deeside, about fourteen miles from Queen Victoria's favorite castle of Balmoral. In 1854 he shipped out as surgeon on an emigrant ship bound for Canada. Landing in Quebec early in the spring, he travelled to Kingston where his brother Deadman was in business. While arranging to set up a practice in Kingston, his brother introduced him to Dr John Stewart, who at just that time was looking for a replacement for Dr Harvey. According to Dr Stewart, as editor of the *Argus*, Fowler was appointed because "he was brought to Dr. Stewart by his brother Deadman Fowler, and introduced as a Scot looking for a gown, a hood and a four cornered hat with two tassels. The *materia medica* chair being vacant, Dr. Stewart very politely told Fife to be seated in it. Thus to the bewilderment no doubt of his Aberdonian relatives, Fife was transmogrified into a learned Professor of the Science and Art of compounding pills and potions."[25] Fowler's memory of the same occasion is a trifle different:

He stopped me on the street without the formality of an introduction, and said: 'You are the man I want,' and clapping me on the shoulder, he continued: 'I want you to take the chair of *materia medica* in Queen's Medical Faculty.' I answered: 'Will the University appoint me?' I was unused to this sudden mode of University appointment. He emphatically answered. 'I John Stewart, appoint you.'[26]

Whatever the actual words of this conversation, the minutes of the executive committee of the board of trustees on 3 October 1854 state that Dr Machar read an application from Dr Fife Fowler seeking employment as one of the medical lecturers in the College and exhibited favourable testimonials which were handed over to the convener of the committee.[27]

Further preparations for the opening of the school continued. The board's executive committee authorized the rental of rooms for teaching at 75 Princess Street and placed advertisements in religious and secular newspapers across the province to attract students.

The chairman of the board, the Honourable John Hamilton, sent Dr Stewart on a foraging mission for equipment and donations to the United States with fifty pounds and a letter of introduction (which implicitly acknowledged the value of the title "Professor," that had been refused to the doctors at home):

To Professors and Lecturers in Medicine, and other Scientific Gentlemen in the Cities of New York, Boston, or Philadelphia.

Gentlemen,

This letter will be delivered to you by Dr. John Stewart, Professor of Anatomy and Physiology in the University of Queen's College, Canada West.

The object of Dr. Stewart's visit to the United States on this occasion is to procure suitable apparatus and other requisite anatomical preparations for the Medical Department in this University, which is now being organized with a view to meet the increasing demand among our youth for a Medical Education.

As the trustees of Queen's College, we beg to solicit for Dr. Stewart your favourable notice and kind assistance. And as the pecuniary resources at our command to devote to this purpose are far too limited to enable us to obtain such a complete assortment of preparations, specimens, plates and apparatus, as would be requisite for a thorough Medical training, we venture to express a hope, that in your liberality you would aid a kindred institution, such as ours is, by such Donations as you may deem suitable, either towards the formation of a Museum or Library, or towards the immediate requirements of a Medical Class.

Any kindness, or benefaction which you may extend to Dr. Stewart, as our Deputy, we should esteem it a privilege and a duty to requite the Donors, should it ever be in our power.

Signed for the Board of trustees of the University of Queen's College
J.W. Hamilton
Chairman[28]

Whether Dr Stewart was able to return to Kingston other than empty-handed is not recorded in Queen's University Archives. We can be sure that the fifty pounds allotted by the board for the purchase of illustrations was probably well spent – by the beginning of the first term, the necessary skeletons and the full-length coloured charts of the human body, so popular with nineteenth-century anatomists, furnished the classrooms at 75 Princess Street.

During the month of September 1854, the Kingston newspapers announced that the medical school was to open on the first Monday in

November. To anyone who knew nothing of the trustees' reservations, the school appeared to be an integral part of the university, not a trial of professional quixotism.

THE TRIAL YEAR

The Medical Department of the University of Queen's College opened its doors on Monday, 6 November 1854. That very day, half a world away, the British "thin red line" was standing down, having just won the smoky "soldiers battle" at Inkerman in the Crimea, a war in which the efforts of Florence Nightingale and the nursing sisters associated with her changed the course of medicine and public health. But these faraway events and their possible outcome were probably far from the mind of sixteen-year-old Mickey Sullivan,[29] whose reminiscences, written fifty years later, supply what little is known of the first year of the school.

Sullivan would have had no trouble finding 75 Princess Street. During his boyhood it had been a hotel. Later, the Royal Artillery had used it as an infirmary or regimental hospital. Despite attempts to modernize the building, the upper rooms were deplorably filthy. According to Sullivan, however, this did not matter much, "as there were no bacteria then in Kingston."[30]

Here, at precisely one o'clock, Dr Sampson declared the school open with a very simple address, outlining the teaching arrangements for the coming session. He then handed the podium over to Dr Stewart, professor of anatomy, who, in his inaugural lecture on the importance of anatomy and physiology to the proper practice of surgery and medicine, quoted Galen's paean to human anatomy as "the most beautiful hymn which man can chant in honor of his creator." He recounted the events leading to the school's founding and exhorted the students to recognize that their future success depended more on themselves than on their professors: the only barrier to that success was idleness.[31]

The medical school consisted of two small lecture rooms and an anatomical dissecting room, accessible from the street by a flight of stone steps with iron handrails. The room of most interest to the students was the one in which they dissected cadavers under the watchful eye of William Hillier, who had been appointed Dr Stewart's demonstrator. Hillier was one of the final-year students who had migrated to Kingston from Toronto. Day after day he meticulously dissected cadavers to the wide-eyed admiration of the young sixteen-year-old Sullivan, the only freshman, who at first was ready to turn tail and run. The furnishings of the room did not help to soothe his vivid imagination. Illustrations and charts of the human body, the results of Dr Stewart's trip to the United States, "flapped against the wall when the winds howled through the ill-fitting windows."[32]

Twenty-three senior students comprised the first class. Nine, who had come from Toronto, Daniel Chambers, Robert Douglas, Samuel Dunbar, Weston L. Herriman, William Hillier, John G. Mercer, William Sumner Scott, H.W. Spafford, and Dugald McKellar, graduated with an M.D. degree in the spring of 1855. Most of the others went on to graduate during the next three or four years.

The small faculty willing to take a chance with these eager students consisted of Sampson, Fowler, Dickson, Horatio Yates, Stewart, and the Reverend Dr Williamson, professor of natural philosophy and mathematics in the arts faculty, who taught chemistry to the medical students. In his memoirs, Senator Sullivan thought he remembered Dr George Baker as one of the first teachers, no doubt because he was a well-known practitioner in Kingston and Bath. Although Baker attended the first organizational meeting in Macdonald's house, his name appears nowhere in the records of the medical faculty. For years he had lived in Bath, at first as an assistant to Dr Carlile. In 1820, he was granted a restricted licence to practise in "physic and midwifery and the lesser operations in surgery,"[33] the first such restricted licence ever granted in Upper Canada. Presumably he had wide experience in midwifery, perhaps lecturing on the subject that first year.

Although Dr James Sampson, because of his duties as the school's president and his age, was unable to give a regular series of lectures, he was always available for consultation. His erudition, his experience as a military and civilian surgeon and his stature as the leader of the profession in Kingston made him an awesome figure in Sullivan's eyes.

The most memorable professor was John Stewart. Sullivan thought he held three chairs – although he could not remember hearing him lecture. What Sullivan did recall, however, – even after fifty years – was that Dr Stewart controlled everything and no one questioned his power.

John Stewart, as he preferred to spell his name, was born in Perth, "that is, Perth in Scotland, not that two penny hapenny Canadian village which stole the name."[34] Little is known of his early life, possibly because, without wife or in-laws, he had no need to fabricate a family history (although he did not hesitate to proclaim a rather dubious royal lineage). He received his grammar school education at the Perth Academy, where he won the prize for French, a feat of which he was inordinately proud, and which he used in later years to scoff at his unilingual medical colleagues.

From Perth, young John Stewart went to Edinburgh to study medicine. "Auld Reekie" won his heart, and as the years passed, it became for him an academic Camelot. The privilege of this experience was not shared, in Stewart's opinion, by medical men trained in less august establishments. As a student at Edinburgh, he fell under the spell of the great Scottish anatomist, Robert Knox, who had not yet had his reputation inadvertently ruined by the murderous resurrectionists Burke and Hare.[35] The Royal College of Surgeons, Edinburgh, has a record that he received his licence in 1834. Why Stewart emigrated to Canada is not known, but after landing at Quebec City, he slowly made his way west. The provincial legal archives reveal that he practised for a short while in Simcoe. In January 1840 the College of Physicians and Surgeons licensed him to practise in Upper Canada (see pg. 9).

Mr Stewart, surgeon, – as he liked to be known – settled down in Kingston and began his practice early in the 1840s. He built up a reputation as a competent, concerned medical man – his dedication to the sick and dying during the 1847 typhus epidemic has become part of Kingston folklore. He had a fine figure and a good carriage, and he knew it. In an era when men were more distinctive in their dress, Dr Stewart stood out as a man of elegance. He and John A. Macdonald were among the most eligible of Kingston's bachelors in the early 1840s, much in demand at the regular social events in the colony's capital. As he strode through the town with his head held high, a Kilmarnock bonnet topping his Scottish red hair, John Stewart must have given the displaced Scotsmen and Irishmen, most of whom had no pretensions to gentility and who were all nostalgic for a homeland now firmly in the hands of the rapacious English, a vicarious sense of elegance and of things that might have been. He wore a Stuart plaid, thrown over his shoulder, fixed with a large Cairngorm brooch, winter and summer.[36]

No evidence exists that Dr Stewart was a great surgeon, scholar, or teacher – although he thought he was all three. It is impossible, of course, to know what Stewart might have achieved had he limited his activities to his profession. But just as his conscience prompted him to abhor humbug and hate hypocrisy, so his personality prompted him to fight them in arenas where he could give his flamboyant wit full rein: journalism, politics, and the law. He used his newspaper the *Argus* to attack social injustice, corruption and hypocrisy and constantly turned to the law courts for recourse. He had a quick tongue and a sharp, even vitriolic, pen, and his emphatic expression of his often extreme – and extremely biased – opinions inevitably led to confrontation.[37]

John Robinson Dickson was the other active teacher in Queen's medical department during its first trial year. Born in Dungannon, County Tyrone, Northern Ireland, 15 November 1819, he was the third son of David and Isabella Dickson. David was a reputable merchant in Dungannon. John had at least two older brothers, both in the British Forces: the eldest, David Jr., a major in the 95th Regiment, and William Dickson, a commissioned surgeon in the Royal Navy.

At eleven, John was apprenticed for six years to Mr McLean, the Dungannon apothecary. Although the indenture papers may have been signed, he does not seem to have finished his apprenticeship. Instead, he left Dungannon to complete a regular secondary education at the Belfast Institute. Although his family wanted him to follow the law, he found the attraction of medicine irresistible. He went to Glasgow, where, after a year or two of study at the Andersonian Medical College, he obtained a licence to practise midwifery. The reasons for his family's emigration in 1838 are unknown, but when they settled down in Upper Canada the young Dr Dickson continued his study of medicine as an apprentice to Dr John Hutchinson, a well-known Peterborough practitioner.

In 1841 Dickson received his full licence to practise medicine from the Medical Council of Upper Canada. By this time he no longer wanted to practise in a small town. On the advice of his Toronto examiners, he attended lectures for a year at New York University in New York City, studying surgery, anatomy, and midwifery under Dr Valentine Mott, Dr Granville Sharpe Pattison and Dr Gunning S. Bedford respectively. In April 1842, he passed the final examinations and graduated M.D. His diploma was allegedly the first to be granted by that university.

Fortunately for the medical school at Queen's, he decided to settle in Kingston rather than in New York. Here he rapidly became accepted as the leading surgeon in town and for the next thirty years was the chief inheritor of Dr Sampson's mantle. Being a strong supporter of the temperance movement did not hinder the development of a close association with Sir John A. Macdonald: he was not only his physician, but friend, business colleague, and political supporter. Dickson's own political career was short and not particularly distinguished, but during his term as alderman for Kingston's St Lawrence Ward in 1854/55, he materially assisted Dr Horatio Yates, his colleague on the city's board of health, in the reorganization of the Kingston General Hospital. His professional reputation throughout Kingston and across the country properly depended on his surgical skill, and it was primarily because of this that he was appointed to the chair of surgery at Queen's instead of Stewart.[38]

If Dr Dickson set an example of excellence in surgery in the new medical school, so did Dr. Yates as lecturer in the theory and practice of medicine. Horatio Yates was born on 11 February 1821, in Otsego County, New York, to Dr and Mrs William Yates, emigrants from Derbyshire, England. At twelve years old, he came to live with his uncle, Noble Palmer, the druggist in Kingston. Five years later he became one of Dr Sampson's apprentices. In 1842, Yates received his M.D. from Pennsylvania Medical College, Philadelphia. He completed his postgraduate medical education at St George's Hospital in London and returned to Kingston where he set up a practice. Although after 1845 he practised all branches of medicine, and was willing to operate surgically on request, he gradually became recognized as a consulting physician.

During the early years of his practice, he contracted tuberculosis. Following the usual routine at that time, he travelled during the winter and spring of 1850/51 in the Mediterranean and Italy. The following year, he spent in Trinidad de Cuba where he completed his recovery. So impressed was he by the change in his condition that he wrote a short article to the *Canadian Medical Journal* on the effects of the climate on tuberculosis patients. He was convinced that all his improvement in health was attributable "to climate, and to cod liver oil."[39]

Returning to his practice in Kingston in 1852, he found the condition and management of the Kingston Hospital deplorable. In January 1854, both he and his contemporary, Dr J.R. Dickson, were elected to city council and subsequently appointed governors of the hospital. Although the lay members of the board of governors suggested closing the hospital, the young medical men fought vigorously, and successfully, to keep it open – a hospital was essential to their plans to sustain a first-class university medical school in Kingston.

ADMITTED WITH ALL THE RIGHTS AND PRIVILEGES

The graduation of nine doctors of medicine by the medical school in 1855 was a significant triumph of enthusiasm over prudence. The Queen's board knew a good thing when they saw it – the medical school had graduated more students that year than any other medical school in Canada West and had submitted to the senate more graduates than the arts faculty, at very little cost. At the annual general meeting of trustees on 20 June 1855, a medical faculty was, as of that date, duly established. The original five professors, with the addition of J.P. Litchfield, were confirmed in their respective chairs in conformity with terms of the university charter:

James Sampson, MD, Professor of Clinical Medicine and Surgery and President of the Faculty
John Stewart, LRCS, Edin., Professor of Anatomy and Physiology and Practical Anatomy
John R. Dickson, MD, Professor of the Principles and Practice of Surgery
Horatio Yates, MD, Professor of the Principles and Practice of Medicine
Fife Fowler, MD, LRCS, Edin., Professor of *Materia Medica* and Pharmacy
J.P. Litchfield, MD, Professor of Midwifery and State and Forensic Medicine.[40]

The sixth member of faculty – and the one with the strangest personal history – was the newly appointed John Palmer Litchfield. The acceptance by the board of the recommendation for his appointment to the medical staff is the first mention of Litchfield in the university records. The original medical school lecturer in midwifery and diseases of women and children, Dr William Hayward, must have found the appointment uncongenial.

For some years Dr Litchfield held both chairs of midwifery and forensic and state medicine. The former included the diseases of women and children, while the latter he shared with Alexander Campbell, barrister-at-law, and John A. Macdonald's law partner. Since he had never been heard of in Kingston before, the founding faculty's decision to ask Litchfield to join the new school suggests that he must have had distinguished credentials or powerful advocates. But whether the board ever saw or even asked for any documentation attesting to Litchfield's education and medical experience is more than doubtful. No evidence is available from other sources to attest to his educational background or even his experience in either obstetrics or medical jurisprudence.

Litchfield's previous career, which can hardly be matched by anyone appointed to an academic chair at Queen's, has only come to light through the tenacity of Dr Thomas Gibson, professor of pharmacology and the history of medicine at Queen's during the 1930s.[41] Gibson was first put on Dr Litchfield's trail by a statement in the records of Rockwood Asylum that Dr Litchfield had, in 1839, been the inspector of hospitals for the colony of South Australia. Further research revealed that early in 1839, one, John Palmer Litchfield, set sail from London to Australia in the barque *D'Auvergne*. The *Adelaide Register* of 25 May of that year carried the following notice:

J.P. Litchfield, M.D. etc., late Physician to the Westminster General Dispensary, Lecturer on Forensic and State Medicine at the Blenheim Street School of Medicine and Physician to the London Infirmary for Diseases of the Skin, has the honour to inform the public that he has commenced the practice of his profession as a consulting physician in Adelaide. Dr. Litchfield takes this method of announcing his intention in consequence of the enquiries which have been made upon the subject.[42]

Litchfield also claimed to have been recognized as a lecturer by the Royal College of Surgeons, London, England and by the Society of Apothecaries. Shortly afterwards, he was made inspector of hospitals for the colony. This appointment was without pay, but was made by the governor, with whom Litchfield began a voluminous correspondence on all manner of public health activities, from the breeding of leeches to the building of a municipal hospital.

Perhaps Litchfield may have overdone his familiarity with the governor; at any rate the governor, becoming a little annoyed with him, began to investigate his credentials and qualifications in England, and found that they did not exist. Litchfield, aware of these manoeuvres, then established Moorcroft House, a private lunatic asylum, a possibility at that time because any lay person in Britain and the colonies could be the administrator or owner of an asylum, although the inmates had to be certified by two regularly qualified medical practitioners to be admitted.

Litchfield still maintained, in the face of the governor's scepticism, that he had a medical degree – this time from Heidelberg. Some colonials, and the governor's secretary suspected that Litchfield had purchased his degree. However, in the 1930s, Gibson inquired of the rector of Heidelberg concerning this matter and discovered that if such a practice ever existed at Heidelberg, it was certainly impossible to purchase a degree after the university's statutes were revised in 1821.

Litchfield was thrown into the Adelaide debtors' prison during the summer of 1841 after his asylum went bankrupt. Fortunately, the judge still believed he had the potential to make a financial success of his life and released him. But Litchfield, recognizing that he was not going to become a social success in Australia, returned home.

Back in England, Litchfield appears to have successfully pursued his natural bent for journalism. He freelanced, writing articles usually related to scientific or medical matters, at first for popular magazines and then for orthodox medical journals and periodicals. He wrote on skin diseases in the *Lancet* and the *Medical Gazette*. On a number of occasions he went to France and the Low Countries as a correspondent for certain London papers. And, while in France he attended the famous medical clinics in the great Paris hospitals.

Following his stint as foreign correspondent, Litchfield held the post of medical superintendent of the Walton Lunatic Asylum near Liverpool from 1845 to 1852. While in this position, apparently mainly an administrative one, he published a number of pseudoscientific papers on insanity. He was particularly proud of one in French, "Essai sur la raison et la folie."

In 1853, he emigrated to Boston for a brief period and obtained a spurious M.D. from Harvard. Next he moved to Montreal where, in 1854, he was editor or leader writer of the short-lived *Montreal Weekly Pilot*, writing literary and popular scientific articles.

When the promoters of the 1855 Paris International Exhibition set up national pavilions, Litchfield, perhaps because of his cosmopolitan experience, was appointed to the Canadian subcommittee. The subcommittee was arranging a small preparatory exhibition from which items would be selected for later showing in Paris. He seems to have made the most of the situation and pushed himself forward with a degree of enthusiasm that ensured favourable notice. Litchfield headed the Canadian adjudicators of the exhibits in Montreal. He moved a vote of thanks to the mayor of Montreal and lunched with the governor-general, Sir Edmund Bond Head. He probably took advantage of the occasion to make the acquaintance of the rising Attorney-General West, John A. Macdonald. It is not inconceivable that Litchfield manoeuvred a chance introduction to Macdonald into a discussion of Isabella Macdonald's psychological illnesses. During this discussion, Litchfield might easily have impressed the anxious husband, who was continually worried about his wife's indisposition. A short time later, we find Macdonald writing on 5 March 1855, to the provincial secretary-Canada West, soliciting the superintendency of Rockwood Lunatic Asylum for Dr Litchfield.[43]

Notwithstanding his lack of documentary credentials, within three months of Macdonald's solicitation, the governor-general appointed Litchfield superintendent of Rockwood, an institution located just outside the village of Portsmouth. This rapid penetration of the Canadian establishment by an almost penniless immigrant can only be accounted for by Litchfield's ability to ingratiate himself with those in positions of influence. He must have possessed the suavity of a confidence man and a Machiavellian manipulative ability.

Rockwood Asylum was instituted to house the criminally insane, who previously had been committed to the basement of the Kingston Penitentiary. The Rockwood estate to the west of Kingston belonged to John Solomon Cartwright, a rich business-man and first member for Lennox-Addington of the United Canada's parliament in Kingston. He built "a fine stone mansion with handsome stables," which, after his death in 1846, was rented out by his widow. Dr Litchfield, an early tenant, opened it up as a boarding house for "well-to-do gentlemen of unsound mind." Until Litchfield's arrival in town, these patients were often committed as "criminally insane" to keep them in the Kingston Penitentiary, close to relatives and prevent them from being shipped off to the only provincial asylum for the noncriminally insane in Toronto.

In October 1856 the government bought Rockwood and its thirty-five acres for $5,000. the main pillared colonial mansion housed the male patients, while twenty-four insane female patients were quartered in the palatial stables, all under the care of Dr Litchfield.

The six founding members of the faculty had little in common but a love of their profession and a desire to see in Kingston a medical school the equal of any in the colonies or Britain. It would have been difficult to bring together intentionally such a combination of distinctive personalities. Their separate strengths nourished the newly founded school in different ways. For the first few years, they acted together and did not allow their idiosyncrasies to hinder university or faculty business; and their strongmindedness undoubtedly enabled the medical school to survive. Only later, as the school grew, did they start to squabble among themselves and with the university officials. Fortunately, by that time, the school had sufficient momentum to overcome all assaults, from within or without.

With the appointment of these six physicians to the professoriate, the board of trustees instituted the Faculty of Medicine and so created a third level of government at Queen's. The university's founding charter had established two governing bodies: the board of trustees (twelve clerics including the principal and fifteen laymen) and the *senatus academicus*, the senior academic body. Initially, the senate comprised all the professors meeting under the chairmanship of the principal. In 1855, the full-time teaching staff for both divinity and arts students consisted of Vice-Principal George, the Reverend Dr Williamson, the Reverend George Weir and Professor Malcolm Smith, with the Reverend Dr Machar and the Reverend Hugh Urquhart teaching part-time. Recognizing that the sudden addition of at least six medical men to the senate might lead to unforeseen consequences, especially if they all voted unanimously for the furtherance of their own schemes or the welfare of their own students at the cost of the rest of the university, the trustees curtailed the senate's wide powers. They restricted its function to degree granting and general academic superintendence, leaving the daily direction of student studies and discipline to the three faculties, theology, arts, and medicine.

For a second time the trustees emphasized that none of the university's funds should support the medical faculty. The members were to continue to derive their emoluments from student fees "and such other sources as may be the liberality of Government or of individuals be specially devoted to that purpose."[44]

The faculty took the hint and promptly applied to the government in Toronto for financial support. The professor of classics drafted the application and it was forwarded to the government, signed by the chairman of the board. The government sent the not unsubstantial sum of £250. This amount was granted to the faculty every year until 1867, when the first post-Confederation government of Ontario under Sandfield Macdonald withdrew it at the same time that it terminated the annual grant of $5,000 to Queen's itself.

With the obvious success of the first trial year and an expected enrolment of forty-seven students for the second session, the medical faculty was welcomed to the campus. At that time, Summerhill was the only building. The medical faculty received quarters in the east wing, while the centre block and west wing were used as general university lecture rooms and as residences for the principal and nonmedical professors.

Although the citizens of Kingston and the trustees of Queen's College were justly proud of their new medical school, the latter even going so far as to call it "the greatest success" in their annual report to the Colonial Committee of the Church of Scotland, some people elsewhere started to view it with a jaundiced eye.

That "Thunderer" of Upper Canada, the *Globe*, looking for something with which to titillate its vacationing patrons during the "dog days" of August 1855, ran an editorial, "The Medical Disturbances."[45] After discussing the shortcomings of the Toronto medical scene, that is, of the Anglican Trinity medical school and Victoria University's medical department, developed from Dr Rolph's private school, George Brown, the editor, asserted that the province needed a nonsectarian school to train young doctors. Predictably, in less than two days this spark ignited Dr Stewart's wrath. In a lengthy letter he blamed the sorry history of medical education in Toronto on Trinity's invidious exclusion of any but those within the pale of the established church. He pointed out that the University of Queen's College had founded a school that granted degrees "irrespective of religious creed – Protestant and Roman Catholic, Episcopalian and Presbyterian,

Free Churchman and Old-Churchman, Wesleyan Methodists and other Methodists being, as disciples of Esculapius, alike to her."[46] For good measure, Stewart intimated that already in its first year the medical school at Queen's had assumed the leadership in medical education in the province, as evinced by the number and quality of its students, to say nothing of its distinguished faculty! Continuing in the same vein, Dr Stewart, who knew his man, expressed surprise that such a self-proclaimed watchdog of the public purse as George Brown should not remember that the people (i.e. the provincial government) had supported the medical faculty at Queen's to the tune of £250.

Brown explained that his lapse of memory was due to the low profile maintained by Queen's medical school. In the chauvinistic manner Kingstonians had become accustomed to, Brown reiterated that only in the resurrection of the Toronto University School of Medicine could salvation be found.[47]

Kingstonians and the Queen's medical students, already aware of Dr Stewart's reputation as a boxer, were not surprised when the next mail boat to Toronto carried this swift hook to the jaw – he accused Brown of deceit, lack of logic, and stupidity, maintaining that the allegation that Queen's did not require a "test" before granting a degree was an unwarranted perversion of the truth; it did not require a sanctimonious religious test, but, he insisted, "Queen's College does require a test – the test of Education." Furthermore, Brown provided the most compelling reason for the existence of Queen's medical school – it was none other than Brown who had described the reputation of the Toronto medical schools as one "with which all are disgusted ... The verdict of the public is that it is a degradation to the medical profession."[48] Stewart quoted Brown's own words: "It is quite plain that no wise parent, or guardian, will send his son to study in a city where he is more likely to learn to stab an adversary than to cure a patient; to fight in the arena than to operate in the theatre; to detect malpractice in an opponent than to learn good practice for himself."[49]

No more was heard from the *Globe* on this matter. Queen's medical school grew sturdier with each passing year, the figures speaking for themselves.

CHAPTER THREE

The Medical Faculty's Early Years

Dr Stewart's bellicose defence of Queen's against Brown reflected the general euphoria and enthusiasm of the whole medical faculty during its first few years in Summerhill. Although the space in the east wing was cramped, it was adequate enough for lectures, which were given in the rooms now part of the principal's quarters. Five students formed the first class to graduate in medicine from Summerhill in 1856: Marshal Jacob Brown, Octavius Yates, Benjamin Franklin, George H. Corbett, and John H. Campbell. Before coming to Queen's they had completed at least three years of study at other universities. Except for Octavius Yates, who stayed in town and joined his brother, Horatio, on the staff of the faculty, most of the graduates went into practice in small Ontario communities. By the 1856/57 session, the faculty was a going concern as Dr Fowler's *materia medica* account book shows. The number of students attending his classes (and consequently supplementing his income) increased year by year: twenty students in 1854/55 (£50); forty-two students in 1855/56 (£102:10s); fifty-three students in 1856/57 (£120:10s).[1]

CURRICULUM

Four academic sessions, of which only one had to be spent at Queen's comprised the required course of study for a medical student at Queen's. This provision permitted the students of the first few years of the school's opening to obtain their M.D.s without losing credit for time spent elsewhere; students were also allowed to spend a year in practice with a senior man before graduation in lieu of a year of lectures. A final year of "walking the wards," analogous to the now universal year of clinical clerkship, was mandatory. Besides practical clinical experience in hospital wards, senior students were encouraged to accompany their chiefs on house calls, particularly when they attended patients during their confinements.[2]

After four years of study, the annual calendar for the Faculty of Medicine assured the students that "the University of Queen's College being incorporated by Royal Charter, those possessing its Degree in Medicine will be entitled to their Provincial License, to practise Physic, Surgery, and Midwifery, by presenting their Degree to a District Judge, identifying themselves on oath as the persons named therein, and paying of $4 – the fee now paid by British graduates in Medicine – to the Provincial Secretary for a License to practice [sic] in the Province."[3]

The Queen's medical curriculum was essentially the same as the one that had developed over the years in the Edinburgh medical schools. The two members of the faculty, Dr Stewart and Dr Fowler, who were most vocal in their pedagogical opinions, had both studied medicine in Edinburgh, and although their temperaments differed, they were both convinced that Queen's should follow the Edinburgh tradition in teaching medicine as well as it did in teaching other subjects.

An academic session extended from the first Monday in November until the end of April. The three years of lectures were structured by the pedagogical imperatives of the curriculum. Courses in natural philosophy, anatomy, physiology and *materia medica* dominated most of the first two years of study. Professor James Williamson's very popular course in natural philosophy, taught in the arts faculty, included chemistry and, to some degree, botany. In addition to his already heavy teaching duties, Dr Williamson served on the executive committee of the board of trustees, and in the 1856/57 academic session, to lighten his burdens, Dr Stewart brought Dr Adolf Wirtz from New York to teach chemistry. Although he only remained at Queen's for one year, Dr Sullivan remembered him as a popular teacher.[4] Practical (surgical) anatomy, the principles and practice of surgery and medicine, obstetrics, and the diseases of women and children and finally, in the hospital, clinical medicine and surgery were offered in the senior year. Every student was required to attend two six-month courses in each of the major disciplines in the curriculum. The substitution of a three-month course in medical jurisprudence for three months of midwifery was permissible. It was a full curriculum, consisting of five lectures a week by each professor.

Dr Stewart was highly regarded as a teacher. After spending the morning seeing patients or conducting other business downtown, he would turn up at the college at one o'clock in the afternoon. He sat alone beside the cadaver, studying and reviewing the day's work in preparation for his four o'clock lecture. Soon finding lecturing somniferous for his students and boring to himself, he adopted the Socratic method of presentation, a highly unusual method at that time, but more suited to his adversarial mentality and certain to keep the students awake.

Stewart enjoyed his virtuoso performances. He would ask what the origin or insertion of this or that muscle was, or what passes through this or that foramen. Then the fun: "Can any first year man answer? Any second year man? Third? Fourth?" The rivalry and competition became keen. A flamboyant professorial performance would follow. The students learned and remembered the important medical facts, which sometimes get lost among the anatomical minutiae covered in the usual lecture.

Occasionally a student raised for discussion a difficult topic mentioned in one of the required textbooks, such as *Ellis, Wilson*, or the *Dublin Dissector*. Stewart welcomed these topics, but if the student had been so unwise as to be facetious, he might be subjected to a tongue-lashing, or even invited to a round of the "manly art" with the professor, who was known throughout Kingston to have the most educated pair of fists in the city.[5]

The students willingly accepted Stewart's academic discipline, aware that they would not survive in their future daily practice without a thorough grounding in anatomy. Dr Stewart admitted that he could not teach physiology with the same sort of order and rigour as he did anatomy. He assigned the students twenty pages of Kirke's *Physiology* three times a week, to save himself from lecturing, examining them towards the end of term "school-boy fashion," presumably orally.

Dr John Watson, professor of philosophy and one of Queen's "greats," was a friend of Dr Stewart's in his old age, and recorded that "in spite of his tendency to brag outrageously, everybody agreed that Dr. Stewart was a first-rate teacher."[6] Dr Stewart's personality was certainly unique. A facility with words, a legalistic mind, a flamboyant style, a love of medicine, and a devotion to his medical students and to the goals he and they had in common made him a born teacher.

In the practical anatomy course, Professor Stewart demonstrated operative techniques on the cadaver in the dissecting room. He taught the proper line for an incision, the tissue layers to be cut through under the skin, and the precise anatomical relationships. The general introduction of ether and chloroform as anaesthetics during the previous decade had made possible a lengthier and more efficient approach to amputations and excision of tumours: blood vessels could be adequately identified and ligatured, and skin flaps for amputation stumps more appropriately designed. An act of the provincial legislature made the bodies of convicts in the Kingston penitentiary available for dissection by the professor, the demonstrator, or students. The dissecting room was open "daily from daylight to dusk for instruction in practical anatomy,"[7] presumably to allow private study by the students on the cadaver itself.

When Dr Stewart was not available, his demonstrator, Dr Meadows, one of the assistant surgeons in the 9th Regiment, Kingston, replaced him. Meadows had no generation gap to leap and was accepted by the students as their friend and confidant. More important, since he had mastered the microscope, the instrument destined to turn medicine into a science, he could teach them what none of their senior teachers knew or had ever even seen. The medical school was proud to advertise that it was equipped with two first-class British microscopes and a few others of inferior value.[8] Meadows's part of the course, perhaps the most advanced in the country at that time, was the forerunner of the departments of pathology and histology. Before Dr Meadows was posted away from the 9th Foot to the Canadian Rifle Regiment, he taught Dr Dickson the workings of the microscope and how to conduct a class in histology.

Litchfield, despite his lack of knowledge of clinical medicine, surgery or obstetrics, was also one of the student's favourite professors. Besides being responsible for obstetrics, he taught forensic and state medicine with the aid, for a short time, of Alexander Campbell, John A. Macdonald's law partner, who was to become, a few years later, the one and only dean of Queen's first Faculty of Law. Litchfield gave his lectures every day, from twelve to one o'clock, for three months: the fee was six dollars. By 1862, the medical school proudly announced in its annual calendar, concerning the course in forensic and state medicine, that "the Professor of this branch being Medical Superintendent of the Rockwood Lunatic Asylum, will have ample opportunities of instructing his class in the important subject of psychological medicine."[9] Doubtless Litchfield had been teaching psychological medicine for some years, it being the one area of medicine that he could legitimately claim to have had experience in, not only at Kingston, but also over the previous twenty years in England and Australia.

Before being posted away from Kingston, Surgeon Thornton gave about half of Dr Litchfield's lectures in obstetrics. Although he was professor of midwifery, Litchfield never, as far as is known, attended a confinement in Kingston. He fully admitted to Queen's board of trustees that he did not practise his profession, only lectured on it.[10] Dr Litchfield made this admission when he asked the board of trustees for the honorary M.D. degrees for himself and Surgeons Meadows and Thornton, who had taught their courses "without any pecuniary return."[11] During 1857, Litchfield offered his resignation from the chair of midwifery. The board, however, delayed acceptance until it was able to find an appropriate replacement. Fortunately for Queen's, in 1858 the young and energetic Dr Michael Lavell moved to Kingston. A pleasant person, he rapidly built up the first specialty practice, devoted mainly to obstetrics and the diseases of women and children in Kingston. When the profession recognized his ability, Queen's, in 1861, accepted Dr Litchfield's resignation and appointed Dr Lavell in his place. Litchfield, in turn, was appointed to the newly established chair of the institutes of medicine.

Litchfield held this chair for only one academic session (*annus medicus* as it was called officially), 1861/62, before Octavius Yates replaced him as the first Queen's medical graduate to be appointed to a professorship in the faculty.

The institutes of medicine course offered lectures on physiology, general pathology, and therapeutics which were supplemented by vivisections, demonstrations with the microscope and samples of specimens from the anatomy museum. Thus, in the British tradition, histology became associated with the teaching of physiology rather than anatomy as is now customary in North America.[12]

Kingston's traditional relationship with the military provided, during these early years, a unique opportunity to offer a course in military medicine and surgery. The course soon became very popular – the Crimean war was still fresh in everyone's mind, and many students knew that they themselves might have eventually to serve as militia surgeons. A number of army surgeons, veterans of the Crimea, were stationed in Kingston at this time, and were eager to pass on the lessons learnt in the heat of battle, where they often improved their amputation techniques and found more efficient ways of dealing with burns or shrapnel wounds. Medical experience gained during the prolonged siege of Sebastopol was particularly interesting to Canadians because of the very similar climatic conditions of the two regions. Ten days after Inkerman, for example, a blizzard blew down all the hospital marquees, in which over 600 British and almost 800 French troops lay, reducing medical organization to chaos. Almost 14,000 soldiers during the following few months were hospitalized with dysentery, cholera, or malaria. The hospitals on land were mismanaged and short of drugs, particularly laudanum and castor oil, while in the hospital ships at anchor in the bay the situation was worse. The newspapers made much of such atrocious conditions, popularizing Florence Nightingale's work in revolutionizing the hygiene and the administration of camp hospitals. Students, aware of these events, probably found Dr Thornton's, surgeon to the 9th Regiment, lectures on military medicine and surgery fascinating.

In keeping with the times, all six members of the original faculty and most of their successors subscribed to the doctrine that although they might teach in the context of a noble profession, they did so *in loco parentis*. All nineteenth-century educators recognized the right and responsibility of parents to direct their sons' education. This was particularly true at Queen's, which had been founded on a patriarchal Presbyterian ethic. Godless secular institutions might flourish elsewhere in the province, but Queen's held firmly, although not sanctimoniously, to the belief that the practice and teaching of medicine was a most worthy expression of the second commandment: "To love thy neighbour as thyself." To reassure parents that this was so, the faculty guaranteed strict supervision of the students' moral behaviour and assured them that arrangements were "made for attendance on Divine worship in the church to which the students may severally belong."[13]

To graduate from Queen's, a student must first have matriculated, specifically in the medical faculty, "in the common branches of English Education, and also on one or more of the following works: – Caesar's *Commentaries*, *London Pharmacopoeia*; Gregory's *Conspectus*; *Celsus: De Medicina*." After matriculation, a primary examination, written and *viva voce*, on anatomy, chemistry, institutes of medicine and *materia medica*, was usually taken at the end of the third year. At the end of the fourth year, the student sat the final examination in surgery, theory and practice of medicine, forensic and state medicine, obstetrics, clinical medicine, and clinical surgery. He was also required to submit, before graduation, a thesis composed by himself, in his own handwriting, which had to be approved by the faculty board. Both the primaries and finals began on 2 March, or the first lawful day following, and had to be concluded before the last Thursday of March, graduation day. The fee for graduation was twenty dollars in the 1860s.[14]

FACULTY FINANCES

Sparse bits of documentary evidence spliced together with a fair amount of conjecture form a picture of the financial arrangements of the medical school. As the school's secretary, Dr Stewart, however badly, kept track of the day-to-day accounts of the faculty. Because he refused to hand over to his successor in office, or to the university, the faculty papers in his possession when his connection with the medical school was severed in 1862, the only remaining pieces of evidence of his administration are those few reports or statements of accounts he rendered under duress to the trustees at the persistent request of Mr John Paton, secretary of the board. They are sketchy, sometimes illegible and, notwithstanding Stewart's high opinion of his own administrative ability, scarcely adequate.[15]

After the faculty's transfer to Summerhill, anatomical preparations, books, and instruments accounted for the faculty's major expenses. Two new British microscopes cost £36 4s in 1856. Dr Williamson was reimbursed £45, Dr Dickson £33 and Dr Fowler £20 for unspecified instruments and apparatus. The routine upkeep of the Summerhill facilities accounted for the other significant drain on faculty resources. Plastering, painting, and carpentry alone cost £66 10s 5d.[16]

Professors collected and kept student fees during the early years as their only emolument. Initially, a ticket granting admission to one year's course of lectures cost £ 2 10s. In 1857 it was raised to £ 3. Dr Fowler, for example, punctilious in his accounts as in all administrative matters, earned an average of £ 120 per year for his first nine years of teaching *materia medica*. Fowler's meticulous accounting became legendary. Many years later, alumni would recall hearing his characteristic Scottish brogue reverberating along the corridors of the old medical building as he shouted after students who were in arrears – "Pay y'ere fees – pay y'ere fees."

The trustees who had voted on principle against the establishment of a medical school appear to have done so primarily on the grounds of financial caution. If the members of Queen's board of trustees have a common virtue, it is that they have kept the trust and protected the endowment, thus ensuring Queen's integrity as the province's only private university. Intense concern for the endowment during the 1850s made the trustees wary of what they thought might be the predatory instincts of the medical men. A number of times during the early part of 1856 the committee called Dr Stewart to explain previous faculty expenditures and justify his request for the balance of the university's original allocation of £250. The trustees saw no valid reason to expend further money on the medical school, coping as it was quite adequately on its annual provincial grant.

The Reverend Dr Mathieson of Montreal was more concerned than any of the trustees about the management of faculty and university funds. He was worried that somehow college property or its endowment might in future be alienated for the use of the medical faculty.

To relieve the Reverend Dr Mathieson's apprehension, Dr Williamson conferred with the Chief Justice, the Honorable Archibald McLean and received the legal opinions of John A. Macdonald, Alexander Campbell, and George L. Mowat, the university's solicitor who unanimously agreed that the worries of Dr Mathieson's Montreal presbytery were groundless: the medical faculty, not being a corporation, had no legal standing apart from being a creature of the university of Queen's College. They did not even follow up Campbell's suggestion that the doctors should individually sign disclaimers because such an action might have indicated some prior right of the medical men to university property which they could thereby voluntarily relinquish.

A more contentious financial problem concerned the ownership and disposal of the annual £250 provincial grant itself. The original government draft for £250 must have been made out directly to the medical faculty, not the university, because even before the transfer to Summerhill (see pg. 32), on 2 January 1855, the executive committee of the board passed a resolution "that the Chairman of the Medical Board be requested to give the Treasurer a power of Attorney to draw the amount of the Grant made by the Government for the Medical School."[17] Old Dr Sampson and Dr Stewart, acting as president and secretary of the faculty respectively, submitted that since the funds were granted for the specific use of the faculty, they were to be disposed of solely by the medical professors. The board, rightly jealous of its own preeminence in university matters, maintained that the funds were granted to the university specifically for the use of the medical faculty, and were to be dispensed to satisfy particular requests of the professors when justified. George L. Mowat supported the board in this opinion. In an attempt to assert its independence, the faculty sought the opinion of John A. Macdonald, who was shortly to become premier of the United Provinces of Canada. Macdonald's 15 July 1857 letter to Dr Stewart affirming that "any grant to Queen's College whether for the Faculty or School of Medicine or for the Faculty of Law or the Arts, is properly payable to the Trustees of that University, and should be appropriated according to the intention of the grant by the Trustees,"[18] ended the medical faculty's first revolt.

THE MEDICAL BUILDING

Having assuaged their apprehensions and affirmed their authority, the trustees set about mending their fences with the doctors. The solution of the grant problem was so much to their liking that they were able to turn an inescapable necessity into an act of apparent generosity.

Even before the medical school made Summerhill its second home in 1855, the executive committee of the board had appointed Professor George, Mr Mowat, and Mr Harper to a subcommittee to meet with the medical men – not yet professors – to consider their request for permission to erect a medical school on a portion of the college land. In the interim, the board, not wishing to spend a large sum immediately, found space for the medical faculty in the east wing of Summerhill. After a year in these quarters, enrolment again increased, and Dr Stewart returned to the fray, using the almost outdated miasmic theory of infection to give added force to his request: how he could "invite students to a place where their health will suffer by continually breathing at lecture hours the impure atmosphere of the dissecting room?"[19]

At this time, the large medical lecture room occupied most of the main floor of Summerhill's east wing, with the dissecting room directly below in the basement, where slabs of limestone served as dissecting tables. The university executive, determined to prevent the "medicals" from expanding into the central block of Summerhill, set up another committee to look into the feasibility of granting "a site on the college grounds for the erection of a building to accommodate the Medical Department."[20] The faculty was expected to remain in Summerhill for only one more session, and had to pay fifty pounds rent out of their government grant for the use of the university's facilities.

By 1858, as no further action had been taken, the problem of overcrowding became so acute that the trustees were forced to take decisive action. They instructed Mr John Powers, architect, to complete plans for a new building at the rear of Summerhill: the board believed that this could most easily and cheaply be done on the spare land where the woodhouse then stood because this location ensured that no money need be wasted on architectural ornamentation. Mr Powers first estimated the cost of the two-story, shingle-roofed building at $7,000. To raise this money the trustees disposed of forty shares, worth $8,000, of Commercial Bank stock.[21]

On 23 August 1858 tenders were opened and accepted from James Stewart for masonry work ($3,752) and Robert Fisher ($3,400) for carpentry and supplies. Three weeks later the architect and mason were complaining of the slowness of the timber delivery, and the university solicitor was instructed to issue the usual warning to Mr Fisher and his guarantors.

Despite delays, by the end of 1858, the partly completed building was insured for $8,000. Though the original estimates had called for a brick building, sometime during the summer a decision had been taken to use Kingston limestone – presumably to carry out the project within the specified budget.

As the weather permitted, construction continued throughout the winter. Once the roof was on, the medical men began to take a proprietary interest in the building. After inspecting the half-completed structure, Drs Dickson and Yates requested alterations in the gallery arrangement in the northeast corner room and several changes in the placing of the doors. Unfortunately, the original plans have been lost and the building has undergone so many alterations that it is now impossible to recognize the original interior. The structure, first known as "the New College Building," subsequently "the Medical," after 1908 "the Old Medical," and briefly in the 1960s "the Anatomy Building," is a well-proportioned block of Canadian Georgian with a smaller wing jutting out from the western side of the main building. Neatby thought that it preserves "something of the fine eighteenth-century tradition," although two of Queen's eminent Victorians considered that it had little merit other than providing shelter from the weather.[22]

The ground floor of the main part became the university Convocation Hall, as the trustees had intended, and it remained so until Principal Grant erected the Old Arts Building (now Theology Hall) in 1878. Final plastering and painting were completed in time for medical classes at the beginning of the 1859/60 session, and the new building had room enough for Dr Williamson and Dr Lawson to teach their arts classes in natural philosophy and chemistry.

FACULTY SQUABBLES

Four years after its foundation, the medical school was well on the way to having its own building and could compare favourably with any other in Canada West. Although on the surface the situation appeared calm, internal bickering partly dissipated the faculty's original apostolic fervour. Dr Stewart, having lost his case to the university trustees in the matter of the provincial grant, began to irritate his medical colleagues.

In preparation for the 1857/58 academic session, Stewart, in his capacity of secretary to the faculty, issued on his own authority a circular announcing the forthcoming session. Somehow the printer's galley proofs fell into the hands of the other members of the medical staff: they were shocked, and no wonder! He had effectively dismissed Dr Dickson from the chair of clinical surgery and Dr Yates from clinical medicine simply by deleting their names and chairs from the circular. He had also removed Dr Litchfield from the chair of midwifery and inserted the name of a Dr Archibald Hall.

Dr Hall, the incumbent professor of obstetrics at McGill, had a national reputation as the editor of Canada's only medical journal, the *British-American Medical Journal*. No evidence exists that he wished to leave McGill or move to Kingston, although Stewart asserted he had applied for the appointment. In any case, Stewart's action was improper because, although Dr Litchfield was finding the medical superintendency of Rockwood Lunatic Asylum a full-time job and had submitted his resignation to the board three months earlier, it had not yet been accepted.

Dr Dickson informed the trustees of this situation in his 11 September 1857 letter. He reported Dr Stewart's assertion that as secretary of the faculty he (Stewart) was not to "be governed by the *majority* of the *medical faculty*" but was "merely responsible to the trustees" for his actions. Dr Dickson asked if the trustees of Queen's College intended "to uphold a professor, who contumaciously bids defiance to all other professors, and states the trustees will sanction his proceedings?"[23] If they supported Stewart, then he and other members of the faculty would, following the example of their worthy president, Dr Sampson, submit their resignations.[24]

This ultimatum placed the board in a most invidious position. Whatever they hoped to accomplish is unclear, but they accepted Dr Sampson's resignation and recorded it in the minutes of the board for 1 October 1857.

In the next two months, however, the trustees realized that they had miscalculated – they could either keep the peace by continued dependence on Sampson's leadership or chance an immediate, irreparable rift by choosing sides. The board decided to solve this potentially dangerous problem by employing a time-honoured technique. It established a committee to draw up a set of rules and regulations for the government of the faculties in the university. It did, however, mollify the anti-Stewart faction by insisting that, in future, all annual announcements of the medical faculty were to be submitted to the board for consideration and approval before publication.

However, Dr Stewart's eleven-page statement answering his critics further complicated matters. Strangely enough, it reads as one of his more rational self-justifications. He argued, citing Macdonald's opinion, that the trustees had a right to control all university monies and also to frame rules and regulations for the governing of the college. By shrewdly invoking the revered example of Edinburgh University, where "Mr. Miller Professor of Surgery of Edinburgh is not Professor of Clinical Surgery, which Chair is held by Mr. Syme ... Are Drs. Dickson and Yates such Medical Luminaries that a different rule must be made for them?"[25], he justified removing Drs Dickson and Yates from their respective chairs. Stewart then turned to a personal attack on Dickson that although, in retrospect, may appear amusing, at the time probably cut very near the bone.

Dickson was interested in real estate and railways, concerns which were probably cemented by his friendship with John A. Macdonald and James Morton, the Kingston brewer and entrepreneur. Coincidentally, at the time of the fray, Dickson and Morton were negotiating for the Grand Trunk Railroad to come right down to the Kingston waterfront. Stewart shrewdly pointed out that the professor of surgery at Edinburgh had been censured for absenting himself from his teaching for only one day to give a major scientific paper at an international meeting in London. Stewart then demanded: "What must be the censure directed against the Professor of Surgery at Queen's College, Kingston who absented himself from class, during *one week*, in Toronto, with no higher aim perhaps than the desire to obtain a railroad through his own potato field?"[26]

Discretion won the day, as much as the trustees might have liked to support Dr Stewart and perhaps divide and dominate the medical faculty, at its meeting on 8 December, the board reversed its acceptance of Dr Sampson's resignation, and corrected the entry in the minutes to read: "it having been the intention of the Board that Dr. Sampson's resignation should merely be laid upon the table, ... the Board do now respectfully request Dr. Sampson to withdraw his letter and resume his duties as President."[27] Dr Sampson complied, Stewart bridled his tongue, and the faculty enjoyed three years of relative peace.

THE APPOINTMENT OF DR GEORGE LAWSON

For some time, Dr Williamson had been asking to be relieved of the responsibility for teaching chemistry to the medical students. Although he was another of their favourite teachers, his duties as professor of natural philosophy and as the most constant member of the executive committee of the board left him little time for the medical faculty. Dr Wirtz taught chemistry during the 1856/57 session, and, in 1857, Dr Sullivan recalled in his memoirs that Dr Stewart went off to Edinburgh, full of self-importance, to find a new professor who he hoped could teach both chemistry and botany – a man, Stewart declared, "from Auld Reekie" who would do for Queen's what the famous Dr Dawson had done for McGill[28] and place preclinical teaching on a sure foundation. The medical men wanted an M.D. to fill the chemistry chair. Dr Stewart offered Dr Lauder Lindsay, superintendent of Murray's Royal Institution for the Insane at Perth in Scotland, and possibly Dr Stewart's school friend, the chair. He accepted, and then refused it.

University records show that in 1858 Dr George Lawson, a Ph.D. from Geissen, Germany, was appointed to the chair of chemistry and natural history on the commendation of Dr Balfour, professor of botany, Edinburgh University. For a young man of thirty-one his salary of £425 was considered very generous: £150, from the ordinary revenues of the college, £150, guaranteed from student fees, and the remaining £125, from the government grant to the medical faculty. It has been suggested that this inducement to Lawson precipitated Queen's first salary negotiations. The Reverend Dr Williamson was thirty years older than Lawson, had been on the staff for sixteen years, and was receiving £50 less. He and the Reverend George Weir, professor of classics, complained to the board, asking to be allowed to keep their class fees like the medical professors. After two years' consideration, the trustees granted them this privilege.[29] For many years after, preclinical medical school teachers of the then-called "natural history" and now "basic sciences" had to bear misplaced aspersions that they were unjustifiably paid disproportionately more than their colleagues in the arts faculty.

George Lawson arrived from Britain in 1858 as the first of a long line of supposedly distinguished nonclerical scholars. According to Dr Stewart (a very unreliable source), Lawson had grown up in disadvantaged circumstances in a small cottage on the banks of the Tay. The *Argus* outlined Lawson's background: "From the hillside George was sent to a pettifogger in Dundee to sweep the office and copy the different contracts entered into by Joannes Doe and Richardus Roe; but not being as adapted to the Roe and Doe business as to the turf, he was wont to neglect his master's office, and was we presume discharged."[30] Sources do not reveal the veracity of Stewart's allegations. Nevertheless, he was, without a doubt, a man of ability who got along amicably with Stewart until he opposed Stewart's application for the penitentiary surgeoncy. Stewart then attacked Lawson's time as professor Balfour's highly thought of assistant in the Botanical Gardens, Edinburgh as being only "head gooseberry pruner in the Experimental Gardens of Edinburgh," and his efforts to obtain a

Ph.D. in Germany as going from "pruning Gooseberry bushes" to scraping "together a pock-o-bawbees [sic], sufficient to purchase a Ph.D.ship," and make "a trip frae auld Reekie to Giessen."[31]

Lawson did tarnish his reputation as a scientific observer when he entered a newspaper controversy over the adulteration of bread, castigating Canadian millers for shipping their flour in barrels previously used to pack arsenic – which, of course, they did not do – shortly after he arrived in Kingston. However, he more than rescued it in 1859 by offering, with the board of trustees' permission, a series of public evening lectures for artisans or working men on "Applications of Chemistry to the Useful Arts of Life." The idea for such lectures, initiated in England a few years earlier in the government School of Mines, spread rapidly across the country. The classes, held in the Convocation Hall on the ground floor of the Medical Building, soon became very popular, and were the first faltering steps of what later became Queen's nationally acclaimed Extension Department and the forerunner of its Faculty of Applied Science.

Lawson was a good teacher, lecturing two hours a morning and teaching in the laboratory three afternoons a week. He was particularly interested in botanical microscopy. In an attempt to upgrade his discipline, he imported six microscopes from Britain. Three were retained for teaching; the other three he sold to students, making for Queen's a profit of $74.83. For taking the financial risk, the trustees' executive committee reprimanded him.[32] He brought order and accountability into the laboratory, compiling careful lists of all chemicals and apparatus and setting up a special balance room. For the first time, students at Queen's carried out their own experiments in quantitative and qualitative chemical analysis.

Apart from Vice-Principal Williamson, Lawson was the first professor at Queen's to hold an appointment in both the medical and arts faculties; the principal only became an *ex officio* member of the medical faculty a few years later. Like a number of his nonclinical successors in the basic science departments of the medical school, Lawson became deeply involved in provincial educational matters not immediately related to the specific well-being of the medical faculty. In 1860, the newly appointed principal at Queen's, the Reverend Dr Leitch, led the crusade of the sectarian universities, McGill, Victoria, Trinity and Queen's, against one of the many attempts by the "godless," secular University of Toronto to monopolize and dominate higher education in Canada. In this fight, Lawson was a vocal supporter of Leitch and appears to have been in contact with colleagues in the other universities across the province. Because he generated expenses "connected with the spread of information on the University question,"[33] he suggested to Mr Paton, secretary of the board, that Queen's should pay all his expenses incurred by his altruistic activities because it would look cheap to ask Victoria and the other universities for contributions.

Botany as a major scientific discipline in Canada can be traced back to George Lawson's founding of the Botanical Society of Canada in December 1860. The early meetings were held in Kingston, and the society rapidly gained acceptance as a national scientific forum.[34] To its fourth meeting, 8 March 1881, it was able to attract the distinguished American professor of botany, Asa Gray of Harvard. At that meeting, Principal Leitch, president of the society, presented a paper "On the Secretion of Saccharine Matter in the Floral Organs of Plants, and on the Economy of Bees; with results on the Sexual Development of Bees."[35] Dr Yates lectured on the history and cultivation of cotton; and Dr Dickson exhibited specimens of Australian seaweed. After Lawson left Queen's for Dalhousie in 1863, the society seems to have declined and become virtually defunct due to lack of funds. A few years later the treasurer of the society (Queen's professor of philosophy, J. Clarke Murray) reported that it was twenty-two dollars in debt, its sole assets being the herbarium and the library. He asked that if Queen's would pay the debt, it could take over both. Queen's complied, laying the foundation of its biology department and carrying on Lawson's enthusiasm for natural history.

The board both underestimated the professional pride of the medical faculty and overstepped the bounds of prudence when on 10 April 1861 they appointed Lawson vice-president of the medical faculty, with the power to call meetings and preside over them in the absence of the principal, who, since Dr Sampson's resignation, had become *ex officio* president. The doctors were willing to accept a non-M.D. as a professor of chemistry, but not as vice-president of their own faculty. They elected Dr Dickson vice-president and Lawson faculty secretary – thanks to Dr Stewart's resignation from the secretaryship "owing to certain improper transactions in that body."[36] The trustees readily agreed to this amicable solution of the faculty's administrative problems.[37]

It is obvious that Lawson was an excellent teacher as well as a good administrator and was highly regarded, with the exception of Stewart, by students and staff alike. Stewart continued his unfair attacks in the *Argus*. After one of them, Lawson's faculty colleagues attended his next chemistry class and read aloud to him this letter:

University of Queen's College,
Kingston, C.W., 31st January, 1862.

Dear Sir:

We the undersigned Members of the medical faculty of this University, feel deeply grieved, and at the same time very indignant, at the foul slander, which appeared in the fourth number of the "Argus" newspaper, in which a laboured effort is made, not only to wound your own feelings, but also to place you in a false position before the public.

The *animus* which actuated the Editor of that paper in publishing such a base libel, is quite evident from the tone of malignancy which pervades its every sentence, and from the daring effrontery which is shown in the distortion, if not the total disregard of truth.

We know you did not come to this country to seek a reputation as a scientific man; a character of that kind you had established long before you came here, before the Medical Department of Queen's College had an existence. We therefore can assure you of our sympathy in the annoyance which you must have experienced at this wanton and unprovoked attack.

We all know full well the admiration in which you are held not only in Great Britain, but also by all learned and sensible men in this country who have had the privilege of making your acquaintance. Your writings have enriched the pages of several scientific journals in Britain, and have been deemed worthy of a place in foreign periodicals, even the press at Athens has issued one of your papers, translated into modern Greek.

You are not only esteemed for your high intellectual attainments, your unassuming manners, and your many social qualities, but also for your intrinsic worth as a gentleman and a Christian.

We beg not only to tender you our sympathy, but to assure you that you will have our entire support and co-operation in whatever course you may think prudent to pursue.

The highly coloured picture drawn in the "Argus" of the 29th inst., descriptive of the part which the Editor of that newspaper played in establishing the medical school here, and the appointment of the Professors, had never any existence except in his own very fruitful imagination. With reference to his ever having presided over any meeting of the Medical Faculty, such an event never happened previous to your advent amongst us, and you well know it has never occurred since.

In conclusion, we beg to assure you that should you ever decide to resign your Chair in the medical faculty, we hereby bind ourselves to have recourse to a similar measure.

(signed)   John R. Dickson, M.D.,
            Professor of Surgery.

Horatio Yates, M.D.,
Professor of Medicine.

Fife Fowler, M.D., L.R.C.S.E.,
Mat. Med. Prof.

M. Lavell, M.D.
Professor of Obstetrics, &c.[38]

Perhaps Lawson should have responded to Stewart's attacks. As he did not, Stewart, even after being dismissed from the faculty in April 1862, repeatedly filled columns of the *Argus* with atrocious half-truths on almost any public action made by Lawson. Although some of them appear amusing, they were doubtlessly deeply wounding at the time.

For example, when, at its spring convocation McGill conferred on Lawson the honorary degree of LL.D., Stewart scoffed at him again, suggesting he was only awarded it because he was a crony of "his Rivrence," i.e. Principal Leitch. And when Lawson placed an advertisement in the *Athenaeum* of London announcing he was opening a boardinghouse for young gentlemen wishing to attend the university, the grammar school or Select Classical School in Kingston, Stewart accused him of setting up "an opposition to the reduced old women of the town who keep boarding houses – A nice use that George makes of LL.D.ship – to decoy British youth to this little 'Sodom and Gomorrah.'"[39] Even in today's permissive society, let alone in the strict Victorian era, one cannot imagine that this description of Kingston would have been appreciated by the city fathers.

The Medical Quadrangle

Early Doctors

Dr James Sampson, president 1854–1860, professor of Clinical Medicine and Surgery

Dr John Stewart, secretary of the faculty and professor of Anatomy and Physiology, 1854–1862

Dr Horatio Yates, dean 1864–1866 and professor of the Principles and Practice of Medicine

Octavius Yates, M.D., professor of the Institutes of Medicine, 1862–1864

Dr John Robinson Dickson, vice-president and dean, Queen's Medical Faculty 1860–1864; president and dean, RCPSK 1866–1882; professor of Surgery

Dr Fife Fowler, president and dean RCPSK 1882–1892; dean, Medical Faculty, Queen's University 1892–1903

Senator Michael Sullivan, M.D., FRCPSK, professor of Anatomy, professor of Surgery, RCPSK; second dean of Women's Medical College (WMC)

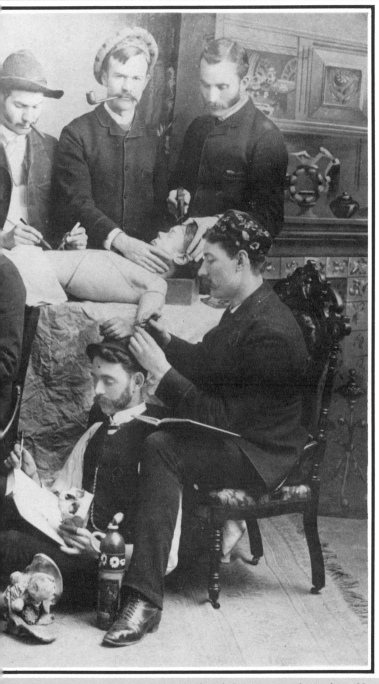

An unscheduled anatomy study session, 1880.

First Lady Meds

Dr Elizabeth Smith Shortt, lecturer in Medical Jurisprudence, WMC

Dr Alice McGillivray, professor of Practical Anatomy, Obstetrics and subdean, WMC

Dr Elizabeth Beatty, medical missionary in India

Dr Sullivan's Surgical Class, 1890, WMC

Medical Coeducation, the Professors

Dr A.P. Knight, professor of Animal Biology, Physiology and Histology

Dr Michael Lavell, FRCPSK, professor of Obstetrics and Diseases of Women and Children, Medical Faculty and RCPSK; first dean, WMC

K.N. Fenwick, M.A., M.D., FRCPSK, professor of Surgery and Obstetrics

CHAPTER FOUR

The Medical Faculty Grows in Stature and Strength

The foundation of Queen's medical faculty and the early years of its development occurred while the university itself lacked a full-time principal. The fourteen years between the Reverend Dr Thomas Liddell's return to Scotland in 1846 and the Reverend William Leitch's arrival in Kingston during the summer of 1860 was a long time for an institution to be without a firm hand on the tiller. Both major historians of the university have seen Dr Leitch's principalship as crucial to the development of Queen's. D.D. Calvin characterized Leitch's principalship as a time of quiet progress;[1] Hilda Neatby, on the other hand, considered that nothing could have been more untrue than the word "quiet."[2] Both scholars were correct – the disparity is derived from their different perspectives. Calvin saw Queen's as a small sectarian college slowly maturing and developing qualities of character that enabled it to withstand internal dissensions and external assaults, while Neatby was impressed by the obvious, highly publicized frailties of human nature and the resulting personal quarrels between faculty members that can be regarded as no more than the exuberances of an unsophisticated human organization passing from adolescence to maturity. Living through the antagonisms probably helped to strengthen the deep moral fibre which developed at Queen's – a fibre common to historic institutions of any longevity.

However historians evaluate Leitch's principalship, he was the first Queen's principal to reject selling her birthright for the mess of pottage perennially held out from Toronto, usually in the guise of government financial support. Leitch's real, quiet legacy was his consistent choice of poverty with integrity rather than affluent subservience as part of a secular provincial university.

At the time of his appointment, Leitch was in his forties, with an ailing heart that was to lead to an early death four years later. He may have seen his tenure as principal at Queen's as temporary, since he never entirely severed his ties with Scotland. Each summer he returned home, ostensibly to rest and, as a widower, care for the upbringing of his two boys. Doubtless, he used these occasions to keep his name well in the minds of the elders of his Scottish church. On one of his trips to Scotland, the chair of divinity at Glasgow became vacant and Leitch's name, along with nine or ten other candidates, were placed before Queen Victoria. Because she chose her favourite preacher, Dr Edward Caird, later master of Balliol and teacher of Queen's future vice-principal and philosopher, Professor John Watson, Leitch returned to his principalship in Kingston.

PRINCIPAL LEITCH'S MEDICAL FACULTY

Following Dr James Sampson's retirement from the presidency of the medical faculty, Leitch, as principal of Queen's, took over and became the first nonmedical man to preside over the faculty. The principal and all his successors regularly chaired faculty board meetings until well into the twentieth century. The day-to-day organization of the faculty and control of the students remained in the hands of the dean, who was always a doctor.[3] Principal Leitch took the presidency hoping that he might allay the continual bickering and discord which arose mainly from Stewart's disagreements with his colleagues in both the faculty and the hospital.

Since the medical school's inception, its professors had formed the majority of the Kingston General Hospital's medical staff. Drs Dickson and Yates conducted their courses in clinical surgery and clinical medicine on "rounds" and in a newly erected lecture theatre. However, the hospital board of governors were sometimes at loggerheads with the university teachers, particularly when the latter began using more and more of the hospital's facilities for teaching.

An unseemly confrontation between the two parties occurred in 1860 over the appointment of a junior house officer. As a rule, newly graduated doctors or senior medical students provided routine daily care of patients in the Kingston General Hospital. The hospital's board of governors, on the recommendation of the medical faculty, usually appointed such persons. In May, a Mr Neil Dunlop was unanimously nominated by faculty. Unfortunately, hospital authorities gave the job to Alfred Sales Oliver, the nineteen-year-old son of a leading Kingston citizen and former mayor, who had been nominated for the position by two of his father's cronies. At a coroner's inquest, presided over by Dr Stewart, it was discovered that this reversal of faculty's recommendation had been masterminded by Dr Horatio Yates because young Oliver was a Kingston boy. Drs Stewart and Dickson – a most unusual alliance – protested vigorously. Dickson was so incensed that he shook his fist violently under the nose of John Paton, lay governor of the board of the hospital (and well known as a sycophantic supporter of those in high places). Both Stewart and Dickson resigned from the hospital board there and then. No evidence exists that the resignations were accepted, but Stewart continued his attack on Drs Horatio Yates and Fife Fowler in the *Argus*; they, in turn, threatened to resign from the faculty.[4]

The possibility existed that this kind of friction might result in the hospital denying clinical teaching to the medical students. As a result, in April 1861, just before resigning the faculty secretaryship, Stewart drafted a petition to the legislative assembly of Canada West requesting that the Kingston General Hospital Act of 1856 be revised to allow the clinical teaching of university students in the hospital. According to Stewart, the 1849 Kingston Hospital Act had already foreseen such a contingency and teaching was implicit in the Act of 1856, since, in the latter act, one of the medical professors of Queen's College was appointed an *ex officio* member of the hospital corporation: why was the appointment incorporated in the legislation if not to ensure clinical teaching? To Stewart, the special association of Queen's College with the hospital existed because of the necessity of providing bedside instruction to the university's medical students. In the petition Stewart intimated that lately the hospital governors had frustrated the aims of the medical faculty and asked the assembly to amend the Hospital Act to grant Queen's College the legal right to place medical teachers in the hospital to impart the clinical instruction which, according to Stewart, was "imperatively demanded by the youth of the Province entering through her the ranks of the liberal profession of medicine."[5] After all, he noted further, hospital experience was a mandatory requirement for anyone wishing to practise elsewhere in the British dominions.

This petition does not appear to have gone further than a draft. At its 13 March 1861 meeting, the board of trustees appointed the chairman, the Honorable John Hamilton, and Principal Leitch to a committee to confer with the governors of the hospital. At its next meeting, it notified the board that a satisfactory arrangement had been made with the hospital authorities for clinical instruction and that this had been confirmed in a letter written by the hospital secretary. The mutually beneficial health care relationship between the university and the hospital continues to the present day.

Oliver eventually was given the appointment, while Dunlop received the dubious distinction of a glowing testimonial in the pages of the *Argus*.[6] In one of his last acts as secretary of the faculty, Stewart tried to block Oliver's graduation on reaching the age of twenty-one by citing him before the faculty board for dishonourable conduct towards a fellow student, insulting behaviour towards his professors and injury to the good name of the university. Dr Stewart sent all of these charges, with the usual embroidery, in a letter to the principal.[7] They appear to have been used by Stewart as an excuse to precipitate his resignation from the faculty secretaryship on 6 April 1861.[8] Dr Leitch, not for the last time, was left in the unfortunate position of not being able to resolve the conflict.

On the other hand, with the negotiations with the hospital success-fully concluded, Principal Leitch noted with satisfaction during his first convocation address, in 1861, that the medical faculty then had an enrolment of forty-seven students. According to Leitch, Queen's clinical facilities were well up to the standards of the British schools and that the students could not now practise outside Canada.

The expression of growing confidence in the academic stature of Queen's medical school was due to its graduates at last beginning to be recognized by British universities. During the summer of 1860, Dr Dickson took a well-earned vacation to Britain. While in Edinburgh, he approached the university to ascertain whether Queen's medical students would be permitted to sit for the examinations in medicine at Edinburgh and subsequently be eligible for licensure within the British dominions. The following extract from the minutes of the *senatus academicus* of the University of Edinburgh, 31 July 1860, explained the situation:

The following report of the Medical Faculty was read and approved of. The Medical Faculty have considered the question made to them by the Senatus relative to Classes of Queen's College and University, Kingston, Canada, and they find that the Medical classes at the University qualify for Graduation here, in so far as the Courses are of the same nature and extent as those given in this University. At the same time, they find that no Professor can be recognized who lectures on more than one of the subjects mentioned in the Curriculum with the exception of Clinical Medicine.[9]

This recognition was of the utmost importance to Queen's. The faculty immediately complied with the caveat – its 1860/61 calendar no longer mentioned Dr Dickson's chair of clinical surgery and Dr Yates's of clinical medicine.[10] The faculty also tried to receive recognition for its curriculum from the senate of London University.

One of England's most famous pathologists, Dr Thomas Hodgkins, took enough interest in the matter to reinforce the principal's confidence. No sure evidence exists, however, of a firm application.[11]

Some of Dr Stewart's public allegations in the *Argus* tried the principal and the faculty. The doctors knew that because they were not all properly qualified, some unfortunate repercussions could arise under the new medical licensing act just recently promulgated in Canada West.[12] At one of the first faculty meetings after Dr Stewart's dismissal, Dr Lavell moved that medical professors receive degrees from Queen's in keeping with the tradition whereby universities conferred degrees or *ad eundem* (equivalent) degrees on their faculty members. The dean, Dr Dickson, with a colleague, examined the other professors. On 13 January 1863, Litchfield and Lavell, and on the twentieth, Yates and Roderick Kennedy, successor of Stewart as professor of anatomy, passed satisfactorily and were granted the Queen's M.D.[13] It is perhaps fortunate that by this time the *Argus* was no longer being published, and so was unable to report on this understandable bit of academic vanity.

DISMISSAL OF THE PROFESSOR OF ANATOMY

Stewart's animosity towards Principal Leitch stemmed from the support Leitch gave against Stewart to the medical faculty in his capacity as its *ex officio* president. This led to his being made the scapegoat for the dismissal of Stewart from his chair of anatomy in the university. Thereafter, Stewart identified Leitch, whenever he was mentioned in the *Argus*, as *Janus*. On one occasion, Stewart explained that the principal was the two-faced leader of "those low scheming fellows who now compose the Medical Faculty."[14]

Stewart brought his dismissal on himself. In the opinion of his colleagues, he had "been guilty of gross misconduct in publishing in his paper foul slanders against gentlemen connected with the faculty"[15] and those slanders were characterized by a spirit of deep malignancy. The faculty's view led to two actions that sealed Stewart's fate. On 7 February 1862, the faculty decided that Principal Leitch and Dr Octavius Yates should replace Stewart as the examiner in anatomy. On 13 February they submitted a full-scale impeachment of Stewart, filling nine foolscap pages, to the board of trustees.

Naturally Stewart objected to being denied the right to examine the students in his own subject – "it is more difficult to *examine well* in Anatomy than it is to *teach well*."[16] However, in an exchange of letters Leitch and Stewart seemed to have reached an amicable agreement, only to have it ruined by Dickson (the dean) who told the students that Stewart's examination would not be recognized by the university. Consequently, Stewart refused to examine the students and Leitch, Dickson and Yates conducted the examination.

The faculty's indictment of Stewart for "certain improprieties of conduct" posed the more serious academic problem for Leitch and the board. The "Statement and Complaint" consisted of seven itemized accusations against Stewart which delineated that: (1) he had published in the *Argus* a statement that he, Dr Stewart, had appointed Professor Lawson to his chair of chemistry, thereby assuming the power and authority of the board; (2) Stewart (according to himself) having gowned, hooded and capped (with a four cornered and two-tasseled hat) Horatio Yates, he was henceforth responsible for Yates's conduct; (3) Stewart had written that he had, on his own authority, installed Fife Fowler as professor of *materia medica*; (4) he had pointed out in the *Argus* the proper duty of the university's trustees and their repeated neglect of it; (5) Stewart had not attended some regular faculty board meetings and also was "guilty of an impropriety of conduct in refusing or declining to appear in (academic) costume with other members of the university on public occasions"; (6) he had published calumnious statements which interfered with "the education of youth in the principles of the Christian religion" and had stated that Queen's medical faculty "had become the most contemptible in the province"; and, lastly (7) in the *Argus* Stewart had called the professors by their nicknames – in particular, he had mocked Dr Michael Lavell as "Mike" – a creature created by Dr Stewart himself.[17]

Two and one-half pages of sanctimonious concern for the good name of the university, the reputations of the faculty members and the maintenance of Stewart's income, which they thought he derived solely from his chair, followed these charges of improper conduct. There was a limit to the amount of annoyance they could tolerate and the faculty recommended that Stewart be removed from office. If not, the whole faculty would resign. To satisfy procedural proprieties, and in keeping with the provision of the royal charter dealing with dismissal, the medical faculty suggested that the board of trustees appoint a committee to investigate the allegations and then dismiss Stewart. The indictment tailed off with a list of Stewart's alleged pecadilloes and suggested ways of correcting them.

On receipt of the complaint against Stewart, the board of trustees directed the new secretary, Mr W. Ireland, to ask for Dr Stewart's confidential comments. Within two days Ireland's letter to Stewart was published in the *Argus*. The board received Stewart's official rebuttal on 5 March 1862 in which he considered the seven charges, one at a time. He maintained that those concerning the faculty were true and justified; the actions of the board spoke for themselves; while any false and malicious statement injurious to the university should be blamed on those who uttered them and not on him for publishing them.

Queen's trustees met on 12 March. The submissions of the faculty and Stewart were read and debated. The minutes state their conclusions:

Having duly considered the same the Board while reserving their final decision on the whole case, yet find that the charges admitted by Dr. Stewart are of so grave a character, and involve such indiscretion and impropriety of conduct on his part as must necessarily tend to the subversion of discipline in this Institution of whose interests they are appointed guardians.

Whilst the board regret to lose the services of a gentleman of Dr. Stewart's zeal and professional ability in so an important a department of collegiate instruction they are nevertheless constrained by higher considerations of a regard to the interests of the institution itself to suspend in the meantime the said Dr. John Stewart from discharge of all the duties and enjoyment of all the privileges of his professorship in the medical faculty of Queen's College and University. The secretary was instructed to send extracts of the foregoing minutes to Dr. Stewart and the secretary of the medical faculty.[18]

On receipt of these extracts, the faculty ordered them to be printed and immediately circulated among the alumni and students, assuring those interested that every effort would be made to counteract any attempt by the "suspended party" to injure the university.

The board, recognizing that it had not dismissed Stewart with the due formality required by the royal charter and, appreciating the legalistic bent of Stewart's mind, reconsidered the case at its April 1862 meeting, and ordered the following extract from its minutes to be sent to the faculty of medicine:

The trustees having instituted an inquiry into a complaint brought against Dr. John Stewart, professor of anatomy, by the medical faculty of Queen's College, find that impropriety of conduct is duly proved and they resolve to remove him, and they do thereby remove him from his office.

The following are the grounds of such removal: '1. That he has publicly arrogated to himself powers that belong to the trustees of the college. 2. That he has published injurious and calumnious statements in reference to Queen's College. 3. That he has conducted himself towards his colleagues in an uncourteous, ungentlemanly and insulting manner. 4. That he neglected his duty in as far as he for a considerable period, refused to attend the meetings of the medical faculty.'[19]

At the same meeting, Dr Roderick Kennedy was appointed to replace Stewart, the young Dr Octavius Yates was elected to the chair of the institutes of medicine, and Dr Litchfield was transferred to the chair of forensic and state medicine.

Three months later, the faculty tried unsuccessfully to recover from Dr Stewart various documents and pieces of equipment they thought he still possessed – skeletons, a microscope, and some embalming instruments.

Although this is the last we hear of Dr Stewart's activities as professor of anatomy in the university, he spent the rest of his life in Kingston. During the remainder of 1862 he continued to print scurrilous attacks on former colleagues in the *Argus*. One of them, libelling Dr Horatio Yates, landed Stewart in the county jail over Christmas 1862. Notwithstanding a petition of 2,000 Kingstonians for his release, he remained in prison over the holiday period because, inexplicably, Queen's senate counterpetitioned for his continued incarceration.[20]

Stewart's subsequent career in Kingston was that of a popular surgeon and figure about town. He contested and lost both the federal and provincial elections, when, in 1867, the Dominion of Canada was confederated. As he aged and mellowed myths grew up around his earlier career and at his death in 1892 he was remembered and respected as one of the colourful founders of Queen's medical school along with Drs Sampson, Dickson, and Yates.

THE STATUTES

Principal Leitch did not only face the controversy over the academic status of the medical faculty members and their personality conflicts. Year after year he dealt with disagreements as to where precisely in the university lay the power to make statutory decisions. Legally all authority derived ultimately from the royal charter of 1841. Article twenty-two of the charter provided that once the board of trustees had appointed a principal and a professor, they and three members of the board became the college senate. Once three more professors had been appointed, no trustee, other than the principal, was permitted on the senate (Article twenty-three). The function of the senate was "to exercise Academic superintendence and discipline over the students and all other persons resident in the college" (Article twenty-two). It had "power and authority to confer the degrees of Bachelor, Master, and Doctor in the several Arts and Faculties" (Article twenty-four).[21] The board retained the responsibility of promulgating statutes, rules, and ordinances for the proper governing of the college. When the board upgraded its medical department to a faculty in 1855, it passed such an ordinance concerning its financing.

However, an unpleasant confrontation between Vice-Principal James George and Professor George Weir of the arts faculty led to further discussion of the rights and responsibilities of the board of trustees and senate. In August 1862, while Leitch was away in Scotland, the senate, with Dr Williamson as senior professor in the chair, asked the board to formulate a set of regulations or statutes applicable to all faculties, dealing with the management of the internal affairs of the university. The board, in turn, asked the senate for a draft proposal. The board turned over the draft proposal to a committee for study. The draft gave significant autonomy to the separate faculties and their deans, with the principal and senate retaining only general supervisory powers. When Leitch returned to Queen's, he was alarmed by what he saw as a curtailment of the power of the board and the principal. He conferred with Mr Paton, secretary of the board. Ignoring the committee appointed by the board to review the senate draft, they drew up another draft reasserting the absolute authority of the board and principal. The committee, represented by Dr Williamson, protested, but Leitch's "Statutes of Queen's University and College at Kingston" were, in the end, the only ones submitted to the board. They were hotly debated for a week, passed and adopted by the board on 26 January 1863.[22]

Principal Leitch's lack of sensitivity to the concern of the senate and of individual professors for autonomy in academic matters and the unseemly haste with which his and Paton's statutes were accepted firmly aligned the faculty of medicine behind their old friend Dr Williamson – this shortly leading to unforeseen consequences.

The members of the medical faculty closely scrutinized all 109 statutes. They were concerned not only about their academic freedom, but also for their personal and professional integrity. Rightly fearful of lay control, the doctors were willing to accept the principal, a nonmedical man, as titular head of the faculty (Statute 24), but his heavy-fisted direction – no! On 21 March 1863, the medical faculty met and after lengthy discussions requested a conference with the board to discuss the possible effect of the statutes on medical teaching. To make sure their position would not be misunderstood during the informal discussions, the faculty delivered to the board a printed memorandum, an extract from its minutes, which set forth its opinions.[23] It identified three statutes as particularly obnoxious. Statute 7 caused the greatest immediate concern. Although allowing the doctors to use the "Medical Hall," which was university property, for the nominal rent of $1.00 per annum, it required that $500 be appropriated for the salary of the professor of chemistry out of the government grant annually awarded to the university for the medical faculty. This requirement violently disturbed the faculty because: first, the grant was originally made to the medical men in 1854 to assist them in founding the school, not to the trustees for the medical faculty; second, the vote in the legislature renewing the grant each year repeatedly indicated that it was for the specific use of the medical faculty; third, by allowing its faculty to derive their salaries from student fees "and such other sources as may by the liberality of Government or of individuals be specially devoted to that purpose"[24] in its original agreement with the medical school, the board implicitly recognized that government financial support was solely the faculty's to use as it saw fit; and finally, this partitioning of the government grant and its allotment by the trustees to special purposes had not received faculty sanction. The medical faculty had never been happy with the arrangement made when Lawson was appointed in 1858; they continued to feel that the salary of the professor of chemistry, since it was an expense not specifically attributable to the medical school, should be supported from general university funds.

Statute sixty-nine stripped the senate of its independence in academic matters and the faculty rallied to its support. Under the statute, the senate could only meet at the call of the principal and then only during the college sessions. Moreover, a motion passed by the senate in the principal's absence could not be acted upon until he had signed it. As there is always academic business to be done during the summer months, this rule was particularly annoying because Principal Leitch made a practice of returning to Scotland as soon as possible at the end of term. The medical men usually abstained from expressing their opinions on matters relating to the faculties of arts and theology, but they saw very clearly that the paramount issue of academic freedom was at stake: were not Vice-Principal Williamson and the senior university professors to be trusted to speak the senate's will without the supervision and imprimatur of the principal?

The medical faculty also considered Statute fifteen "very objectionable." By this statute the board constituted itself "a Court of Review and Appeal" with respect to any decisions of the senate and faculties.

The members of the medical faculty recognized this as a denial of the senate's rights as the ultimate academic authority, and viewed the statute as a layman's attempt to meddle in traditionally professional matters: who but the medical faculty is competent to judge a candidate's fitness to be granted an M.D.?

Following the long summer vacation, the full board met on 1 October 1863, and although it received several recommendations to amend the statutes, it refused to do so. Events then began to move quickly. Within a month of this rebuff of the senate and faculties, the popular Dr Lawson resigned almost immediately to take a chair at Dalhousie University. No doubt, this action upset the trustees because they had been given such short notice. They reprimanded him, however, not for his precipitous departure, but because he used the occasion to discuss the controversy over the statutes with the students. The trustees alleged that this free expression of opinion brought disrepute on the board. The medical faculty responded by spending a whole faculty meeting composing a laudatory address to Lawson. The next day the faculty met again and expressed its deep regret that the executive committee should have arraigned Dr Lawson on mere hearsay evidence.[25] After Lawson's departure, the board appointed Mr Robert Bell as interim professor of natural history and chemistry, without first consulting the medical faculty.

When the faculty of medicine, not recognizing Bell as a member, met without him on 21 January 1864, five of "the most respectable and reliable students" appeared before faculty to give testimony on "the great disorder" and "the extreme want of discipline" in the chemistry class. The students stated "that they considered it at times unsafe to remain in the class, owing to the billets of wood and other missiles being almost constantly thrown through the room, and frequently aimed at the lecturer himself." They commented further that "when the lecturer goes to the blackboard, he invariably makes mistakes, and lately when he attempts to go there, he is obliged to turn his face to the class every few seconds, as when his back is towards the students they pelt him with chips and the pieces of mouldings which they tear from the benches – Snowballs are also frequently thrown through the class, and the lecturer and his assistant are often thus assailed."[26] Even though he did not have an M.D., Bell might have been accepted by the faculty had he recognized, like Lawson, the vocational aspects of medical school teaching. But, as events proved, although he was knowledgeable in geology, he had no idea how to handle medical students.

The inadequacy of Mr Bell's teaching worried the faculty especially because of the real possibility that it might provoke students to leave Queen's. Dickson reported to the board of trustees:

Several of the students assert that unless some other lecturer is appointed to the Chemical Chair, they will not return to Queen's college another session, but will go either to Montreal or Toronto, as they are satisfied they cannot learn Chemistry from the present lecturer. His experiments invariably fail when his students as invariably commence to pelt him, and this usually excites the uproar ... the faculty after serious deliberation unanimously agreed that some other teacher of Chemistry must be appointed or the Character of the Medical School would be destroyed, and while the members of the Faculty sympathize with Mr. Bell, they at the same time regret that, he should have undertaken to teach Chemistry to a Medical Class without being (as the students assert) sufficiently prepared."[27]

Initially the faculty tried to remedy matters itself by choosing a small committee to meet with Bell to "inform him in as gentle a manner as possible that the members of the Medical Faculty were fully satisfied that it would be for the best interest of the College, as well as his own interest to sever his connexion with the College, as his continuance would drive many of the students away."[28] Their efforts produced no results. A month later Dr Dickson reported to the faculty that Bell was obdurate in his rejection of the students' grievances and blamed Dr Lawson for inciting them to revolt even though he had left Queen's some months earlier.

Mr Bell kept the main thrust of his *apologia* for his letter of 8 February 1864, addressed to the trustees. He denied the allegations, cast aspersions on the faculty's honesty, and refused to offer his resignation. He followed his letter the next day with a formal application for the chair of chemistry. In his letter of application, Robert Bell affirmed his fitness for the permanent appointment on several grounds: one, as a geologist of seven years, he would have no trouble "in the management of students" (this showed how little he knew of that mythical creature "the average medical student"); two, that three brothers had graduated from Queen's, even though he had not; and three, that his father had donated his whole geological cabinet of 3,000 specimens to the university.[29] He wrote not a word about his commitment to the medical faculty, which was being made to pay the lion's share of his salary. At its next meeting, the board converted Bell's interim appointment into a permanent one as professor of natural history and chemistry. The medical faculty was dismayed by this action of the board – they considered Bell unsuitable and saw in his appointment the realization of another of their fears.

Not only was half the faculty's government grant to be allocated to Bell's salary, he was also to be allowed to retain the medical students' class fees. Many thought that he was being paid excessively from medical funds while the medical professors, who did much more teaching in the medical faculty, received fees but no stipend. Since he taught in the faculty of arts, they felt that the university board should have funded most of his salary from its own operating account.

The conversion of Mr Bell's interim appointment as professor of chemistry into a permanent position has been charitably described by Professor Neatby as "another apparently dubious and even in its origin faintly discreditable appointment."[30] The trustees' lack of sensitivity and concern for the well-being of the medical faculty and its students remains incomprehensible. In retrospect, their action appears to be, if not the result of sheer incompetence, the first expression of a desire to oust the medical faculty from the university, or, worse still, an ill-conceived attempt by the board to subvert the universally recognized traditional academic autonomy of a professional faculty. The medical men knew from historic precedent that it was only a short step from the Bells of this world to quackery and intellectual irrelevance in medical education. The whole episode stands as an example of the continual struggle of professional faculties for academic freedom and excellence in the face of an incompetent individual academic on the one hand, and intransigent inept lay authority on the other.

Professor Bell's time in the medical faculty cannot have been happy. Little of him appears in the minutes over the next two years. In 1865 he charged a medical student with disarranging some of his chemical apparatus and taking away a bottle of lime water. Bell wrote to Principal Snodgrass and the senate asking for a full investigation of the outrage. The following year Bell made a much more serious charge of insubordination against another student – he was sustained and the student rusticated. By this time, late April 1866, Bell must have realized that if the medical faculty seceded from the university, as seemed increasingly likely, his own relationship with it would have to come to an end. He wrote to the board in an attempt to justify his salary, which the board would, in the event of secession, have to pay in full, despite his decreased teaching responsibility. He offered his services as curator of the museum, since he would only have two classes in arts a week.[31] Shortly thereafter, probably recognizing he was not born to teach, he rejoined the Geological Survey of Canada and became the chief geologist in 1890.

Mr Bell's short connection with the medical faculty would doubtless have been forgotten were it not for the fact that both of the university's official histories implicitly connect Bell's permanent appointment and Dr Dickson's resignation. However, the anticipated reaction from a dean of Dickson's calibre, one, moreover, who had withstood the outrageous Stewart at his worst to the inappropriate appointment of a junior professor, would be to shrug it off, get on with running his medical school, and obtain his personal relief from bureaucratic myopia by looking after his patients – unless, of course, a matter of principle which impugned his own good name or that of his faculty or profession were at stake. This was the business of the statutes.

In his 15 February 1864 letter to the board, Dr Dickson clearly states the reason for his resignation. "As soon as I saw those very objectionable Statutes, which were sanctioned by the Trustees, I determined to sever my connexion with the College, and only deferred doing so at the solicitation of my colleagues, as they felt assured that some of those statutes would be repealed." Since they were not, he resolved to submit his resignation, although he promised "to take a deep interest in the Medical Faculty, and endeavour to advance its prosperity in every way in my power."[32] Dr Dickson's colleagues requested at the next faculty meeting that Dickson withdraw his resignation until the statutes' validity, still *sub judice*, was tested.[33] The board appears to have accepted his resignation, without regret, on 9 March. The next day Mr William Ireland informed the faculty "that Dr. Dickson's resignation had been accepted by the trustees to take effect on the 31st inst."[34]

With this abrupt communication, the board showed a graceless lack of appreciation of one of the founders of Queen's most successful faculty. The trustees' statement hurt Dickson deeply; he and others considered the manner in which the trustees handled the affair to be an undignified display of bad manners, quite unbecoming gentlemen. The students and professors determined to show their appreciation of Dickson by preparing sympathetic laudatory addresses to be delivered at the coming medical convocation.

At the ceremony, Dr Horatio Yates would present the faculty's address of appreciation to Dr Dickson, while newly graduated Dr Andrew Dunn was to speak on behalf of the graduates and students. Learning of this plan, three local trustees, Hon. John Hamilton, Mr John Paton, and Mr George Davidson, fearing the disapproval of the board, forbade Dr Williamson to permit anything other than a routine convocation programme. But the faculty found a way to circumvent this pettiness. Towards the end of convocation, Williamson, the presiding senior professor, turned to Dr Dickson, who then invited the assembly to adjourn upstairs to his lecture room. Between 150 and 200 people went to hear the testimonials. Dr Dickson spoke more in sorrow than anger. He looked back on the school's ten successful years and expressed the hope that soon the heavy cloud which overshadowed the university would pass away and that the sun would shine gloriously on the graduates' Alma Mater. After this melancholy affair, the company reassembled in Convocation Hall to receive Professor Williamson's benediction. Much to the annoyance of the local trustees, a full report of the convocation proceedings appeared the same evening in a Kingston paper.[35]

Three weeks after Dickson's departure, the faculty met to consider necessary changes in staff appointments. The members nominated Horatio Yates as dean, Fife Fowler, secretary; Roderick Kennedy was to be transferred from anatomy to surgery and Michael Sullivan, promoted from demonstrator of anatomy to the chair. The faculty sent these nominations to the board unaware that it had received a letter of application for the chair of surgery from Dr Donald Maclean, an alumnus of the arts faculty who had subsequently qualified in medicine at Edinburgh. Dr Maclean, before going into private practice, had fought on the Union side in the American Civil War, where he gained valuable clinical and pathological experience in the Union's large military hospitals. In his letter of application, he assured the board that he would be as devoted to the duties of the chair and the university as he was to the church with which it was associated.[36]

After its dealings with Dr Dickson over the statutes, these sentiments were presumably very acceptable to some of the trustees. At a 28 April meeting, the Reverend Dr Urquhart moved and the Reverend Dr Mathieson seconded that Dr Donald Maclean be appointed (inexplicably) to the chair of the institutes of medicine, held by Dr Octavius Yates. Although some members of the board suggested it might be appropriate to refer the whole matter to a committee to confer with the medical faculty, the suggestion was set aside, a vote called, and the main motion was carried by the casting vote of the chairman, the Honorable John Hamilton – Dr Maclean was duly appointed professor of the institutes of medicine, not surgery. The board transferred Dr Octavius Yates, whose chair had just been given to Maclean to the chair of surgery.[37] By taking these actions without consulting the medical faculty, the board (and especially its chairman) clearly meant to show the professors who really ran the university. Dr Horatio Yates and Fowler were confirmed as dean and secretary respectively as of 21 May 1864, in keeping with faculty recommendations.

DETERIORATING RELATIONS
WITH THE UNIVERSITY: THE
END OF THE BEGINNING

Principal Leitch died in May 1864 and the Reverend William Snod-grass was appointed to the position in August 1864. He presided over the meetings of the medical faculty with more diplomacy than his predecessor, and consequently a situation of greater mutual respect developed, destined, unfortunately, to last only for the next two years. The minutes of the medical faculty meeting for 1864/65 and 1865/66 consist, in the main, of a record of examination results, matriculations, and routine faculty business. A number of changes were introduced. The dissecting room remained open during the evening of working days and on Saturday mornings, under the supervision of Dr Sullivan. The hospital accepted Dr Maclean as clinical lecturer in surgery because his skill as a surgeon had soon become appreciated by his colleagues. A summer session was introduced for the first time in the medical school on 15 May 1865. But while the faculty itself was managing its own business without incident under Dr Yates as dean, relations with the university board of trustees were becoming more strained.

The university trustees had gradually become disenchanted with the medical students, who set a bad example with their boisterous behaviour. They were also less amenable to discipline than the divinity or arts men. The medicos were not only publicly intemperate, but it was widely known that they occasionally stayed in bed on Sunday mornings and sometimes even missed divine service. Some of the trustees must also have suspected the medical professors of a similar lack of religious devotion, perhaps even of secularist free-thinking.

In 1859, Darwin published *On the Origin of Species* and for the first time since Galileo, biophysical concepts threatened the metaphysics of the established religions. Because the medical men were the only group in Kingston who were scientists by profession, they tended to be seen as secular, irreligious radicals. The other scientists in town were senior clerics of the stature of Principal Leitch and the Reverend Dr Williamson, whose beliefs were above reproach. Even though all the doctors on the faculty of medicine were churchgoing men, the trustees must have feared that they would be especially susceptible to revolutionary ideas.[38] The board was well aware that not one of the medical faculty publicly accepted the tenets of the Presbyterian persuasion, a condition normally required of all Queen's professors. Even though some of them did so privately, the faculty seemed to agree that they should not be required to submit publicly to Presbyterian doctrines. In`this way, they would avoid the consequences of denominationalism suffered by Toronto's Trinity medical school: nine medical students, who could not accept the Anglican Thirty-Nine Articles, had been prevented from graduating and received their degrees in medicine from Queen's – precisely because the university erected no such sectarian barriers.

This situation deeply disturbed some members of the board of trustees. At a meeting during the summer of 1865, Judge Malloch moved, seconded by Mr Edward Malloch and carried, that application should be made to the Presbyterian synod for a formula of faith which, in keeping with the university charter, should be signed by all Queen's professors not in the theology department.[39]

The statutes had already asserted the dominance of the board over the academic senate and the faculties in matters of finance and of appointments; this motion seems to have been either an attempt to deny the medical professors freedom of religious thought or the board's desire to use religion as a wedge to separate Queen's College from its medical faculty and consequently restore the university to its pristine Presbyterian purity.

Principal Snodgrass, an enlightened cleric and a clear-minded scholar, had the unhappy task of trying to reconcile the intransigence of the religious zealots on the board with the pragmatism of the medical men who were being forced to take a secularist position in support of freedom of conscience, even though most of them personally accepted the trustees' doctrinal position on the Westminster Confession of Faith.[40]

The majority on the board was about to insist on the medical faculty's submission to the confessional requirements when Principal Snodgrass, who had conferred with the faculty, realized that a deadlock was rapidly approaching. To save irretrievable loss of face by either party, the principal suggested that a series of meetings should be held during the spring and summer of 1866.

Despite his attempts to reconcile the trustees and the doctors, the disagreement gradually increased. On 19 April 1866, Principal Snodgrass, as president *ex officio*, read an extract from the minutes of the board of trustees to the medical faculty. It explained that he and Judge Malloch had been appointed to meet formally with the faculty to try to reach a compromise by which the terms of the university charter could be met, particularly the doctrinal one.[41]

The meeting was adjourned *sine die* without discussion of the principal's ideas. The faculty members were divided among themselves. Some wished to maintain the status quo, and were willing to sign the Westminster Confession. At least one, Dr Sullivan, being a Roman Catholic, could not, in conscience, sign. Others, presumably, were simply unwilling to get involved in religious matters which had nothing to do with medicine.

Meanwhile, Judge Malloch even refused to meet with the medical professors and with the principal to try to arrive at a *modus vivendi* that might have saved the university from its own self-denying ordinance. As it turned out, Judge Malloch was unable to get the board to press the synod to draw up the desired religious formula. Accepting this as a lack of confidence in his position, he resigned from the Queen's board because he continued to believe that, in keeping with the spirit of the royal charter and common justice, the medical men should subscribe to the same formula required of other professors.[42]

However, the incident had pushed some of the medical faculty too far. Some decided to secede from the university. The confrontation had provided the medical men with an excuse to take over complete control of the medical school and its destiny. By the end of the summer of 1866, the medical faculty had separated itself from the university. Paradoxically, by withdrawing from the university, the medical faculty in the long run perhaps saved the university from its own narrow sectarianism, by making it realize that without a medical school it might become a simple bible college with a liberal arts appendage.

MEDICAL PRACTICE AND TEACHING IN THE MID-NINETEENTH CENTURY

Between the founding of Queen's medical faculty and its dissolution, significant changes occurred not only in European and North American medicine, but also in the legislation controlling the medical profession of Upper Canada.

At Queen's, the successful graduation of 161 M.D.s during its first twelve years bred self-confidence in the medical school. The academic standing of the school had been enhanced by the performance of its graduates and the recognition of its M.D. by the universities of London and Edinburgh and the Royal Colleges in the United Kingdom (see p. 62).[43] Because almost from the beginning professors were encouraged to publish their case histories in the British, American, and Canadian medical journals, an academic atmosphere came to pervade the school.

Clinical teaching at McGill's medical faculty, founded thirty years before Queen's medical school, was based on the venerable but rapidly declining tradition of medicine that stretched back to Hippocrates, Galen, and Paulus Aeginata. In contrast, the teaching at the University of Western Ontario, founded just over a quarter of a century after the medical school at Queen's, was irrevocably in the era of modern medicine. Queen's fledgling faculty of medicine lived through this intellectually exciting time, making its first tentative steps within the crumbling empiric tradition while at the same time warily accepting novel nineteenth-century concepts of scientific medicine.

Changes in the scientific methodology of medicine did not suddenly occur during the decade or so between the middle 1850s to 1860s. Scientific medicine gradually changed, reaching beyond causal association between symptoms observed during life and gross macroscopic findings postmortem. Controlled observation, correlation, and classification became the springboard for investigation and experimentation. Microscopy and urine examination for specific gravity, protein, casts, and blood were becoming commonplace among academic clinicians to further their diagnostic capabilities. Medical teaching underwent a parallel shift in emphasis. For example, while Sir William Osler was still in primary school and at least sixteen years before he introduced his course in medical microscopy at McGill, the microscope was being used for teaching pathological physiology in Queen's medical school.[44]

When the faculty was founded in 1854, gross human anatomy reigned alone as the preclinical or basic science in medicine, although tentative searches for the chemical infrastructure of health and disease had already begun. The functional aspects of structure were identified, and consequently the separate science of physiology slowly, but irrevocably, became differentiated from anatomy as a discipline to be taught in its own right. This was most obviously evident at Queen's when a separate course in institutes of medicine, taught by Dr Litchfield, was established in 1861. Gross pathological changes were routinely recognized and classified postmortem. By the middle of the 1860s, autopsies were conducted in Kingston for scientific and pedagogical reasons as well as when required by the coroner to provide evidence at an inquest.

The general acceptance of the thermometer and the gradual introduction of the ophthalmoscope further advanced clinical acumen at Queen's, as elsewhere. Although the ophthalmoscope was not commonly used, its availability led to the establishment of one of the earliest surgical specialties – ophthalmology. A Queen's student, R.A. Reeve, who graduated in 1865, was among the earliest practitioners. He took up his specialty in Kingston within fifteen years of Helmholtz's first successful use of the ophthalmoscope. Because it was a garrison town many retired soldiers with eye diseases settled in

Kingston after serving in the Near or Far East, where diseases of the eye were endemic.

Although the hypodermic syringe was used by the middle sixties, there was no great increase in the therapeutic armamentarium for which it could be employed. Morphia was the only drug given in this manner, although numerous physicians had tried unsuccessfully to use intravenous therapy as a technique of treatment. The other truly significant advance of the middle 1800s was general anaesthesia. During the early years of the faculty, ether and chloroform were still considered mixed blessings for operations, although they eliminated pain, inefficient antiseptic care in hospitals often led to erysipelas, gangrene, and septicaemia and patients died anyway. The full benefits of operative anaesthesia had to wait for the general acceptance of Lister's antiseptic carbolic spray, introduced in 1867.[45]

The relatively unrestricted frontier society in the United States enabled any sect or individual to practise medicine in his own way, controlled solely by criminal and civil law. The more aberrant practitioners, usually itinerant, were recognized as quacks or charlatans, and, when too unacceptable, were probably dealt with appropriately. A number of the more plausible sects or schools of medicine supported a single cause theory of disease or the benefit inherent in a particular therapeutic regimen. The slicker and more persuasive of these practitioners gave a verisimilitude to their medical practice by believing, teaching and proclaiming widely that their methodology was based on a philosophic truth either not appreciated or actively rejected by regularly qualified practitioners. The most successful of these sects in Ontario were the homeopaths, the eclectics, and the botanics. These sects pejoratively labelled the traditionalists as "allopathic physicians," in an attempt to make them, before the law, just one of the many sects of medicine. Allopathy, they suggested, was a health-care delivery system no more valid than any other. A small number of the nonallopathic sects were sufficiently well organized in Upper Canada to sway legislative committees and recommend changes in the medical licensing laws that would protect their interests.

Orthodox physicians and surgeons saw in legislation a distressing evidence of the persuasive power of the sects. The legislative assembly gave legitimacy to the homeopaths in 1859 (22 Vic. c.47, Canada) and to the eclectics in 1861 (24 Vic. c.110, Canada),[46] endowing them with virtually the same professional status as university-educated physicians still being licensed under the Medical Act of 1827. Fortunately, however, students of these sects were required to attend a recognized medical school for at least two of the four mandatory years of medical education before they could present themselves as candidates for the licensing examination in homeopathic or eclectic medicine. It is impossible to know with any certainty whether the fine Italian hand of the allopathic medical fraternity influenced these bills. Although some of their criticisms seem, in retrospect, to be tongue-in-cheek, the orthodox traditionalists who had founded and controlled the medical schools of Canada West were so vocal in their journals, in the newspapers, and in the legislature about the sects that they may well have been able to influence the educational requirements demanded of the homeopaths and the eclectics.

Nevertheless, the very persuasiveness of the sects worried the profession (although, fortunately for the citizens, none of the sects appears to have had a large following in Kingston, probably because of the high standards set by Dr Sampson and Dr Horatio Yates as consulting physicians and professors of clinical medicine.

The medical profession had other concerns. Any military surgeon or graduate of a British medical school could obtain a licence to practise in Her Majesty's North American colonies, and because many were settling in the province, the profession feared the loss of self-discipline in the profession. Furthermore, because the universities controlled the admission of medical students, by the early 1860s the profession in the province began to worry that its autonomy was slipping away. MacNab has pointed out that "the inevitable enactment, which came in 1865, represented a compromise between the demands of the profession and the growing influence of the universities."[47]

The 1865 parliamentary bill was as significant to organized Canadian medicine as the Medical Act of 1858 to the British medical community. It guaranteed the autonomy of the profession with respect to entry into the profession and discipline of its own members and ensured its influence on the educational process and curriculum content by legalizing its power to examine. Bill 29 Vic. c.34 (Canada) managed to balance the sometimes conflicting interests of the practising profession, on the one hand, and, on the other, the medical academics whose loyalty rested in the universities.

The newly appointed General Council for Medical Education and Registration (Medical Council) set up by the act of 1865 was the product of the compromise. Twelve members were to be elected from Canada West's territorial districts. Each medical school or university that had the right to grant degrees in medicine was allocated a seat, which had to be held by a licensed practitioner. Dr Horatio Yates, the dean of medicine, represented Queen's senate. Dr Dickson, former dean and vice-president of the faculty, was elected as the local territorial representative and, because of his seniority and national reputation, he became the new Medical Council's first president.

The act stipulated that the licence to practise in the province was to be granted only after a certificate of graduation or an M.D. degree had been issued by an authorized medical school in the province and to those entitled by previous legislation. Medical men from the universities directed the examinations for these certificates. Although the Medical Council lost its right to hold its own examinations – that had been one of the responsibilities of its predecessor, the Medical Board of 1827 – it retained the power to set matriculation standards and supervise curricular content and the medical schools received the right to control examinations.

The governor-in-council of the Medical Council had the power to ensure a degree of conformity in curricular formation, thus effectively holding in check the grosser aberrances of the homeopaths, eclectics, and botanics. The 1865 act implicitly required that all medical students spend at least two years attending an approved school. A neophyte practitioner then had to decide whether the psychic and fiscal rewards from practising other than allopathic medicine were worth it. In fact, this provision of the 1865 act effectively sounded the death knell for the sects in Ontario.

The 1865 bill contained a number of noneducational regulations which had, however, an indirect bearing on the development of medicine in Ontario: for example, it restricted the prescription of drugs to licenced practitioners, who also were the only people permitted medical appointments in the militia or provincial service.

The Medical Council, in its advisory role to the governor-in-council, could report on the adequacy of a particular medical school's curriculum. If unsatisfactory, the council could then recommend that the governor refuse to license candidates from that school. This is the earliest legislated accreditation process in this country.

As a result of the Medical Act of 1865, medical education became a direct concern of the licensing council elected by the practising members of the profession. Although the physicians were reasonably pleased with the restoration of their autonomy, the lay-dominated senates of those universities with medical schools saw in the provisions of the act concerning curriculum an erosion of their cherished educational responsibilities. Rather than accept the status of a simple provider of medical training without academic authority, the senate of Queen's preferred to wash its hands of responsibility for medical education. In this decision the senate seems to have found solid support on the board of trustees. In the year after the medical bill's enactment, the university and the medical men accepted, with a fair degree of equanimity, the closure of Queen's faculty of medicine as a teaching institution and the formation of a newly incorporated Royal College of Physicians and Surgeons of Kingston, affiliated with the university.

The Royal College of Physicians and Surgeons, Kingston: Foundation and Affiliation with Queen's

The first incarnation of Queen's medical school legally existed until 29 August 1866. On that day, by resolution of the board of trustees of the university, medicine ceased to be taught in Queen's College. By then, however, royal assent had already been given to incorporate the Royal College of Physicians and Surgeons, thus ensuring the continuation of the tradition of medical education in Kingston.

THE ESTABLISHMENT OF THE ROYAL COLLEGE

Friction between the medical faculty and the board had come to a head over the Westminster Confession. Principal Snodgrass's suggestion for meetings between the board, represented by himself and Judge Malloch, and the medical faculty came to nothing as Judge Malloch refused to participate. The faculty's position also hardened, with a majority coming to favour independence from the university.[1]

At the end of April 1866, Principal Snodgrass, following the meeting with the medical faculty, reported to the board the implications of the 1865 Medical Act and the reactions to it of both doctors and the senate. Word seems to have spread through Kingston that the medical men were discussing among themselves how to secede from the university but still maintain a medical school in town. Snodgrass explained to the board the feasible alternatives available: (1) the complete break-up of the medical faculty and consequent cessation of medical teaching in Kingston; (2) continuation of the school in the university as a purely denominational body thereby restricting the number of Kingston professional men whom it could call upon to teach; and (3) a complete severance from Queen's by the doctors and the inauguration of a new medical school which, though legally separated from

Queen's, might be amicably affiliated with it for the purposes of degree granting. This third option was doubtless the principal's own suggestion and recommendation.[2]

Snodgrass laid before the board the advantages to the university of secession. Simple affiliation with a separate, legally incorporated medical college would eliminate the conflict and animosity naturally arising from confessional loyalties. Separation would also divest the university of unpleasant student discipline problems, and it would enable the university to rent the Medical Building to the new college and thus recoup some of the money it had laid out eight years before.

Because most of the faculty thought that the existing situation could not continue, the principal recommended that the board accept the idea of affiliation with as much grace as possible. He intimated that the trustees would then reciprocate the courtesy and amiable spirit already expressed by the members of the medical faculty.

By the time Snodgrass had reported to the board, the doctors had taken the first steps towards the incorporation of a new medical school. Their intention was to obtain licensing and teaching powers from the government while retaining the option, through continued affiliation with Queen's, for their students to earn a university medical degree.

Little documentary evidence remains in Queen's archives of what must have been a summer of feverish activity for a few of Kingston's medical men, although much can be inferred. The university and the medical school both had to make accommodations of some importance.

First of all, however, the legal requirements had to be met. During the months of June, July and early August 1866, three meetings were held of the provisionally organized, but as yet unincorporated, Royal. Present at all three were Dr John R. Dickson, the unanimous choice as president, Dr Fife Fowler, registrar, Dr Michael Sullivan, and Dr Michael Lavell. Other Royal College founders, Drs R. A. Reeve and Donald Maclean, also attended one or more of these early meetings. Of this small but distinguished group, five of the six in their time were deans of four different medical schools, four became president of the Ontario Medical Council, two president of the Canadian Medical Association, one president of the American Medical Association, one president of the British Medical Association, and three close advisers to Sir John A. Macdonald in either a private or public capacity.

The provisional corporation, as a first unofficial act, read the act of incorporation drafted by Dr Lavell. The draft was approved by the meeting and "handed to Dr. Dickson for transmission to the member for the city" (John A. Macdonald).[3] Then a letter was read from Dr H.

Yates, dean of Queen's moribund faculty, in which he expressed a willingness to join the new college. Principal Snodgrass's invitation to meet with the university representatives was also considered. Dr Lavell's legal bent was again expressed at the second meeting when his provisional set of by-laws were ordered to be held *in retentis* until the college should be incorporated. By the third week of August, incorporation had been accomplished.

Bill No. 214, 5th session, 8th Parliament, 29/30 Victoria 1866, An Act to Incorporate the Queen's College of Physicians and Surgeons of Kingston was received and read for the first time on Wednesday 18 July. The second reading occurred the next day. It received royal assent on 15 August. Although this was essentially a private member's bill, it was considered for constitutional purposes to be a public one. John A. Macdonald steered the bill through parliament. According to Dr Dickson, the Honorable Alex. Campbell and Alex. Morris, M.P.P. assisted Macdonald.

In Queen's archives a handwritten draft is extant, Act to Incorporate – College of Physicians and Surgeons, Kingston, Canada, that presumably formed the basis for the printed legislation. The draft omits the adjective in the title, indicating it only by a dash. Was it to be *Queen's* College of Physicians and Surgeons, Kingston or the *Royal* College of Physicians and Surgeons, Kingston? It had obviously become common knowledge during April 1866 that certain of the Kingston medical men who were considering the feasibility of establishing a medical school were about to approach parliament for the incorporation of the organization to be named Queen's College of Physicians and Surgeons, Kingston, Canada. The similarity of the name to "Queen's College of Kingston" agitated the university trustees. At their board meeting of 27 April they agreed that the principal should ask the doctors to change the name. The doctors apparently agreed; but when Bill No. 214 was first printed, An Act to Incorporate the Queen's College of Physicians and Surgeons, Kingston, appeared on the outside of the schedule, while the first line of the text read An Act to Incorporate the Royal College of Physicians and Surgeons of Kingston.[4]

The name of the new medical school suggests that it was a royal foundation, meaning that it had received Her Majesty's consent and a royal charter of incorporation like Queen's University twenty-five years earlier. But as no written evidence exists of either Queen Victoria's consent or of the existence of a charter, it can be presumed unlikely that one ever existed or for that matter was ever sought. The minutes of neither the corporation nor the faculty of the college mention neither consent nor the existence of a charter. Besides, a royal charter would have been expensive to obtain and would have required lengthy discussion, because the college treasury was always short of funds.[5]

The handwritten draft of the act of incorporation appears to have been written by Dr Michael Lavell. In general, the wording of the legislated act parallels that of the draft. The draft was clarified and tightened up by the parliamentary writer, who, in the process, compressed Lavell's ten paragraphs into eight by omitting unparliamentary verbosity. The first paragraph or section in both draft and act names the incorporators and constitutes them as a body politic. This corporate body was to have perpetual succession and a common seal, "with power to break, alter or renew the same . . . it may sue, be sued, plead and be impleaded in any courts of law or equity in this Province [i.e. Canada], may purchase, lease, take and hold real estate, etc. etc . . . provided always that the said estate held by the said corporation does not exceed the value of twenty thousand dollars."[6] Paragraphs five, six, and seven of the act deal with items relating to the Royal's academic, as distinct from its corporate, functions and with students' certificates of qualification, the Medical Act of Upper Canada, and college affiliation.

Paragraph five controlled the students' access to practice. This section placed the college on an equal footing in matters of medical education and licensure with any degree granting university within the British Empire:

Whenever any student shall in his medical studies, and in all other particulars have complied with the requirements of the corporation of the said college, and of the existing, or any future law regulating the practice of the medical profession in Upper Canada, it shall be lawful for the corporation of said college to grant him a certificate of qualification, or diploma, or such other credential, or any or either of which shall entitle him to registration.[7]

Paragraph six conferred on the Royal the rights granted by the Medical Act of Upper Canada (1865) to specific medical colleges in the province and required it to make certain declarations and returns to the Medical Council. On payment of the stipulated fee, persons whose names and addresses had been notified to the council would be placed automatically on the medical register.

Paragraph seven of the Royal's act was most important for the future of medical education in Kingston. Parliament gave the college the right to affiliate with an established university, should it deem it advisable or expedient, in order to procure for its students degrees in medicine, surgery, and midwifery: "It shall be lawful for such purpose to affiliate with any university empowered to grant degrees in this Province, and such university is hereby empowered to affiliate and grant such degrees."[8]

John A. Macdonald seems to have undertaken all the legal and parliamentary work on behalf of the Royal during the summer of 1866; notwithstanding the urgency of affairs of state – specifically the building of the original Canadian confederation and preparations to repulse the Fenians – he managed to find the time to act as midwife for Kingston's newest medical school. On the same day that the Royal College bill received royal assent, 15 August 1866, Regiopolis College in Kingston was elevated to university status. It also was granted the right to award the M.D. degree, although to date it has never taken advantage of the privilege.

At Queen's, as both sides recognized the *fait accompli* of the separation of the medical school from the university before the actual passage of the act, they were able to set about reaching an accommodation on specific regulations which would meet the terms of affiliation. The senate was concerned that its academic prerogatives be protected, while at the same time the Royal College corporation wanted to ensure that its regulations were legally in tune with the forthcoming act of incorporation.

The board set up on 8 June to discuss with the provisionally organized Royal the terms of affiliation. The university board appointed Principal Snodgrass, as chairman, Dr Barclay, Messrs Logie, Davidson, and Paton, while the Royal was represented by Dr Dickson and Dr Fowler. On 24 July 1866, the principal presented a report to the university's board of trustees in which were laid out the Royal's conditions for affiliation. The most important condition stated "that the senate of the University of Queen's College confer the degree of Doctor of Medicine on all candidates whom the College of Physicians and Surgeons shall recommend."[10] To counter the senate's probable objection that this condition pre-empted its academic decision making, Principal Snodgrass pointed out that the Royal's request was not unreasonable because the Medical Council of Canada, since its establishment the previous year, had set down strict requirements respecting the education of medical practitioners. The matriculation requirements set by the Medical Council for admission to the licensing process were higher than those hitherto enacted by any college, including Queen's. Furthermore, the Medical Council had defined a stiffer curriculum and set stricter attendance requirements than Queen's itself had previously demanded. Had Queen's continued to retain a medical school, it would, like the Royal, have had to adjust to these higher standards. Dr Snodgrass assured the board of trustees, and by inference the senate, that its level of academic excellence would be more than maintained.

At the same time, however, the principal and his colleagues presented to the board four reasons why it would not be proper for the senate to denude itself completely of its powers or hold in abeyance the performance of its duties in connection with the granting of medical degrees. In the first place, the honour of the university was involved in the conferment of degrees and the trustees and senate had an obligation to see that it was bestowed only on deserving candidates. Second, the Medical Act of 1865 required the University of Queen's College to observe its enactments and the university had a legal duty to uphold the act. Third, the university had an interest to try to raise the standard of medical education which, Snodgrass suggested, should be attempted separately from the Royal. Finally, although the by-laws of the new college appeared adequate at the moment, they might become unacceptable in the future.

The physicians' representatives saw some merit in the principal's position but were unhappy with the thought of their students sitting two different examinations to obtain an M.D. from Queen's. The doctors, however, eventually accepted the two-examination idea and also a set of by-laws drawn up by the nonmedical members of the senate to implement the affiliation: the senate could inspect and approve all necessary tickets and certificates issued by the Royal and retain the "right of examination." This right was regularly exercised by the principal and one or more senior members of the senate (by necessity nonmedical men), attending all the Royal's final oral examinations. Through the exercise of this right, Queen's retains an unbroken record as the longest surviving independent medical school in English-speaking Canada. The idea of a conjoint university-Medical Council and Royal College examination was envisioned but never put into effect. Many years later, however, after the demise of the Royal, conjoint examinations were held.

The Royal's proposal that the university rent to the corporation of the college the building and appliances then used by Queen's medical faculty for an annual rental of $250 formed a second major contentious issue. Snodgrass and his fellow board members felt that such an offer on the part of the medical men was scarcely adequate, particularly if the deterioration of the equipment was taken into account. They recommended acceptance of the offer, however, at least until the Royal got on its feet. The university's committee closed its report to the board of trustees by recommending that a legal contract be drawn up by the university solicitor covering all the normal housekeeping arrangements – six-month's notice to void the contract, rent to be paid semiannually, tenants to maintain the building and carry out repairs except those due to ordinary wear and tear, and the university principal's right of access to the building.[11]

The full board received the committee's report and the draft of the Royal's act on 25 July 1866. They approved both but particularly the terms of affiliation. While the joint committee was working out the mechanism of affiliation, the senate was formulating its own regulations for matriculation and eventually bestowing the M.D. degree on the Royal's students. The academic by-laws drafted for the senate during August 1866 were similar to those in force in the university's arts and theology faculties at the time.

Although the faculty of the Royal did the actual teaching, the formal lecture courses stipulated in senate regulations were essentially those required by the Medical Council for licensure.[12] Two six-month courses were to be taken in the following subjects: general and practical anatomy, chemistry, *materia medica* and pharmacy, physiology (or institutes of medicine), theory and practice of medicine and midwifery, and diseases of women and children. One three-month course in each of practical chemistry, botany, clinical medicine, clinical surgery, and medical jurisprudence was also obligatory. In addition, each student was required to compound medicines for twelve months in the office of qualified practitioner, to attend at least six cases of midwifery, and to pass a primary and final examination. The senate, expressing its adherence to high academic standards, also insisted that each candidate compose a thesis on some medical subject.

Kingston's new medical school was already legally established when Queen's board of trustees met on 29 August 1866 to discuss the future of medical education in the university. The board received reports from its various committees and listened to the Act to Incorporate the Royal College of Physicians and Surgeons of Kingston. The minutes reflect the solemnity of the occasion:

After deliberation it was resolved
I. To accept the resignations of Professors Litchfield, Fowler, Lavell, Kennedy and MacLean, and of Dr. M. Sullivan, Assistant Professor of Anatomy, and the same are hereby accepted.

II. To discontinue the Medical Faculty of the University in so far as the teaching department of the said Faculty is concerned and the same is hereby discontinued with instructions to the Secretary of the Board to intimate this resolution to Dr. Horatio Yates, heretofore Professor of the

Principles and Practice of Medicine, Dr. Octavius Yates, heretofore Professor of the Principles and Practice of Surgery and Dr. Robert Bell, heretofore Professor of Chemistry in the Medical Department.

III. To approve of the reports of the committee appointed to confer with the Royal College of Physicians and Surgeons, and of the draft of Bylaws prepared for adoption by the Senate, and the same are hereby approved of, with instructions to the Secretary to engross the supplementary report after entering this minute in the Records.

IV. To affiliate 'the Royal College of Physicians and Surgeons of Kingston' with this University, and the same is hereby affiliated, the connection thus formed to continue so long as it shall be agreeable to this Board and the corporation of the said Royal College or their successors respectively, it being agreed, in virtue of this affiliation – (1) That all actual students in the College being already matriculants in the Faculty of Medicine of Queen's College shall have rank in this University as undergraduates in Medicine, provided they have been registered or so soon as they shall be registered in the register of Queen's College. (2) That hereafter students in the said College shall take rank as undergraduates or graduates of this University in Medicine upon complying with the terms and requirements respecting matriculation and registration on graduation respectively as set forth in the reports and draft Bylaws approved of in the third of these resolutions. (3) That the Senate of this University shall in every way consistently with duty to the University consult the convenience and interests of the said College in all their arrangements for the examinations required for the admission of students to the rank of undergraduates and graduates.

And the Board record their earnest hopes that the Royal College of Physicians and Surgeons now affiliated with this University shall be eminently prosperous and successful in the important work upon which it is about to enter, and that the relation thus formed shall have a lasting, useful and honorable existence.[13]

Medical education in Kingston now rested in the hands of the corporation and the faculty of the Royal.

THE ROYAL AND QUEEN'S

The minute books of both the corporation and the faculty of the Royal are still extant. The minutes of the corporation are sparse, taking up only 39 foolscap pages even though they cover almost forty years; those of the faculty, which reported its meetings only until the Royal rejoined the university in 1892, take up 127 pages.

Royal assent to the act of incorporation was granted on 15 August 1866. The corporation held its first meeting on 21 August at Dr Fowler's house on Brock Street. The Act to Incorporate the Royal College of Physicians and Surgeons, Kingston was read into the minutes. Only five of the eight incorporators attended the inaugural meeting. Drs John R. Dickson, John Mair, Fife Fowler, Michael Lavell, Roderick Kennedy, Donald Maclean, Michael Sullivan, and Richard A. Reeve. Mair remains the most enigmatic of the original eight incorporators. No evidence exists that he ever attended a board of faculty meeting or played the least part in either the teaching or administration of the college.[14] Almost as elusive are Reeve and Kennedy. Even though they were members of the teaching faculty, they appear to have attended only one of the early board meetings. In 1869, three years after the college's foundation, Dr Reeve resigned to pursue a distinguished career in Toronto as an ophthalmologist and eventually as dean of the medical school. Dr Kennedy, who had been teaching anatomy (rather ineptly), became the Royal's first professor of *materia medica* and pharmacy.

For the rest of the Royal's existence as a corporation, its board held forty-five meetings at which attendance was recorded. Dr Dickson took the chair until April 1882, the year he died, with Dr Lavell, Dr Fowler, and Dr Horatio Yates occasionally presiding in his absence. Fowler, who succeeded Dickson as president, was without doubt the sustaining force of the corporation. He attended every meeting of its board while it had a separate existence, that is, until the "Royal" returned to Queen's in 1892. Eighteen medical men, at one time or another, were on the board.

It appears from the minutes that the major function of the corporation's board was to ratify academic decisions made previously by the "Royal's" faculty board, which usually consisted of the same people.

At its first meeting as a legally empowered body on 21 August 1866, the corporation accepted the by-laws drafted by Dr Lavell. The first by-law approved was the description of the corporation's seal: "a crown, encircled by a wreath of maple leaves and the name or designation of the College."[15] The seal was to be affixed to all diplomas and other public acts of the college.

The quorum for a meeting of the corporation was set at five. It was a rare meeting which had more than a bare quorum. Occasionally fewer than the required five attended. In light of this fact, the registrar, Dr Fife Fowler, must have had his work cut out when matters of importance needed to be decided. After the president, and the registrar, who was also secretary-treasurer, the college's most important appointment was the representative to the Medical Council. In 1866, Dr Dickson was president of the Medical Council for Upper Canada, so the politically astute Dr Lavell was elected to the position.

By-law seven dealt with appointments. Members of the college corporation appointed to the teaching faculty had to be registered under the Medical Act of the province. Presumably the incorporators wrote this into the by-laws to keep nonmedically qualified professors out of positions of power in the medical school.[16] The chairs or professorships established were the same as those accepted by the senate of the university before it agreed to affiliation. Those who held them were also to be registered practitioners: John R. Dickson M.D., M.R.C.P.(L.), M.R.C.S.(E.), F.R.C.S. (Edin.), professor of the principles and practice of surgery; Fife Fowler, M.D., L.R.C.S. (Edin.), professor of the theory and practice of medicine; Michael Lavell, M.D., professor of obstetrics and diseases of women and children; Roderick Kennedy, M.D., L.R.C.S. (Edin.), professor of forensic and state medicine; Donald Maclean, M.D., L.R.C.S. (Edin), professor of the institutes of medicine; Michael Sullivan, M.D., professor of anatomy; Richard A. Reeve, B.A., M.D., professor of chemistry; and Roderick Kennedy, M.D., L.R.C.S. (Edin.), professor of *materia medica* and pharmacy.

Three physicians, not members of the corporation, were also appointed to the faculty: Thomas R. Dupuis, professor of botany, James Neish, demonstrator of anatomy, and Henry Skinner, member of the Pharmacy Society of Great Britain. He ran a wholesale druggist establishment on Princess Street in Kingston and became Dr Kennedy's assistant.

The next order of business at the first meeting of the corporation dealt with the registration of students and the setting of fees (by-laws twelve and thirteen). Twelve dollars was the fee for each class per session, with the exceptions of botany and practical anatomy, which were to be $6, and clinical surgery and clinical medicine, $3 each. All fees were payable in advance. The registrar issued tickets on payment of the fees, and possession by a student of two tickets for any course or lectures entitled him to a perpetual ticket. The total fees for the five-year programme were approximately $265, which included the $4 for a ticket permitting hospital attendance during the whole period of the student's study.[17]

By-law fourteen immediately admitted as fellows, without examination or fee, the eight doctors named in the act of incorporation of the Royal. Thereafter, all candidates for fellowship in the college, before being admitted to the examination, had to produce evidence of being graduates in arts, "or undergo an examination equivalent thereto." They also had to offer proof that they had been engaged in the practice of the profession for at least five years and pay fifty dollars – a considerable sum in those days. These requirements set a high standard for what may have been the first organization in Upper Canada to be specifically concerned with postgraduate continuing medical education. The requirement of an arts degree was undoubtedly an attempt to place a fellow of the Royal firmly within the ranks of learned physicians and to demonstrate that the profession's leaders were scholarly by the university community's own criteria. After its return to Queen's campus in 1880, the medical faculty made a particular point of ensuring that candidates for the fellowship of the Royal were reasonably well read in English literature and other subjects. To this end, they set out the following requirements, for example, for examinations in English language and literature – Shakespeare's *Merchant of Venice*, Milton's *Comus* and *Lycidas*, and Pope's *Essay on Man* – and in mathematics and physical sciences. In addition to the above, candidates were to be examined in the practical subjects of medicine, surgery and obstetrics.[18] There are no records, however, of candidates actually sitting the examinations.

After the first meeting of the corporation, most meetings were devoted to ratifying licentiates' diplomas, granting fellowships (only twenty-five in its whole history), and appointing members of the corporation (eighteen in all). The corporation authorized the issuance of the calendar. It occasionally directed the negotiations for property, and once it reprimanded a colleague for alleged professional misconduct (drunkenness).[19]

As the years passed, partly perhaps because the members of the corporation were also senior faculty members, and because administrative problems arose less often than academic ones, the corporation's minutes were less punctiliously recorded than a historian would like. After the Royal's return to Queen's campus, the activity of the corporation of the Royal, as an entity distinctly separate from the faculty, can at the best be described as somnolent.

Most of the minutes of the faculty board of the Royal are in the handwriting of Dr Fife Fowler. The faculty board dealt with all academic business. The first matters attended to were the appointment of matriculation examiners and of clinical lecturers at the Kingston General Hospital. After some discussion, they reached the conclusion that parchment was appropriate for the university diploma of M.D., but fine cartridge paper was sufficient for those of fellows and licentiates of the Royal. It was agreed that previously graduated Queen's M.D.s in good standing could become licentiates without further examination upon payment of the required fee. *Ad eundem* licentiates were granted to Edward Clapham, M.D., professor of anatomy at Iowa State University, Dr Ramsay of Cleveland, and Surgeon Thornton of the 9th Regiment without examination. The latter had played a significant role during the early years of Queen's medical faculty as its first lecturer on military medicine; the other two were probably attempting to obtain a licence to practise in Canada.

As early as the second meeting, the faculty board heard, with pleasure a letter from the president of the Royal College of Surgeons of Edinburgh:

I am instructed to inform you that the College having considered your application and your printed regulations for examination of students, unanimously agreed to continue the recognition of your new Incorporation which they formerly granted to the Medical Department of the University of Queen's College, Kingston.[20]

This type of approbation encouraged the Kingston medical men in the pedagogical risk they were taking; it also put to rest misgivings by the university and other scholars that the Royal might not be an academic institution worthy of international recognition.

At the same meeting, the faculty accepted a motion that might sound strange to modern ears: "in the case of Mr. Mark, in that as he has expressed in writing his intention to devote himself as a Medical Missionary he be admitted to examination without paying the usual fee."[21]

By February 1867 the faculty of the Royal was assuring the principal of Queen's that every effort would be made to erect its own building and vacate the university's major teaching building as soon as possible. Correspondence between Principal Snodgrass and Dr Fowler suggests that the Royal was very seriously considering approaching the board of trustees of Queen's University with the suggestion that it sell to the Royal College "one quarter of an acre, forming the corner of the college grounds, on Arch and Stuart Streets, for four hundred dollars, provided the College agree to erect upon it a sightly building to be used as a Medical School."[22]

The offer tempted the board, particularly in view of its recent Commercial Bank losses, even though the proposed price of the land was not quite what might have been obtained on the open market. When news of the proposal leaked out, however, Kingston residents were vehement. In April 1867 a number of owners and tenants of properties on the south-east periphery of the campus presented the following petition.

April 22, 1867

The Chairman and Board of Trustees of the University of Queen's College Kingston

Gentlemen

The Petition of the undersigned resident Freeholders and Householders in the vicinity of Queen's College

Humbly Showeth

That your Petitioners have learned that it is the intention of the Royal College of Physicians and Surgeons of Kingston to Purchase the piece of ground belonging to the College at the corner of Stewart and Arch Streets to build a Hall thereon for anatomical purposes. That whilst your Petitioners are in favour of practical science being carried out for the benefit of mankind, yet your Petitioners are of opinion that a more suitable place and one less offensive to your Petitioners could be selected.

That the lands belonging to Queen's College are sufficient to allow a more convenient place for the contemplated Hall – and if you would not consider it presumptuous in your Petitioners to offer an opinion – they would name a piece of ground directly opposite the Kingston Hospital as the most suitable and convenient site and as the least obnoxious to them.

That a number of your Petitioners who having spent a life of economy and having worked hard for the attainment of the property they now possess, consider that in the event of a dissecting room being established on the contemplated spot, i.e. corner of Arch and Stewart Streets, would be the means of depreciating the value of their property and in fact would be the cause of driving away those persons now renting premises from them.

Believing that it is not the desire of the Trustees being put in possession of the wishes of your Petitioners to favour such a project and also believing that the Medical Faculty of Kingston who compose the Royal College of Physicians and Surgeons will not in opposition to expressed wishes of your Petitioners insist on the erection of such a building.

Your Petitioners therefore pray that you will take the matter into your consideration and act thereon in such a manner as will conduce to the best interests of your Petitioners.

And as in duty bound
Will ever pray[23]

The trustees, realizing that the best interests of their petitioners coincided with their own, agreed – to this day, the university property in front of Summerhill is considered one of the most scenic spots on the campus. The medical faculty, whose newest building, Botterell Hall, overlooks the site, is particularly pleased, even over a century later, with the trustees' decision.

Two years later, to the embarrassment of the faculty, the provincial government withdrew the $750 annual grant to the Royal as a result of one of Mr Sandfield Macdonald's electoral promises. A committee was appointed to submit to the board of trustees of Queen's College a financial statement on the condition of the Royal and to convey to them that owing to altered circumstances (the loss of $750 annually) the Royal could no longer pay the university rent for teaching space.[24] A temporary accommodation must have been arrived at, however, because the college remained on campus for another year.

Nothing indicates in the faculty minutes the traumatic months during 1870 when the faculty had to vacate the university building behind Summerhill because the university discovered that it required the building to house its own increased enrolment. The letter Principal Snodgrass wrote to Dr Fowler in January clearly shows that by this time he had come to the conclusion that no continuing benefit would accrue to Queen's from its association with medical education. In reply to the Royal's submission that it was unable to pay rent, he explained that the university itself was $4,000 in debt because of the collapse of the Commercial Bank, in which the trustees had deposited an inordinate amount of the university's money, and was in no state to support aspirations of Kingston's medical fraternity. He also suggested that the university community was beginning to lose interest in medical education as it was becoming apparent that the Medical Council of Ontario was to have an increasing influence on the development of medical school curricula throughout the province. This very real power, derived from its control of licensing procedures and examinations, would naturally increase at the expense of the university senate.[25]

No mention was made in the faculty minutes of the Royal's short sojourn at the House of Industry on outer Montreal Street, two miles from the hospital, where it set up business after being evicted from Queen's campus. During the 1870/71 session, the Royal rented a building on lower Princess Street. In September 1873, the Royal offered to buy the building for $1,800 from the dominion government but eventually accepted the minister of the interior's offer of $2000. The Royal borrowed the money from the Frontenac Loan and Investment Society and insured the building for $3,000.[26] This site was to remain the home of the Royal for the next ten years, before Principal Grant invited it back to Queen's.

Although the Royal had left the university campus, through the 1870s the faculty regularly, and the corporation occasionally, held their meetings in what is cryptically designated as "Queen's College Building," a name used variously to describe both Summerhill or the Old Medical Building – either would have afforded a reasonable venue.

During the 1877/88 session, George Munro Grant became principal of Queen's University. The faculty minutes record that Dr Lavell was directed to prepare an address to be presented at the inaugural ceremonies expressing the loyalty of the affiliated medical school. The actual inauguration took place at four o'clock on 5 December 1877, in the university Convocation Hall. That evening, in the city hall, Principal Grant delivered his inaugural address with all the academic pomp and circumstance the occasion demanded. Immediately after the prolonged cheering which greeted the new principal's arrival, the chancellor, the Reverend Dr Cook, presented, in order of precedence, those bearing congratulatory messages: Dr Dickson brought greetings from the medical school, immediately followed by Mr R. W. B. Smith, Critic in the Aesculapian Society, who spoke for the medical students. In his reply, Principal Grant assured the medical professors and their students that "they might depend on his sympathy in their work, and his best counsel they might command at any time."[27]

The practical direction Grant's sympathy might take was implicit in this part of his speech:

Queen's is no mere Divinity Hall. It is a University with a Royal Charter. It has its Faculty in Theology, a well-equipped Faculty in Arts, and a Medical College affiliated and in living connection with it. The relation of the Medical College to the University is peculiarly happy. The Professors manage their own affairs and pay their own way; but their action shows that they recognize the importance of being united to a University that is not only an Examining Board and a Foundation of Honor but also a Teaching Body. Their students are thus enabled to avail themselves of the classes in Chemistry, Botany and other branches of natural history, and also of those classes that are universally recognized as essential to a Faculty in Arts, and to a liberal education. Such a liberal education every intending physician should resolve to acquire. It should not be enough for him that he has studied his own bread-and-butter subjects. Any merely professional education gives a one-sided development to the powers of the mind, and leaves the student with marked limitations of ideas, and altogether an imperfect, because a one-sided man . . . It is then a matter for congratulation that the connection of the Medical College with Queen's is of such a nature, that intending and actual students of medicine can study those subjects which, according to the testimony of all nations, tend to produce faculties and capacities in their relative subordinations. May the connection become more cordial and increasingly useful! May the result be, that the majority – if not the whole body of physicians who go out from Queen's College, shall be Bachelors of Arts or of Science as well as Doctors of Medicine! And to this prayer – which regard for my own physical well-being inspires in me – all the people say, Amen; – for they are all deeply interested in such a consummation.[28]

These words were music to the ears and honey to the taste of the assembled medical men; they put the university on notice that medicine was about to resume its status as a senior academic faculty at Queen's. From that moment medical education in Kingston and throughout Canada had a new champion.

Canada's "Old Chieftain," Sir John A. Macdonald, was among the distinguished speakers on the platform that night to congratulate the university, the principal, and the medical faculty. He regretted that the faculty of law was not present, but acknowledged that had it been at convocation an embarrassing situation might have arisen. Who should take precedence, the medicos or the legal fraternity? He reminded his audience that an old decision gave the lawyers the right to walk before the doctors, presumably because the thief always preceded the executioner.

Dr Michael Sullivan, whom Sir John A. was soon to elevate to the senate, followed with a brief congratulatory address to the new principal. He affirmed the loyalty of all the medical alumni, not only of Queen's old medical school, but also of the "Royal." According to Sullivan, some of these men occupied high positions all over the world. In his inimitable way he assured the principal that as far as the medicals were concerned, Dr Grant's sentiments were sound and more than welcome.

Four months after his installation and true to his word, Dr Grant was present, along with his senior colleagues, Professors Williamson, Mowat, and Watson (all members of the senate), at the next meeting of the Royal's faculty board. They announced primary and final examination results to the students. It would appear from the 29 March 1878 minutes that the principal had attended afternoon and evening sessions of the faculty specially called together as an examination board, and had been present while the students were being examined.

Faculty minutes reveal that from the time of Principal Grant's appointment, matters of mutual interest to the college and the university surfaced with increasing frequency. For example, in

August 1880 the faculty received a notice that the board of trustees would permit the Royal to teach in the building they had previously used but which was currently in the hands of the arts faculty. For this Queen's University was to receive one-third of the graduation fees, while the medical faculty of the Royal was required to insure the building. The gesture was scarcely an offer to the prodigal son, but the faculty happily accepted it. They promptly made arrangements to move in, and from that day to the present, the Old Medical Building has been a centre of preclinical teaching.

Early in 1881, the students petitioned that the degree of C.M. (Chirurgiae Magister – Master of Surgery) be conferred on those who passed the university examination for M.D. The faculty concurred, and Grant indicated the terms on which the senate would institute the degree. He also suggested that the medical professors sign the diploma for the university M.D. This was a most unusual concession because the faculty of the Royal were not legally members of the university professoriate at that time. Dr Grant, however, did not acquire his reputation as Queen's greatest manager of men for nothing. Following the proffer of this olive branch, he immediately requested that the faculty discuss the possibility of some closer union, other than affiliation, and ways this might be done. The principal had cast his bait. The faculty rose to it and instructed Dr Fowler "to inform the Principal that the Faculty felt honoured by his proposition and are favourably disposed to any scheme of connecting as a Faculty with Queen's College but at the same time retaining their own autonomy."[29]

Dr Grant believed, as we have seen, that without a medical faculty Queen's College could not be the national university he intended it to be, while the faculty of the Royal knew that a medical school without a university would inevitably degenerate into a trade school and lose both its credibility and its students. Nevertheless, it took another eleven years for an organic union to be fully effected.

In the middle eighties, Toronto University made one more move to extend its hegemony over professional and other higher education throughout Ontario. The Kingston medical faculty refrained from expressing any opinion on the general merits of Toronto's proposal for college federation – the nineteenth-century euphemism for academic takeover. But the Royal was emphatic in its views on the professional aspects of the proposal, protesting "against the centralization of professional education in Toronto as implied in this scheme, feeling that this would reflect a great injury on the cause of medical education in the Province and be manifestly most unjust to an institution that has for upwards of thirty years laboured zealously to promote it.[30] After widespread canvassing of the various university constituencies, the Queen's board of trustees sent a letter to the minister of education stating "that the constituency of Queen's is practically a unit in favour of declining to enter the proposed confederation and of Queen's remaining permanently at Kingston as a University."[31]

Two years later, Toronto Medical School generated a similar problem for the province's independent medical schools. Trinity College invited the other schools to join it in opposing the Toronto Medical School Act, then before the legislature.[32] Their combined efforts were unsuccessful; Toronto became a provincially supported medical faculty while the others found themselves with growing financial difficulties.

The Royal's own financial problems arose partly from its need to update its facilities; in 1886 it spent $250 on thirteen microscopes from Ernest Leitz and a further $500 on other teaching equipment. Unfortunately, the Queen's treasurer coincidentally complicated matters by demanding payment of graduation fees in a lump sum instead of by instalments as before. The costly attempts to keep in step with Toronto's provincially funded medical school forced the Royal to seek affiliation with Trinity.[33]

On 13 April 1887 the corporation of Trinity College accepted a recommendation from its executive committee to permit the Royal to hold examinations in Kingston for the M.D., C.M. (Trinity). Dr Garrett of the Royal was appointed a member of the Council of Trinity College and the Royal, for a short time, became legally affiliated with two universities, Queen's and Trinity.[34]

Two years later, a deputation consisting of Principal Grant and Judge McLennan met with Trinity's executive committee. Together they formulated the following recommendations for acceptance by both universities:

1. That each University should appoint two members on the Board of Medical Studies of the other university.
2. That the Board of Medical Studies of each university should nominate at least one Examiner on their Board of Examiners to represent the other University.
3. That the students at Queen's University who desire to take the degree of M.D., C.M. in Trinity University shall be required to register not later than the end of their second year.
4. That the Final written Examination of Queen's be accepted for the degree in Trinity.
5. That Candidates shall however be required to pass the final oral Examina-

tion conducted by the Examiners of Trinity University before admission to the degree of M.D., C.M.

6. That clauses 3, 4 and 5 shall apply *mutatis mutandis* to students of Trinity desiring to Graduate in Queen's.

7. That the fee for the degree of M.D., C.M. be $30 to be paid by the Candidate in installment viz. $14 before presenting himself for the Primary Examinations and $16 before presenting himself for the Final Examinations.

8. These regulations are to come into effect at once but the additional requirements are not to affect those who have already registered – Students of the third and fourth year registering before March 15th 1889 shall obtain the benefit of this arrangement.[35]

Had these recommendations been carried out the Royal would have doubtless been effectively deprived of students and would have ceased to function in Kingston. But the Royal survived and Principal Grant in 1892 advised Queen's trustees to set up a joint university/Royal College committee to frame terms of reference and regulations for "an organic union" whereby a medical faculty could be reestablished within the university. Dr Fowler became dean of this faculty while continuing as president of the Royal, which maintained its separate corporate existence for a further decade. Trinity, however, was eventually cannibalized by Toronto University Medical School in 1903.

CHAPTER SIX

The Royal College: Curriculum, Staff and Students

At first the Royal continued the same blend of clinical and preclinical instruction as the medical school at Queen's before the dissolution. Because of the Royal's legal affiliation with the university, the curriculum was announced in the university's annual calendars, thus making students and others aware of the requirements for the M.D. Official curricular changes also appeared in the minutes of the joint (Queen's/Royal) Board of Medical Studies, established in 1887. But as in other aspects of the Royal's life, faculty and student opinions, whether found in minute books, diaries, letters or notes in the *Queen's College Journal*, help fill out our understanding of late nineteenth-century medical education in Kingston.

MEDICAL CURRICULUM AT THE ROYAL

The general regulations controlling the medical school curriculum during the seventies and eighties followed closely those first delineated in the Queen's senate and Royal's faculty board affiliation agreement. After 1865, all medical schools' curricula in Ontario had to be acceptable to the provincial Medical Council.[1] Normally the complete medical course lasted four years, but credit was often given for one year if a student was a graduate in arts or had spent a year in the office of a medical practitioner.

Apart from this exception, the full course of instruction included provision for the student to spend one year (later reduced to six months) compounding medicines in a doctor's office and required him to produce evidence of attendance at not fewer than six cases of midwifery. In keeping with the British system, it became necessary to pass a primary, intermediate, and final examination. The primary was held at the end of the second session (botany, institutes of medicine and theoretical chemistry); the intermediate after the third year (*materia medica*, anatomy, practical chemistry, medical jurisprudence and histology); and the final examination, in April of the fourth year (principles and practice of surgery, theory and practice of medicine, obstetrics, clinical medicine, clinical surgery, and sanitary science). *Queen's College Journal*, commenting on the introduction of this scheme in 1882, felt that three examinations – even though "suspiciously homeopathic" – would obviate cramming.[2]

During the first year of the medical course, botany and chemistry were taught on Queen's campus by the university professors in these disciplines. Professor James Fowler gave botany lectures every day during the first half of the year. Where appropriate, drawings, microscopic sections and, whenever practical, living plants or dried specimens from the university greenhouses (which he had been instrumental in setting up) illustrated his lectures. Chemistry, under the direction of Professor Goodwin, consisted on lectures and practical classes. The lectures covered chemical physics, chemical philosophy, inorganic and organic chemistry. The calendar for 1887/88 proudly announced that the professor possessed abundant apparatus for experimental investigation, and that practical work under his personal supervision would include blow-pipe manipulations and toxicological investigations.

Anatomy was the most important preclinical discipline at the Royal. It was taught in two courses, each under a different professor. Professor Thomas R. Dupuis gave five lectures a week, which were illustrated with fresh cadaveric dissections performed by two of the best dissectors among third-year students. The students themselves dissected under the direction of a junior professor. The professor and two demonstrators were supposed to be available for teaching in the dissecting room from eight in the morning until six in the evening every day of the week; occasionally friction developed between staff and students over the regularity of the professors' attendance.

In the same way that we know little of the students' everyday life a century ago, we have only a modicum of detailed knowledge of the routine medical curriculum at the Royal – that is, apart from a few cryptic remarks in the "brief notes" column of *Queen's College Journal*. Fortunately, however, more detailed information is available to us about the *materia medica* and physiology courses taught at the Royal in the early eighties. Miss Elizabeth Smith was one of the students who studied these subjects under Dr A. S. Oliver and

Dr K. N. Fenwick respectively, and her lecture notes in these subjects are still extant.[3]

Miss Smith's *materia medica* notebook consists of 197 pages of careful writing. The notes are so neatly kept and so clearly organized and legible that one must presume that they were either taken *verbatim* in class, following slow precise dictation by Dr Oliver, or compiled after the lecture from a set of rough notes now lost. This latter alternative is probably the more likely.

Apart from writing prescriptions and identifying the action of particular drugs, the course in *materia medica* consisted of therapeutics (the discovery and application of remedies for disease), and pharmacy (the act or practice of preparing, preserving and compounding substances for the purposes of medicine). The major portion of the course classified medicines into evacuants, depressants, narcotics, excitants, revulsives, antacids, and alternatives. We can appreciate, from the detail covered in this lecture course, the aptness of Dr Michael Sullivan's vociferous condemnation of the excessive amount of students' time spent on *materia medica*.[4]

Dr A. S. ("Holy Al") Oliver not only lectured on all aspects of *materia medica*, he also instructed the students of the Royal (and subsequently the Women's Medical College) in the correct manner of compounding the mixtures or rolling the pills they prescribed. He also made sure that they knew how to package a bottle of medicine and seal it as elegantly as any pharmacist. Mr Pickwick's friend, Dr Bob Sawyer, would probably have been more able than today's medical student to pass Dr Oliver's examination. Some of his questions in the 1880s were: "How are quinine, Sulphuric Ether and Calomel made?"; "Give the composition of Compound Extract of Colcynth, Compound Rhubarb Pills, and Compound Jalap Powders"; "Give the doses for internal use of Extract of Belladonna, Tincture of Nux Vomica, Phosphorous, Protiodide of Mercury, Corrosive Sublimate, Nitrate of Silver and Tannic Acid, and Hypodermically of Atropia, Apomorpha and Hyoscymin."[5]

The last thirty-two unnumbered pages of Miss Smith's *materia medica* notebook, which she set aside for special prescriptions, provide a small glimpse into medicine a century ago. The range of prescriptions with their date of copying down or attribution suggests a type of general medical practice in some ways similar to today's but in others, quite alien. The following short selection of topics, apparently written down when she first entered practice, gives an insight into some of the problems she was faced with:

For the Hair – Tried and proved (Mother's), Aunt Mary's tonics (Edgar), Cure for colds, Gargle – (from Mother's 'Dr.' book), for nervousness, Nipple wash (Dr. Alice McG.), Gastralgia, Chapped Hands, Varicose Veins, 'After pains', a recipe for Shoe Blacking.[6]

Every physician had his own similar list of favorite prescriptions, which might include those handed down to him from his preceptor or those he had found particularly successful in the early years of his own practice.

The physiology course (institutes of medicine), taught by Dr Fenwick in the Royal, was attended as assiduously as possible, given the circumstances, by Miss Smith and her colleagues, Mrs McGillivray and Miss Beatty.[7] Odious interruptions marked the 1882 fall session, leading to the male students threatening to leave the Royal. In spite of the turmoil in the lecture theatre, Miss Smith took notes. Her physiology notebook consists of two volumes.[8] The first, apparently covered the subject matter lectured on before Christmas, the second, dealt with the remainder of the course.

The spectrum of topics taught by Dr Fenwick in physiology during the 1880s was becoming more and more like a modern course because, as a younger faculty member, he accepted some of the recent European research and teaching. Histology and a little pathology appeared in his lectures. Miss Smith's lecture notes cover, among other subjects, the proximate principles of physiology and structural composition of the body (i.e., cell biology), nutrition, then the functions of blood, the gastro-intestinal tract, respiration, the skin, the liver, the kidneys, the breast, and finally a substantial presentation of what was known about the nervous system.

Two of the five examination questions set by Dr Fenwick's successor as professor of physiology and histology, Dr D. Phelan, in the physiology examination in 1887 were:

1. If a man eats dinner consisting of beefsteak, potatoes, bread and butter, state where and how each article is digested.
2. State the mechanism of ordinary and forced inspiration, and state the average vital capacity, and mention how it is tested by the spirometer.

Dr Irwin taught jurisprudence and sanitary science. His lectures in jurisprudence embraced a full range of topics including "post-mortem appearances, insanity, infanticide, death from cold and heat, signs of death, personal identity, drowning, hanging, suffocation, microscopic chemical and microspectroscopic tests for blood stains, etc. etc."[10] The lectures in sanitary science dealt with the purity of drinking water, drainage of soil, removal of excreta, and the effects of atmosphere on health. The professor usually stressed nutrition in health and disease, and the proper preparation of disinfectants for combatting contagious diseases. Students in the course on medical jurisprudence were required to visit "Rockwood Asylum for the Insane and the Criminal Asylum at the Penitentiary"[11] where, so the calendar announced, cases of insanity could be studied in all its forms.

In an attempt to maintain what it perceived to be the excellence of its own standards, the Royal invested heavily in many of the newer aids to medical practice and teaching. During the summer of 1881, Drs Sullivan and Fowler were sent to New York to purchase, among other equipment, a Pond's sphygmograph, a new microscope with pathological and physiological slides, an ophthalmoscope, a laryngoscope, a thermocautery, a Keith's spray producer (for carbolic acid to be used during surgical operations), a chemical thermometer, a set for testing urine, and an obstetric manikin.[12]

In clinical medicine every student was required to take histories and do physical examinations as well as follow two complete lecture courses in the theory and practice of medicine. Professor Michael Sullivan taught the principles and practice of surgery. This course placed special emphasis on the use of instruments and surgical apparatus. The professor performed on a cadaver in front of the whole class. Students also attended the surgical teaching in the operating rooms and at the bedside in the Kingston hospitals (K.G.H. and the Hotel Dieu).

Two quite different accounts throw some light on how the idiosyncrasies of individual professors affected the manner in which these academic and professional disciplines were taught. Dr William Mather, a graduate of the Royal in 1886, was a country general practitioner for fifty years. In 1936, the Hastings and Prince Edward County Medical Societies gave him a Jubilee celebration dinner and gold-headed cane as expressions of their appreciation and respect. His acceptance speech contains a brief account of his teachers and he remembered them:

Dr. Fowler was our Dean, a sober-looking, dignified old Scot, who scarcely ever smiled, cold and reserved in disposition, spoke slowly, but plainly, and delivered his lectures like clockwork. He was indeed a fine sample of the old-fashioned Scottish gentleman.

Dr. Oliver was our Professor in Materia Medica and Therapeutics, a solemn, serious-looking chap, whose given name was Allen or Alvin and on account of his impassive statue-like face was nicknamed by the students 'Holy Al.'

Dr K. N. Fenwick was Professor of Physiology, a clever up-to-date fellow and at that time was doing advanced surgery, stating one day at lecture that he had opened the abdomen five times, quite a feat at that time. Unfortunately he died in middle life from bloodpoisoning contracted while operating. His death was greatly lamented and a serious loss to the hospital.

Dr. Sullivan, commonly called 'Mickey' was Professor of Surgery, a great talker, somewhat absent-minded, often forgetting when his lecture hour was up and continue talking, a very clever, well-read lecturer and a witty little Irishman.

Dr. Dupuis was our Professor of Anatomy, commonly called, 'Thomas R.', quite a literary fellow and somewhat of a poet, was a good teacher and knew his work well.

Dr. Lavell was Professor of Obstetrics, a well-posted and clever man in his day and generation but his teaching that childbed fever was of a malarial nature would not be accepted now.

These six, with Drs. Garrett, Irwin, and Henderson as occasional assistants constituted our Faculty. Rev. Dr. George Grant was Principal of the University and supreme head over both Arts and Medical Colleges.[13]

A short commentary on the changing medical theory and practice in Kingston during the early 1880s and the students' response to them followed Dr Mather's memories of his teachers:

When I started on my medical course, germs as a cause of disease, were practically unknown and antisepsis never practised. After an operation in those days, there was pus galore 'good, healthy, laudable pus' and in major cases plenty of it. I remember well the first operation I witnessed. It was an amputation of the leg above the knee and was performed by our Dean, Dr. Fowler. There was no boiling of instruments, nor antiseptics used. The older doctor did the operation dexterously and rapidly. Surgeons at the present time who consider that the old M.D.s of fifty or sixty years ago were slow, rough and clumsy were greatly mistaken. After this amputation, there was any amount of the 'good, healthy, laudable pus' of those nonantiseptic days.

At this time Lister and Pasteur were deeply engaged on the germ and antiseptic work. The former had announced that germs caused disease and Lister, about the same time had discovered that carbolic acid spray would destroy germs, and under the supposition that the latter might cause erysipelas and other deathdealing troubles that often followed operations, Lister began using carbolic acid spray in the operating room during operations. The results were said to be almost miraculous. The senior medical students at Queen's asked Dr. Sullivan then our chief surgeon, to give a demonstration of Lister's method of using carbolic acid spray at operations. The doctor did so using the spray so profusely that everything in the operating room was pretty well drenched with it, even the students' faces. As everyone now knows all this spraying was unnecessary although it apparently did much good as was shown in the way patients progressed after operations in cases done under the spray. The spray was used under the supposition that the germs were in the air, and although it apparently killed nothing in the air, it eventually did so on the patient, instruments and hands of the operators and assistants. This was, I think, the first antiseptic surgery that was done in Kingston and was in 1882 or 1883.[14]

This student's poem written for the *Queen's College Journal* in 1889 provides another less orthodox perspective on the medical school:

The Royal and Her Faculty

Kind friends, your attention I'll ask for a while,
For I think that the Royal's throwing on too much
    style,
Bacteria small, which we never do see,
Are sought with great zeal in our new 'Ology.'

To the building at first your attention I'll call,
No 'subs' as of old adorn the front hall;
And the incense their presence exhaled heretofore,
Is locked up secure in the vat on the floor.

The professors all strive to teach us with care,
We trust that their words are not thrown 'way on air,
When full fledged we emerge armed with an M.D.
The fruits of their labors they plainly will see.

Dean Fowler does love to point out 'petechiae,'
But better he likes the new man with his fee;
The latter may ask him, 'Sir where is the Gym,'
But all it is gone, and it's future is dim.

'I'll just mention it in passing,' Dr. Sullivan
    will say,
'And refer to it at length on some future day.'
Dr. Fenwick will say, 'This is your A.B.C.,
The anterior plane, it's so easy you see.'

Dr. Dupuis delights in wielding the knife,
Just to give the poor patient a chance for his life;

His eye it is searching, his scalpels are keen,
He curettes the ulcers and scrapes the bone clean.

Dr. Henderson's dome is all polished with thought,
His lectures on Glenvale are carefully wrought,
On the stethescope, too, he is quite at his best,
'This part is the ear piece, and that for the chest.'

In Dr. Mundell's museum bacteria fly,
But we never can catch them, they soar, perhaps,
     too high;
The cocci are off on an 'aureoid' spree,
While we struggle and labor in Pathology.[15]

The Royal's curriculum remained quite stable throughout its lifetime. Small changes were gradually introduced in the content of the subjects following modifications in treatment or alterations in preclinical concepts. As usual, these changes followed the appointment of younger men to the faculty who had spent some postgraduate time in the major medical centres of the United Kingdom or Europe. Occasionally, when student criticisms or petitions were recognized to be valid, the faculty adjusted either the manner or the timing of the teaching programme. Sometimes, however, "student power" was put in its place. In November 1875 thirty-eight students petitioned for Dr K. N. Fenwick, a popular young surgeon, to be appointed to the chair of the institutes of medicine. The faculty, with nineteenth-century courtesy, explained academic niceties to the students, that "it was resolved that the Registrar be instructed to inform them that after full consideration of the matter the Faculty feel that the claims of standing Professors to any vacancy which may occur cannot be overlooked."[16] As a result, Dr A. S. Oliver, who fifteen years earlier had been the cause of much faculty annoyance, was pointedly elected to the chair of the institutes of medicine, while Dr Wafer received the chair of medical jurisprudence. Dr Fenwick, however, was appointed demonstrator of anatomy on the gracious motion of Dr Oliver with Dr Wafer seconding the motion. Before the spring term was over, however, Dr Wafer died of tuberculosis contracted while serving in the Union Army during the American Civil War. Even then, Dr Fenwick was not automatically promoted – he had to wait another year until he was appointed professor of the institutes of medicine.

In 1878, an often repeated criticism surfaced: the students became restive and complained that they were given too many didactic lectures, particularly by junior staff in the Kingston General Hospital. What they really wanted was practical bedside experience. They were told in no uncertain terms that the attending medical officer would continue to give clinical lectures, and while no change could be made in that session, the faculty would endeavour to make the lectures as practical and instructive as possible in future.

Possibly because of the ubiquitous presence of Principal Grant, or because of one of those inexplicable agitations which periodically afflict medical faculties, the year 1882 saw a tightening of the Royal's academic standards and a reorganization of the medical school's curricular requirements. For example, Dr Charles Lavell, professor of practical anatomy, was to have full control of the dissecting room and the disposition of cadaveric extremities. He was also required, subject to the approval of the faculty, to draw up regulations for the guidance of students who dissected.

Examinations were also reorganized. Special ones were set for those wishing to take honours or to strive for the faculty prizes. In order to qualify as an honours candidate, a student had to obtain forty percent of the marks attainable in chemistry and sixty percent in all other subjects. They were required to take a special oral examination which was intended to be as practical as possible. Each candidate was asked the same questions. Immediately after being examined, he was passed into a room where he was unable to communicate with others going up for the examination that day. In 1881, gold and silver medals were instituted for undergraduate competition in both primary and final examinations.

The Royal, the Kingston Women's College (founded in 1883), and eventually Trinity University Medical School all held the examination standards set for the Queen's M.D. in high esteem. This was shown by their recognition of the authority of the jointly established (Trinity, Queen's, Royal and W.M.C.) Board of Medical Studies at Queen's set up in 1887. The composition of the standing committee ensured its overall authority and the importance of its decisions. Principal Grant and George M. Macdonnell represented the Queen's board of trustees, Professors Dupuis and Goodwin, the senate, and initially Dr A. P. Knight, the university council. Drs Fowler and Lavell represented the Royal and the Women's Medical College respectively. Dr W. B. Geike, the famous Toronto medical educator, attended as the representative of Trinity University. In 1891, the temporary arrangements between Trinity and Queen's ended.

Between 1887 and December 1891 the board met nine times. Its prime function was to appoint the university's medical examiners and establish the dates of examination in each subject. A rule enunciated at the first meeting forbade any examiner from making known to anyone an examination result until it had been officially announced by the senate. The board confirmed the practice of permitting a student to appear for a rereading and reevaluation of his paper and ratified the custom that the reread be done by a professor other than the original examiner. It recognized the academically mature concept of appointing external examiners and, when possible, examiners from outside the Kingston medical community. During 1888 the idea of substituting numbers for the candidate's name on the examination papers was also introduced. In 1891, for the first time and at the request of the Aesculapian Society, examination questions were printed by the university printer under the control of the chief examiner. Previously the chief examiner read the questions to the candidates at the beginning of each examination.[17]

In 1890, the Board of Medical Studies permitted the appointment of associate examiners to examine the papers of any candidate who made less than fifty percent in any subject. They were also required to be present when these candidates came to be examined orally.

In the early 1890s, the Medical Council of the College of Physicians and Surgeons of Ontario became particularly interested in curriculum standards across the province. Dr Pyne, registrar of the college, wrote for a copy of the Queen's curriculum requirements for the granting of its M.D. and to the university's Board of Medical Studies for its opinion on the ideal medical curriculum. Younger faculty members welcomed this invitation. At the Board of Medical Studies' meeting of April 1891, a small committee consisting of Drs Knight and Goodwin made the following report, which was adopted after some discussion:

1. That the number of didactic lectures in Anatomy, Physiology, Chemistry, Materia Medica, Practice of Medicine, Surgery and Obstetrics be reduced from 200 to 100 in each subject in order to leave time for practical study in these kindred subjects.
2. That in each subject there shall be two courses of lectures, a junior and a senior, and that the lectures of the senior course shall be different from those of the junior, as suggested in the appended schedule.
3. That Comparative Anatomy and Comparative Physiology and Bacteriology be added to the Curriculum.
4. That pass Matriculation Physics be required of Matriculants or that Candidates be required to take Junior Physics in Arts in the first year of the course.
5. That the Departmental Pass Matriculation which has been accepted by the Universities for Arts should be required for Medical Matriculation.[18]

The schedule set out what was then considered to be an ideal medical education:

Anatomy	Junior 3 hours a week, Bones and Muscles Senior 2 hours a week, Nerves, Organs
Physiology	Junior 3 hours, Senior 2 hours Physiological Chemistry 1 hour.
Histology	Normal 1 hour, Pathological 1 hour
Chemistry	Junior 3 hours, Senior 2 hours practical 3 hours
Botany	30 Lectures
Materia Medica	Junior 3 hours (Mat. Med.) Senior 2 hours (Therapeutics and Medical Pharmacy)
Practice of Medicine	Junior 2 hours, Senior 3 hours
Surgery	Junior 2 hours, Senior 3 hours
Obstetrics	5 hours
Clinical Medicine	3 hours This teaching was to be conducted at the hospital bedside and at clinical lectures in the new hospital theatre.
Clinical Surgery	3 hours At bedside and in operating theatre.
Medical Jurisprudence	3 hours It included toxicology, post mortem appearances, etc.
Comparative Anatomy and Physiology	2 hours lectures, 3 hours practical
Pathology	2 hours a week of lectures
Bacteriology	2 hours a week

The last meeting of the Board of Medical Studies, on December 23, 1891, saw its recommendations generally accepted by the Medical Council of Ontario;[20] bacteriology and pathology, for example, became required courses throughout the province. Although this programme was not fully executed at the Royal, it was implemented at Queen's when the medical faculty was reestablished there the following year.

COLLEGE LIFE

The corporation, the faculty board, and the Board of Medical Studies are the warp of the Royal's historic tapestry; the weft is the sparse record of the students' opinions and activities at that time, most often found in the *Queen's College Journal*. These sources provide a shadowy picture of the daily life of a Canadian medical school a century ago, sometimes made clearer by the Kingston newspapers or by the diaries, memoirs, papers, or speeches of those who were associated with the Royal or Queen's.

The physical separation of the medical school from the university campus led to the formation of the Aesculapian Society in 1872. This society was restricted to medical students and became their official voice. Originally it was a free and separate body; only later did it become one of the constituent societies of the Alma Mater Society. A year later, *Queen's College Journal* first saw the light of day and from that time until the present fitfully reported the activities of the Aesculapian Society.

Queen's College Journal hailed the foundation of the Aesculapian Society as the institution of a forum which would "increase the harmony and good feeling amongst the students, promote the diffusion of knowledge amongst them, as well as to form a bond of union in after years."[21] The *Journal* expressed the wish that even though the Aesculapian Society had an initial membership of thirty, it would not become a rival to the Alma Mater Society but rather emulate it. The *Journal*'s reports of the proceedings of the Aesculapian Society and the activities of the medical faculty or alumni initially seemed to depend for their regularity on the literary enthusiasm of an individual medical student reporter. For example, the first issue devoted considerable space to a history of the medical school. Although the editor lamented the decline in student enrolment, he was sure the Royal would soon "regain the position of being the leading Medical School of Ontario." The *Journal* frequently included early Aesculapian Society debates and discussions on topics such as "Tobacco as an evil," "Women's rights," "Vivisection" and "Is bile a product of arterial or venous blood?"

The vicissitudes through which the Aesculapian Society and other student organizations passed during the 1870s and 1880s no doubt reflected the general mood of the students. In some years students seem to have been keen on the Glee Club; in others, dancing was the prevalent fad. For a time, the Y.M.C.A. was popular; popularity of the temperance movement waxed and waned (in 1887 two students were publicly castigated for not having "signed the pledge"). The Aesculapian Society itself went through the usual cycle of university institutions – birth, enthusiastic growth, general lethargic acceptance, senility, and slow decay – until 1883, when, as Queen's *Journal* promptly reported, it underwent "a resurrection" (an allusion to the allegations that medical students habitually frequented graveyards to "resurrect" lately buried bodies). The Aesculapian Society's resurrection was more respectable, as it rededicated itself to the "mutual improvement and the promotion of social intercourse among the students."[22]

The *Concursus Virtutis*, the judicial branch of the Aesculapian Society, usually maintained student discipline at the Royal. This student court was a copy of an older court founded in the arts faculty of Queen's – the *Concursus Iniquitatis* – a venerable institution whose foundation is hidden in the mist of student myth.

Dr Knight, the first full-time professor of physiology at Queen's, wrote in 1914 that the *Concursus Iniquitatis* was already functioning when he arrived at Queen's in 1868.[23] He thought that originally some arts students, wishing to become lawyers and wanting to practise their debating and adversarial skills as though they were "pleading at the bar," had founded the *Concursus*.[24] Dr Knight felt that its secondary object was to curb the "cheek" of the cocky freshmen undergraduates. The *Concursus Iniquitatis* had predictable ups and downs during its first twenty years of existence. When Principal Grant first arrived at Queen's he looked with disfavour on the frivolousness and puerility of the court. As the years passed, however, he realized it provided a formal outlet for the students' high spirits. Occasionally, thereafter, he turned to it to serve his own purposes.

It was widely believed that the medical *Concursus* had been established following a wager between the medical and divinity students. The point at issue was which group could drink the most beer.[25] The perceptive placed their bets on the Scottish tradition and were rewarded when the "divinities" won outright. Perhaps it was this previously hidden talent of those destined to serve the Kirk that led the medical students to institute a *Concursus Virtutis* rather than another *Concursus Iniquitatis*. A subtle doctrinal issue may also have had some bearing in the choice of the court's title.

The Queen's *Journal* seemed to subscribe to this distinction in legal nomenclature:

The venerable *Concursus Iniquitatis'* has a rival which bids fair to eclipse it in dispensing justice to the unfortunate freshmen. It is styled the '*Concursus Virtutis'* and its object is said to be the elevation of the morals of students in general and the meds in particular. Its sittings are held in the 'den' and are of the most solemn and awful character![26]

Various charges of solemn and awful character were levelled against those medical freshmen and juniors thought to have transgressed the niceties of the *Concursus*. One prisoner in the dock was alleged to have accompanied a young lady home from choir practice and thus to have usurped the place of a senior man. Another was required to explain where a long blond hair, which the sheriff removed from his shoulder, had come from. One felon "had the audacity to neglect washing his upper lip, and thus had endeavoured to force the growth of unseemly capillary appendages on said upper lip, thus threatening the peace of this venerable University with a moustache!" This same scoundrel had shocked the whole student body by swaggering up and down Princess Street in an ulster overcoat. He disported himself in every conceivable manner and threatened with his cane "every poodle dog or lean and hungry cur that crossed his path."[27] When the *Concursus* was not guarding the morals and etiquette of the freshmen, the Y.M.C.A. kept them in order by example and the velvet glove.

The medical students called the common room reserved for their use, where they could relax between classes or hold informal gatherings, the "den." Whether in the Royal on Princess street or in the Medical Building on Queen's campus, it was in the "den" that they hatched their plots and planned revolts. Occasionally they went too far.

On Christmas Eve 1881, a concerned faculty met to discuss the medical students' outrageous behaviour on the evening of 16 December. The faculty and principal, acting for the senate, met during the Christmas vacation to plan their strategy. When the students returned in January, a lengthy document was read to the entire student body, in the presence of the faculty, discussing the unbecoming behaviour of several students at the Christmas party; the unauthorized importation of spiritous liquors into the Medical Building had led to conduct of the grossest kind, including damage to property and reputation. Restitution had to be made, and the faculty was gravely distressed.[28]

Three weeks later the senate added clout to the faculty's verbal whip-lashing by assessing the students $200 for damages. It was pointed out, quite explicitly, that if this amount were not paid to the university treasurer, the students would not be allowed to sit for any further examinations. The students responded to the senate's action by disclaiming any connection with the fire that occurred on the day of the party, in which some of the belongings of Thomas Coffee, the janitor, were destroyed. Part of the money collected from the students was given to Tom to help him recoup his losses. The rest was turned over to the registrar.

Obviously the senate was satisfied with the students' repentence because no further mention was made of the "outrage." The hooligans who shocked the senate on this occasion were the same ones who also objected to the presence of ladies at lectures in the medical school during the following semester (see chapter seven for more details).

The medical dinner was the most significant social event of the year at the Royal. It was held under the auspices of the Aesculapian Society in one of Kingston's larger hotels and usually reported in *Queen's College Journal* (the reports were particularly laudatory whenever the editor received a free dinner ticket). Regularly the governor-general, the prime minister of Canada, the lieutenant-governor, and the premier of Ontario were invited, and just as regularly sent their regrets. But the mayor of Kingston and Principal Grant, along with the majority of the Royal's faculty, nearly always attended and inevitably each succumbed to the temptation of making an after-dinner speech.

At one of the earlier dinners, "a young man named _____ made a great deal of noise during the evening, interrupting every speaker at least twice. He also made a speech in which passages from Homer, Galen, Isocrates, Virgil and other familiar authors, in praise of Medical Students abound."[29] The suggestion that those authors were "familiar" was perhaps made tongue-in-cheek, although it was doubtless well received; such a speech would probably be received today with uncomprehending shock by the students and with amazed incredulity by the faculty.

Often in the relaxed postprandial atmosphere the professors would lightheartedly admonish the students, while they, in a similar vein, would point out to the faculty some of its shortcomings. Principal Grant, on one occasion, confessed that "he knew not the origin of these dinner customs, but they were good – socially, physically and intellectually. If a man did not enjoy them there was something radically wrong about him."[30] Professor Watson, the philosopher, once held the assembled diners spellbound with a metaphysical appraisal of medicine and its traditions. On another occasion, the controversy over one of Toronto's repeated attempts at a university hegemony could not dampen the spirits of the students nor the wit of Principal Grant, who pointed out that being at Queen's they were at the "heaven ordained centre" – "here in the east" the students were "therefore among wise men."[31]

In 1886 the situation changed. It seems, not for the first (or the last) time, the dinner degenerated into bun-fights interspersed with bouts of monotony induced by excessive speechifying. Just before Christmas, the Aesculapian Society, following the example of the YMCA and the Alma Mater Society, held a *conversazione* instead of the annual dinner to restore to the minds of Kingston citizens the high opinion they had previously held about the manners, morals, and intellect of the medical students. The medical *conversazione* was recognized as "the very first event of the season" and seen as the occasion for the Kingston debutantes to be presented – "all the fair rosebuds," all the other maidens of beauty, and all the young men of fashion. The patronesses – and anyone who was anyone – were also out in full force. The Arts building blazed with light and was festooned with evergreens. A concert started at nine o'clock with several glees and solo numbers. Mr Rechab Tandy, with his robust tenor voice, offered three songs and an encore. During the concert, Dr Sullivan and Principal Grant made short witty speeches, while Dr Dupuis lectured in the history classroom on "The Skeleton." Drs Clarke and Millman, alienists from Rockwood Asylum, not to be outdone, gave a magic lantern show. The subject of the entertainment remains unrecorded, but Dr Clarke's "very felicitous" remarks were widely appreciated. Mr Cox, the caterer, provided refreshments and dancing started at nine thirty and continued until two o'clock in the morning.[32]

The editorial columns of *Queen's College Journal* occasionally expressed the medical students' academic and political concerns. In December 1879 the students' annoyance at having to write a thesis for their M.D. degree surfaced. Although the Royal's faculty generally agreed with students, the doctoral requirement was not done away with for a considerable period of time because such action was the senate's responsibility.

Shortly afterwards, the students complained that "if a fair share of time is not spent by the teacher in classifying his ideas and facts, the result is to confuse rather than enlighten."[33] The professors were also gratuitously advised to take more interest in their pathology museum, which the students found to be a useful adjunct to their learning.

The Ontario Medical Council itself was not above censure by *Queen's College Journal*. For many years the final council examinations were held at the same time in April in both Toronto and Kingston. In 1880 the council set the examination for 13 April and had the date printed in all medical school calendars. A few weeks earlier, however, a notice appeared in the *Globe*, the *Mail*, and the *Canada Lancet* stating that the council's examinations had been postponed two weeks to suit the convenience of Toronto University, whose own examinations were to be held on that date. *Queen's College Journal* attacked:

and as Toronto University is the high and mighty one before whom all other institutions of learning must bow low in the dust, it was of course necessary that the Medical Council examinations must be postponed until it should please the grave and reverend seignors who run the University of Toronto to graciously deign to give them an opportunity to hold their wholly unimportant examinations.[34]

Apart from minor disagreements, the Royal's students still remained on good terms with their Toronto counterparts. In 1879, both student groups held their annual dinners on the same evening and exchanged complimentary telegrams. The Royal wired, "May the spirit of generous rivalry for excellence in our profession continue to characterize our schools . . . ," and Toronto replied, "May the friendship existing between the two schools long remain as warm as now . . ."[35]

Although the medical students owed their professional loyalty to the Royal, on any and every appropriate occasion, they expressed their pride in being members of the Queen's community, along with the arts and divinity students, by singing Queen's unofficial anthem before the introduction of *Oil Thigh na Banrighinn a Banrighinn gu Brath*.

On the Old Ontario Strand

My father sent me down to Queen's
That I might there become a man;

The Meds., with grand and noble aim,
Get lore by many a curious plan,
For they often rob the graves,
Of defunct and extinct braves,
On the Old Ontario Strand.[36]

Yearly, during early spring, Queen's University assembled in convocation to bestow degrees on those whom the senate deemed worthy to receive them. Because the tradition was well established by the time the Royal returned to the campus in 1880, a comprehensive record of the medical convocations - who graduated, who won prizes or medals, and sometimes the *verbatim* report of the medical valedictory - exists. Although the valedictorians offered, on behalf of their graduating colleagues, a formal farewell to Queen's and the Royal, they quite often took the opportunity to express the distilled wisdom of four years in medical school by praising or criticizing the facilities, the curriculum, or even the faculty. The subjects they spoke on, apart from the mandatory platitudes praising the generosity of Kingston's citizens and the beauty of their daughters, often reflected the concerns and interests of the graduating students about the college they were leaving behind or the nature of the profession they were about to enter. For example, earlier valedictorians went to great lengths to impress on their junior colleagues, and indirectly the Kingston public, that medical students were not really "bone pickers and body snatchers," as they were "dubbed by the street urchins."[37]

Meds '85 chose well when they selected George Spankie as their valedictorian. He spoke first to the junior classmen, pointing out that the graduating class, on becoming doctors of medicine, could share the same platform as the professors. In addition, "the student ... is granted the privilege of publicly expressing his approval or disapproval of the treatment and teaching received by him during his college course. Our verdict today is approval; we express it with deepest gratitude to our professors, for they many acts of kindness towards us."[38] To the professors this was not trite tribute. It meant the implicit promise of hard cash in the years to come, through the referral of patients by country general practitioners to their consultant specialist teachers back in Kingston. For the next fifty years, Dr Spankie, while practising across the length and breadth of Wolfe Island, was as good as his word - he repeatedly referred patients to his former teachers. The "approval" he spoke of, gained and cherished by the faculty, partly arose from an updating of the curriculum and the introduction of specialist clinics and lectures in dermatology, diseases of the nervous system, and of the eye and the ear. The facilities at the Royal, Queen's, and Kingston General Hospital were those which "senior students of other and larger medical schools have publicly admitted to be superior to their own." Looking into the future, Dr Spankie upbraided the Ontario Medical Council for not requiring, before licensure, a university education "which would provide a preliminary literary and scientific education for medicine." He expressed a fear that if Latin and Greek were banished from the medical curriculum, the day might come when the student would neither appreciate where his *levator labii superioris alaeque nasi* was, nor understand what it did. Among his many observations he reminded his listeners of Mr. Gladstone's opinion "that the influence of the medical profession, great as it now is, is destined to grow in greater proportion than that of other professions."[39]

The valedictorians also criticized the Royal. In 1887, for example, after the ritual acknowledgement of the Royal's pre-eminence as a medical school, Dr M. James condemned the Medical Council of Ontario for putting the literary education of medical students on the level expected of third-class teachers. He found fault with the facilities provided for the medical students at the Kingston General Hospital. The students:

all disapprove of its poor supply of medicines, the lack of surgical instruments and appliances, and the poor quality of those it possesses, the uncleanliness of some of the rooms in the basement, the untidy and apparently unclean hospital dress of the patients, the lack of a waiting room for students, and the ill furnished appartments of the house surgeon ... At the same time the resident officials complain of improper food.[40]

In the same year, Toronto University was trying to control all medical education in the province, and James knew how to aim his criticisms: "when members in the Ontario House assert that students cannot obtain a thorough medical training in Kingston or London on account of the poorly equipped hospitals, it behooves the friends of the Royal and those interested in the hospital to make a certain effort to place it on a better footing." Worse followed: "If it had even one good knife, one whole pair of scissors, one probe, one unrusted needle ... there might be some room for saying that we as medical students speak unjustly."[41]

Dr James may have felt his intemperate remarks were justified, but they naturally caused quite a stir. Within days the *Daily British Whig* printed a rebuttal by the indignant board of governors of the hospital. They denied Dr James's charges, and pointed out that "the question has been repeatedly debated at the board, when that students have been unruly, stolen dead bodies, and otherwise misbehaved themselves, and the only reason why the counsel of the older heads, to cut off the students has not been followed, has been the desire to help the Royal College."[42]

Dr Fife Fowler, the dean, recognizing that clinical teaching might be in jeopardy, wrote to the board disclaiming any responsibility for the unjustifiable remarks made about the hospital by Dr James. The publication of this letter in the local press seems to have satisfied the governors of the hospital.[43]

Towards the end of the Royal's separation from Queen's, the

valedictorians became less controversial, even though they continued to follow the formula containing an acceptable blend of piety and politics. The last of the Royal's valedictorians, Dr A. Haig, expressed the students' hopes for the future of the school with courtesy and such common sense that presumably it led to their fulfillment: the sanitary condition of the Medical Building was improved; the museum was enlarged, and an infectious disease wing of the Kingston General Hospital was established. Dr Haig, expressing the students' hopes, foresaw the need for curricular changes and the necessity of decreasing lecture hours, while the Board of Medical Studies was already moving in this direction. He concluded with the ritual appreciation of Kingston's elegance, its daughters' beauty and its citizens' generosity.[44]

The story of the Royal and of Queen's Medical Faculty would be incomplete without mention of Thomas Coffey. During the development and growth of any institution, many, who contribute to its survival, remain unknown to all but their contemporaries. In a medical school, the professors, teachers, and clinicians usually remain vividly in a student's memory. Occasionally a few, no less important in a student's education, who as they only "stand and wait" have a far less widespread reputation but are far more familiar to the students at their most impressionable age. Paradoxically, these necessary members of the medical school are often forgotten by the historians. The Royal had such a character: Tom the janitor.

Thomas Coffey was born in County Limerick, Ireland in 1836. At eighteen, when the Crimean War broke out, he joined the 21st Royal Fusiliers of the British Army. After the war and a further ten years of enlisted time, spent in various parts of the empire, he returned to England. Civilian life did not suit Tom. He rejoined the army, this time the Canadian Rifles, stationed in Kingston, where he met the young lady he married as soon as he had completed his term of service. Dr Fowler offered the veteran Tom Coffey, immediately on his return to the city, the situation of janitor of the Royal. Over the years Coffey's broad Irish brogue, with its natural simplicity, became known to and loved by generations of medical students, first in the lower Princess Street College, and then in the Medical Building on Queen's Campus. The innate dignity of the man was one of those enduring memories held by students and faculty alike.[45]

It was Tom's duty to care for the dissecting room and make sure each student had his "sub."[46] While in the dissecting room one day he cut himself slightly. The ensuing bloodpoisoning was the only occasion during the whole of his working life at the Royal or Queen's when Coffey was not in his usual place to keep an eye on his boys.

Tom protected the first few ladies attending the Royal medical lectures from the most outrageous tactics of the discourteous male medical students who were harassing the ladies during the unfortunate times of the early 1880s. For the rest of their lives they remembered him with gratitude.

Tom Coffey, respected and admired by all who knew him, retired in 1903, after twenty-five years of loyal service, first at the Royal and then at Queen's medical faculty.[47] Unfortunately, he was not to enjoy a lengthy retirement because what was probably cancer of the stomach killed him within two years.

CHAPTER SEVEN

Medical Coeducation at the Royal and Queen's

By the middle of the nineteenth century, open-minded men were beginning to accept the idea that no good reason existed why women should not practise medicine. But liberal views on sexual egalitarianism were slow to permeate European and North American societies, and when it came to putting them into practice there was often hesitation and occasionally outright obstruction. In Kingston, a reasonable opinion seems to have prevailed.

This short entry in the faculty minutes of the Royal, 18 June 1877, indicates a truly historic landmark for medical education in Canada. "A letter was read from the Rector of the Collegiate Institute, Hamilton asking if ladies would be allowed to attend medical classes. The Secy. was instructed to inform him that no objections would be made to the attendance of ladies at medical classes."[1]

When the faculty of the Royal made the decision to admit ladies to its classes, two women doctors were already practising in Toronto. Emily Stowe was the first woman to practise medicine in Canada. She was born, the eldest of six girls, to a Quaker family in 1831. Not being able to enter Toronto medical school, Emily took up teaching and soon became Canada's first female public school principal. After teaching for some years, giving birth to two children, and caring for a tubercular husband, she decided to study medicine in New York. She graduated M.D. from the New York Medical College for Women in 1867. Although she promptly set up a practice in Toronto, she did so illegally and only became properly registered in 1880, at the age of forty-nine.[2]

The other woman doctor, Jennie Trout, did not have to fight the male chauvinists head on. Her husband, Edward, was the financially successful publisher of the *Monetary Times and Trade Review*, and a force to be reckoned with in Toronto society. He supported his wife's ambitions when, after teaching for a few years like her older friend and mentor Emily Stowe, she attended the Toronto School of Medicine for one year and then enrolled in the Women's Medical College of Pennsylvania in Philadelphia. She graduated in 1875 and immediately sat the Ontario College of Physicians and Surgeons' licensing examination. Since she had completed the mandatory year of medical studies at a recognized Ontario medical school before going to Philadelphia, she was registered and licensed to practise in the same year. After graduation, Dr Trout began the successful Therapeutic and Electric Institute on Jarvis Street in Toronto; at the same time she supervised a free dispensary for the poor. After seven years of this hectic work, she gradually turned her attention to the cause of women's medical education. It was during this phase of her life that she influenced the development of Queen's and the Royal as coeducational institutions by encouraging young women to enter medicine and the citizens to establish medical schools both in Toronto and Kingston solely for women.[3]

While Jennie Trout and Emily Stowe were practising medicine in Toronto, the Kingston medical establishment accepted the inevitable with a degree of courtesy rarely seen elsewhere. The request by the rector of the Hamilton Collegiate Institute was probably stimulated by the desire of one of his students, Elizabeth Smith, to be a doctor. A year later this young women, confirmed in her idea to study medicine, went to Toronto to sit the matriculation examination of the Medical Council of Ontario in English, Latin, French, and mathematics. Miss Smith passed in English and mathematics but unfortunately failed in Latin and French.[4] In the following year she was reexamined in these two subjects – she passed them and successfully matriculated.

The examiners for matriculation on Easter Tuesday 1879 were Mr Archibald MacMurchy and Mr A.P. Knight, rectors of the Toronto and Kingston collegiates respectively. These high school principals were obviously sympathetic to the hopes of Misses Stowe, Smith and another now-unknown candidate. During the examinations Mr Knight asked the candidates where they intended to study medicine. Augusta Stowe, Dr Emily's daughter, had already decided to go to Victoria University's Toronto School of Medicine. Because Principal Nelles of Victoria was a Stowe family friend, Augusta was welcomed in its medical school. In 1883, she graduated to become the first Canadian woman doctor wholly educated in Canada. Elizabeth Smith told Mr Knight that she was going, on the suggestion of Dr Jennie Trout, to Ann Arbor medical school in Michigan, which at that time had a yearly enrolment of sixty women. In the course of conversation with Mr Knight, she discovered that the Royal might be sympathetic towards the admission of women. He probably also explained to her the advantages of studying medicine in Kingston, where she would get not only a thorough education in Canadian medicine, but also an M.D. degree from Queen's University. She seems to have taken Mr Knight at his word, because on 4 September 1879, the faculty of the Royal met to consider a letter Dr Michael Lavell had just received from Miss Smith asking the faculty to admit ladies. The discussion between Drs Yates, Lavell, Sullivan, Oliver, Dupuis, Fenwick, and Fowler which led to the momentous decision is not recorded in the faculty minute book, but in the end it was moved and resolved to establish a summer course for women – from April to October – equal in character to that given to young men. It was also decided that Drs Lavell and Fowler should "prepare and publish a circular giving intimation of the intention of the faculty."[5]

Before Elizabeth Smith approached the Royal – the medical college, that is, not Queen's University, as is usually thought – she had placed an announcement in the 29 July 1879 issue of the *Globe*: "Ladies wishing to study medicine in Canada will hear something to their advantage by communicating with Box 31, Winona, P.O." From her diary we find that a number of people wrote to her expressing interest in the project. Some were discouraging, some ambivalent, but quite a few were eager to join her in the great adventure. The Stowes, mother and daughter, devoted as they were to Victoria University, attempted to pour cold water on the idea of a separate medical course for women in Kingston.

Unfortunately, when the time came, many who had intimated they wished to join Elizabeth in Kingston were forced to drop out. As she recalled many years later when describing these times, "parents were willing to make sacrifices to send a son to college, but had not yet become convinced of any equal claim of a daughter." She wistfully described how as the spring of 1880 approached "letter after letter of despair came to announce the fact that they could not manage the financial end of it."[6]

THE FIRST SESSION OF WOMEN'S MEDICAL EDUCATION AT QUEEN'S

When the great day arrived, the second Monday of April 1880, only three young women enrolled in the Royal: Elizabeth Smith, the only daughter of a reasonably well off family who supported her aspirations to become a doctor; Elizabeth Beatty, who intended from her first days at the Royal to be a missionary doctor; and Alice Skimmen

McGillivray, "a very young person - fair to see, good to talk to, has been married over a year and is not yet nineteen, determined - clever and girlish, a very good companion in labor,"[7] as Elizabeth Smith described her in her diary.[8]

On 13 April, the day after classes began in the medical school, Elizabeth Smith described in her diary the beginning of the great adventure:

The Rubicon is passed. We cut the rope - we are adrift - on the sea of study. God help us to win the day. The morning was fair - we had a good sleep and felt ready to begin warfare. Went to Dr. Fowler's office he told us to go down to College, that Dr. Depuis [sic] would be there to give us his first lecture. We went but being late found he had left. Went to his office & he returned with us - gave us a short lecture on the bones of the back - showed us over the College, the chamber of horror i.e. the dissecting room and was very agreeable. Dr. Fowler came down also - we had some talk & then after appointing hrs for lectures tomorrow we returned with Dr. Depuis to his office where he gave a scapula & some illustrations of it.[9]

The three young women were proud to be pioneers, or "*rarae aves*" as they saw themselves, and they really enjoyed it. They were made welcome by the faculty, professors, and students, by the university, particularly Principal Grant, and by the townsfolk of Kingston, to whom they were a continual source of curiosity and admiration. This was especially evident on their daily trek from the Royal on lower Princess Street to their chemistry classes on Queen's campus. They boarded together during these early days and facetiously but prophetically named themselves Shadrach (Elizabeth Smith), Meshach (Alice McGillivray), and Abednego (Elizabeth Beatty). Little did they realize that all too soon they would be steeled in the fiery furnace!

Because there were only three of them, the young women received almost individual attention from their professors. It is very likely that during the first month or two they regarded Dr T.R. Dupuis, professor of anatomy in the Royal, and Professor N.F. Dupuis, professor of chemistry at Queen's, as father figures. Chemistry at Queen's was not markedly different from any other university natural philosophy course, apart from the brilliance of Professor Nathan Dupuis's teaching - it was his brother's first anatomy lecture that took the women across the Rubicon. Dr Dupuis talked that first day about the scapula. The particular bone he gave them had belonged to a Betsy Kerr who not long before had died in the local jail. The girls soon learned that

Poor Betsy Kerr has gone away
She would if she could, but she couldn't stay;
she had two sore legs and a baddish cough,
But her legs it was as carried her off.[10]

On the second day, Dr Dupuis lectured on the humerus. By the end
of the week the girls were well accustomed to their "sub":

Today Saturday we dissected from 8:30 to eleven thirty and we did pretty
well. One forgets when at work that the sub. ever had the breath of life in it,
or that it is anything but mere mechanism. The Sub. I may put here for after
merriment was an old schoolmaster in Down, Ireland – died in hospital and
his wife was too poor to afford him burial & so gave him for dissection. An old
man about eighty years old. We have just the upper part. Today I dissected
the side of the chest. It would have been terrible to me to have seen myself
had I not taught myself will power or even had I not been studying med. I
would have been fearfully shocked. As it is I really do not mind it so much as I
anticipated – & ate a hearty dinner after the orgies.[11]

In 1916, thirty-five years after the event, Elizabeth Smith Shortt,
M.D. wrote her reminiscences for the *Queen's Review* and described
the programme she and her colleagues followed every day:

These days were crammed with work as we were zealous students and had
literally no counter attractions. Up at six, down to the Royal at eight,
practical work, one and a half hours and to Anatomy at ten. Then Physiology,
Histology and Therapeutics, dinner, and back at two for Materia Medica.
Then up to Queen's University for Chemistry 3:30 to 4:30, and again for a
time in the early evening to the Royal for practical work and back to study till
late bed time.[12]

The first three months passed quickly. The women worked at a
rate far beyond that usually expected of the men during the normal
winter session. They worked so hard that the professors made them
take a midsummer break.

The candid entries in Elizabeth Smith's diary give some idea of the
courage and bravery of these young women, who were determined to
be as strong as their male colleagues. On 12 May they first watched a
surgical operation:

Today for the first time we went to the hospital to see an operation. An old
man was to have his foot cut off. Dr. Depuis did it, some other M.D. &
students were there. The hospital is a nice large stone structure – very clean

& neat looking indeed. The ward where the man lay had about 10 or 12 beds, some in their beds – some by them, such fearful mishaps. This old man had gangreen [sic] foot. They had him brought into the operating room. Mr. Mac & we three ranged ourselves into the observers seats & prepared to see the performance. They gave him chloroform. This was hard to as he groaned & struggled so hard, then bared the lower leg & tied rubber tightly round it & cut off the foot by the metatarsus bones left enough skin & flesh for a flap to cover the bare end and sewed it over it. Just before the finishing of it when I heard the joints parting company & the foot go spat on the water, I felt kind o'sick & Miss Beatty & I left. I did not faint but was very white & weak. Soon after I went out – Oldham & Day came out to see if I had a fit or anything as that & out comes Mr. Mac & drops on the bed, dead sick. He did look bad to say the least. Dr. Day introduced Chown – B.A.M.D. to us. They took great satisfaction in staring at us & were glad I think that I was sick. I seemed quite an interesting monstrosity to whom they were very kind. I'm bound to get over this – but oh it did leave me less strong than before. They say it is common for the men to faint – so I'm not so very bad.[13]

Towards the end of the 1880 summer session there was talk of the women joining the men's regular winter course, but unfortunately it did not materialize.

In December 1880, an editorial in *Queen's College Journal* commented favourably on the first successfully completed session of Canadian women's medical education during the previous summer:

But it is very desirable that a further trial should be given this experiment. It is watched with interest by many who are hopeful of its ultimate success ... It is with pleasure that we note this attempt by the Royal College to rectify the errors of a conventional past; and we trust that success may attend its efforts.[14]

Alice McGillivray (it was her husband, "Mr. Mac," who had fainted in the operating room) remained in Kingston throughout the winter and continued to attend Professor Dupuis's chemistry classes. The following April, only two new students joined the original three; Helen Reynolds and Margaret Corliss, who, it is thought, still holds the record as the oldest person – she was forty-four on admission – accepted into medicine at Queen's. Since the enrolment was so small, and the number of hospital inpatients declined during the warm months, faculty and students decided to cancel the separate 1881 summer course and set up a bona fide coeducational course in the following October. All but one professor were in favour of this proposal and the women students eventually coaxed him into agreement as well. By the fall of 1881, Principal Grant had invited the Royal back to its former home on Queen's campus. The Medical Building (now the Anatomy Building in the quadrangle behind Summerhill) provided ample and comfortable quarters for the women's separate classroom, dissecting room, and a waitingroom or cloakroom.

MEDICAL COEDUCATION:
SUCCESS THEN FAILURE

During the 1881/82 academic session, the male students, on the whole, welcomed the women and expressed pleasure whenever they answered correctly in class. The senior men conducted themselves with gentlemanly courtesy, and it looked as though all was going well. Unfortunately, after the graduation of the senior men in the spring of 1882, the harmony of this first Canadian experience in medical coeducation turned into discord.

In contrast to the previous year, the 1882/83 session was distressful for the Queen's women. While Augusta Stowe was forging ahead at Toronto in frigid isolation, in Kingston the junior male medical students, released from the standards set by their seniors, seemed to take an active dislike to their female colleagues and started to harass them openly. Graffiti appeared on the classroom walls – disparagement, sly innuendoes, catcalls, and blatant discourtesy became the order of the day. In these disruptive activities the students were led by "a certain Falstaff from some American School." Tom Coffey, the janitor, tried to protect the girls' sensibilities. Every morning before class he would go into their waiting room and call out in his inimitable brogue, "yez can be goin' in now leddies." Only when he was sure they were safely seated in the classroom would he ring the bell to bring the "bhoys" from their "den."[15]

By November 1882 Shadrack, Meshach, and Abednego were truly in the furnace. The senior faculty members, Drs Fowler, Lavell, Sullivan, Yates, Oliver, and Dupuis, extended every sympathy and kindness towards them. Elizabeth Smith Shortt wrote much later that they received from the better class of students every evidence of good will, particularly in the anatomy classes, but the majority were antagonists. Elizabeth Smith's diary reflects her increasing apprehension:

Dr. Depuis said this morning to the class! He was proud of Miss Smith & which brilliant remark was elicited by my answering several successive questions, & I heard a boy behind me say to another 'so are we, so are we all.'

I wanted to sink through the floor but it was obstinately firm & I drooped . . .
I believe Fenwick thinks we have cancelled any chance we might otherwise
have had of clearing our names, by entering med. coll. His reasonings are
often this wise likely 'Any good looks a girl may have were given her purely &
solely to get a husband with,' & and as we were quite lacking in that respect
we took to medicine in despair, never dreaming of such a hope in that state of
life.[16]

Within two weeks the young women were beginning to feel the
pressure. It must have seemed to them that each of the young men
tried to outdo the others in discourtesy. On 22 November Elizabeth
wrote:

No one knows or can know what a furnace I am passing through these days at
Coll. A furnace fiery & severe as any could be & not affect one directly,
physically. Not a day not a lecture passes at Med Coll but something makes
me shrink something hurts me, hurts me cruelly, & why? Not because there
is anything in the whole range of medicine that should make me blush or feel
hurt in the tenderest part of a woman's nature. It is not that, oh no. . . . It is
late now, I have not studied tonight. I tried in the early evg. But it would not
do. But as I am too proud to fail in answers tomorrow I must study yet
tonight.[17]

By Friday, 8 December 1882, the medical faculty grapevine was
more productive than usual. The *Daily British Whig* carried the
heading "College Difficulty: Remark of a Professor Causes the Female
Students to Leave the Room – Resolutions."[18] Ten days of crisis in the
life of the Royal ensued; ten days when the reputation of Queen's
University swayed in the balance; ten days of real worry to the
citizens of Kingston who had sincerely taken the women students to
their hearts. The crisis seems to have been triggered when Dr
Fenwick, while lecturing on the larynx, compared the higher pitched
voices of women to those of the great apes. The *Daily British Whig*
reported, with the minimum of comment, the male students' version
of the facts:

A difficulty, which has been anticipated, occurred in the Medical College a
few days ago. One of the professors, in the course of his lecture, gave
utterance to a natural fact. It appears to have been received as an insult by
the ladies, and they arose and left the room. The Professor, whose character
is above reproach felt grieved at the proceedings. From our knowledge of his
life we must say a purer minded man cannot be found, and his desire to see
graduates well versed in medical science is his only excuse for using

expressions that have been wrongly construed. The students (male) met and unanimously carried a series of resolutions, indicating their sympathy with the Professor and urging the Faculty to close the College against females. They now presented the resolutions to the Professor, who, in replying, said that hitherto he had suppressed important information owing the presence of the ladies; but in future he would not do so. The ladies had adopted the profession of medicine and should not feel aggrieved when any plain statements were made in its study. He would be the last person to say ought that would bring a blush to the cheek of the most virtuous. Another Professor seems also to have incurred the ladies' displeasure and they will not attend his lectures. This gentleman, whose reputation is widespread, holds the same opinion as the Professor first alluded to. He believed that if ladies desired to study medicine, to become specialists they would have to discuss every portion of the human system. Whether they became missionaries or otherwise they should verse themselves in all departments, so that when they graduated they would be an honour to the institution. The Professor declared that everything he said to the students in his lectures should be known by them in the interests of science; no utterance of his was made for any other purpose. The ladies have absented themselves from a number of lectures. This evening the Faculty meet and deliberate upon the question.[19]

During the following week the crisis became a national issue. On Saturday, 9 December, Elizabeth wrote of her anguish in her diary. She thought that Dr Fenwick, lecturer in physiology, was courting popularity with the male students by being unnecessarily rude to the women. She also worried about one-sided views presented by the *Daily British Whig* and hoped their representation would not be copied uncritically by the rest of the press:

This has been a terrible day a terrible day, a day of trouble, of which little can be said in words. It was all in the shadow of our disaffected Prof. Dr. K. Fenwick. The crisis that has been impending came ... We know how delicate a matter it is for members of a Faculty & fraternity to come out openly publicly against one of their no. in this way. The more so as he is quite a popular physician, being one of those bland smiling men of external polish who within is black as midnight. We do not see the end as yet but in any case it is intensely disagreeable. That the press in all places will take pains to copy the pack of falsehoods that appeared in Friday's Whig, goes without saying.[20]

A snowstorm blew up on Sunday, preventing Miss Smith from going to church. It did not, however, prevent the medical faculty from holding a meeting. Although neither the corporation nor faculty minutes of the Royal provide any evidence of this meeting, the *Daily*

British Whig reported on it. The faculty received and rejected outright a petition signed by forty-six students who declared that unless the institution were closed to women they might complete their studies elsewhere.

The next morning, the students met in their "den" on the ground floor of the Medical Building to examine the faculty's reply to their petition. The only action the students took, according to Monday's *Daily British Whig*, was to prepare a letter correcting some inaccuracies in the reports which had appeared in the Toronto newspapers on the previous Saturday. By Tuesday, 12 December, the confrontation between the male medical students and the professors had become worse. The students had received the faculty's reply, which they construed as an insult. Only four students stood against the majority. In keeping with a resolution of the previous day, the first, second, and third year students refused to attend classes. On the same day, the *Daily British Whig*, not satisfied with reports and opinions, published *verbatim* the students' original ultimatum and the faculty's reply.[21]

Not all the newspapers were a cause of grief to the young women. The next day, the *Daily British Whig* and the Toronto papers at last began to appreciate the young women's position and their rights. A second severe snowstorm that week kept Miss Smith at home again. She managed to write extensively in her diary:

These are dreadful days, stormy in every sense, now the snow is blowing terribly a regular whirlwind of snow – & oh such stormy times at Coll. We are passive now, the war has passed from us to the other students & the Faculty & we wait the issue, confident for ourselves. Such a fabric of false cowardly statements as have appeared in the papers here, is hard to conceive possible. They have lost sight of the first issue & now are all intent on having us sent from R.C. wh. endeavor we may lay to the charge of Fenwick & his aide de camp – that despicable of all despicable people Jack Herald ... The gentleman, Mr. Shortt who boards here has been a staunch friend throughout & he & Prof Lavalle [sic] are about the only ones who have come out scatheless to my eyes in the whole affair. It all seems like a horrible dream from wh. I must awaken but yet has been long & terrible.[22]

News of the faculty's discomfort spread quickly across the country. The medical faculties of Toronto, Trinity, Western, McGill, and Bishop's in Montreal received telegrams from the Kingston students asking for admission with *ad eundem* standing. Trinity became the subject of public odium, because it sent a telegram to the Royal's students offering them immediate admission. The temptation to score off the Royal and Queen's must have been great for those senior faculty members who remembered the desertion of nine of their own students to Queen's, for doctrinal reasons, almost thirty years earlier. Dr Fulton, Trinity's dean, and some of its professors suggested with some graciousness that initially they had no desire to injure Queen's itself and were upset by newspaper reports to the contrary.[23] The other medical faculties replied in the newspapers that a certificate from the Royal attesting to three months attendance in Kingston was necessary for admission. The medical faculty of Western University in London was particularly tempted. It had been in existence for only twenty months and an infusion of fifty or more students immediately with the possibility of many more in the future was almost irresistible. But it resisted, maintaining, in consequence, its self-respect and the public's high esteem.

Since the beginning of this eventful week the faculty had been trying to talk sense into the male students – mostly without success. On Tuesday evening Dr Sullivan went to the "den" and spent an hour talking with them, to no avail. The faculty, at last appreciating the intransigence of the medical students, decided to meet in Dr Lavell's office at eight o'clock on Wednesday evening. At the request of the students, however, they transferred the meeting to the Medical Building on campus. The students held their meeting at the same time in a different room.

The *Daily British Whig*, Thursday, 14 December 1882, again presented the relevant documents, which describe the situation more clearly than any reporter's account. It simply headed its report "Fruitless Meetings – The Faculty and Students of the Medical College at Sixes and Sevens – A Final Answer."

The Faculty meeting was attended by nearly all the Professors. The students' petition was carefully considered. After a deliberation of several hours a conclusion was reached, such as they thought was wise, and calculated to meet with public approval, such as appealed to the better side of mankind. They did not capitulate, but delivered their opinions in the following way:

The Faculty having received a further communication from the students, in which they disclaim any disrespect, and indicating that too extreme a view of their request has been taken by the Faculty, it is resolved that in view of the difficulty which has occurred in the co education of male and female students in Medicine, for the present session the female students occupy the ante-room during all the lectures, and that until united action among the Medical Schools of Ontario be had on this subject the Faculty feel that they are bound in honor and law to aid the female students now attending here in completing their course, either by recurring to summer sessions, or adopting such other means as will secure harmony.

Fife Fowler, Dean[24]

The resolution was conveyed to the students, who at once took it into consideration. They replied as follows:

To the Faculty of R.C.P.S.K.

Gentlemen, - We have received and considered your communication. While we would be willing to make any concessions which we can in honour do we cannot accept your offer. In the first place we cannot agree that the females take lectures with us this winter. In the second place we fail to see that you are legally bound to allow them to finish their course here. Should the College be closed at the end of this session we could not bring an action against you, no more do we see that the females could do so should you close this as a female College in the Spring. In the third place we would like your word that no more females be admitted. Should you agree that the females can have no connection with this College after Spring we would be willing to attend classes as you suggest during this session.
- Yours truly,

A.N. White, Secretary[25]

Thursday morning saw a hardening of the students' position and the presentation of their final ultimatum:

To our Respected Faculty of the R.C.P.S.K.

Gentlemen, - Whereas the Faculty have now shown their willingness to consider our complaints and make all legal concessions, but whereas, they declare that they cannot legally reject the females now in attendance until they have finished their course.

Therefore be it resolved that we accept the following as meeting the spirit of our petition:

(1) That no more females be admitted into our College.
(2) That those now in attendance shall not be admitted after the Christmas holidays, but shall be compelled to finish their course as was the original intention by taking summer sessions.
(3) That hereafter males and females be kept separate in every respect.

And now, gentlemen, in conclusion we respectfully present this document as our ultimatum in the matter. After careful deliberation we are resolved to stand by each and every resolution herein contained, and while we will regret exceedingly to leave the Royal College if so compelled by an adverse decision on your part we feel it our duty to go elsewhere to complete our medical studies. Respectfully yours,

THE STUDENTS.[26]

After drawing up this document, the students adjourned until nine-thirty that evening.

In the meantime, word of the seriousness of this irrevocable stage in the confrontation spread and the city's establishment became deeply concerned. During the afternoon Mayor Gaskin and former mayors McIntyre, Gildersleeve, and Pense met. They realized that if the students carried out their ultimatum, Kingston would lose an excellent institution – one of which it had been extremely proud. In the afternoon the mayor's committee interviewed the professors and the students separately, in order to get hold of a thread by which they could unravel the difficulty. They suggested the possibility of a double course of lectures, one for the men, one for the women. In the early evening they met again with the faculty in Dr Lavell's office. The faculty agreed to the "double teaching" option and to abandon the practice of admitting women as long as other medical colleges of Canada were not in full harmony upon the subject. Although the professors stated that it was wrong for the public to think that much valuable material was left out of their lectures because of the presence of the women and that they might be open to an action in Chancery if they forced them out in midsession, they accepted that no more women would be admitted after the graduation of those then in the college.

At half past nine that night in the "den" the mayor's committee confronted over eighty medical students. Each member spoke to the students and presented the propositions, which would allow each side to withdraw gracefully and which met most of the students' demands. At first the younger students wanted to stand on their honour because they had signed the ultimatum. At one o'clock in the morning, after nearly every student had spoken, the following motion was put and carried:

Resolved that having heard the gentlemen who have acted as mediators between the Faculty and ourselves, and the assurance that in future the Faculty agree to give an education to the male and female students separate and distinct in every particular, and that it is not their intention to admit females in the future, we accept the same as a satisfactory settlement of existing difficulties.[27]

The students immediately voted a motion of thanks for the deputation before they expressed their true love of the Royal and Queen's in song. They visited each professor's home and demonstrated their restored loyalty with cheers. The following piece of official correspondence ended what may well have been the greatest student-generated crisis in the history of Queen's or its medical school:

A.N. White, Secretary to Students of the Royal College.

Dear Sir – I am in receipt of your letter of this morning, enclosing a resolution passed at a meeting of the students last evening and desire to say that the Faculty accept the suggestions of the gentlemen who have interested themselves in their present College difficulties. The Faculty agrees to give in future to the female students now attending College a medical education separate and distinct in every particular from the male students, and, as the Faculty believe that under existing circumstances, co-education in medicine is a failure, there is no intention of admitting female students in the future. – I am, yours faithfully,

Fife Fowler, Registrar[28]

The *Daily British Whig*'s lead editorial, 16 December, proudly announced "All in Harmony." It recognized that "women's medical college is a necessity for Ontario," and expressed the opinion that small classes for women should be a thing of the past (only six ladies attended the Royal, one at Toronto and two who were being privately educated at Trinity). *Queen's College Journal* was able in its 21 December issue to sum up in a *post hoc* olympian fashion:

Last week the Royal College proved a perfect Godsend to the quidnuncs ... The press all over the Dominion chronicled the changing phases of the conflict while the local newspapers apparently instructed their reporters to take note of nothing else ... On another [question] the attitude of Trinity Medical College, there can be no two opinions, except perhaps among the inmates of Rockwood or Trinity ... It is unnecessary to say a word more about Trinity Medical Professors. The one comfort in connection with the whole embroglio is that those gentlemen went out for wool, and returned home shorn; shorn of their honour and without the least mite of the wool they so desperately longed to get.[29]

Christmas 1882 passed with the week of chauvinistic discourtesy remembered beyond Kingston only by that unforgiving commentator on human weakness, *GRIP*. Barney O'Hea, a valorous Irishman, moved by the injustice done to the women students, wrote a letter to the editor that has lost none of its bite in the intervening one hundred years:

But its meself that's losht in amashement at the wonderful ingenooity dishplayed in the plan they tuk to get the girls banished out av the medical college, widout renderin' thimselves liable to the lash av the law. They cudn;'t scare them out wid a dishplay av their shupayrior talints – the girls could bate them there. Nayther dursht they be anything but civil, seein' some av them had brothers who could handle a horse whip, so they hit upon the manly, glorious, pious, an' immortally characteristic plan av blushin' them out av the class-room. Whooray for the Kingston medicos!!! The bowld brave fellows!!! They couldn't drive out the girls by any manes, until sayzin the Axecalibre av blackguardism, they routed them with ribald laughter, an' thin petitioned the faculty not to let thim in agin![30]

When this issue of *GRIP* appeared on the Kingston newsstands, the medical men bought up all the available copies to prevent the women seeing their "manly behaviour" mocked. The women eventually got hold of a copy, possibly with the help of Adam Shortt, a philosophy student in the arts faculty who had sided with the women students – particularly with Elizabeth Smith. To say they were very pleased and amused would be a gross understatement.[31]

A new term started for Shadrach, Meshach, and Abednego on 8 January 1883, their last as students of the Royal. Elizabeth Smith probably expressed the feelings of all three when she wrote, "as we go back to K. tomorrow, to take up the battle of life in an especial earnest – I dread it – dread it."[32]

Arrangements were, in general, in accordance with those accepted by the faculty before Christmas. Drs Sullivan, Oliver, Dupuis, and Lavell lectured, with the women in an adjacent room; Dr Fowler, lectured to Miss Reynolds in his office, as she was the only women taking the *materia medica* course that year. Dr Fenwick who had told Mr Knight, the matriculation examiner, he was going to continue his anecdotes, kept to the letter of the agreement to give separate lectures to the women. However, Elizabeth noted, "on no day does he give us more than twenty minutes sometimes so rapidly and incoherently that we could not possibly take it down."[33] By the end of January most lectures, except Dr Fenwick's in physiology, were satisfactory. With an increase in the workload towards the end of term, and examinations, Elizabeth's diary tails off and the rest of the women's medical education at the Royal seems to have continued uneventfully. The three original female medical students needed just one more year of study to graduate from Queen's with their M.D.s.

A CIVIC MEDICAL SCHOOL: THE WOMEN'S MEDICAL COLLEGE, KINGSTON

The forced withdrawal of the young women from regular classes at the Royal seemed a victory for the male medical students. This was, of course, a delusion. In the short run they won, but lost the advantages of medical coeducation. In the long run, however, all the women of Canada won their right to professional equality in medicine. The citizens of Kingston who had mediated the compromise, the faculty, and the women medical students united to develop an acceptable, possibly an improved, environment to continue women's medical education. The result of their efforts culminated, that summer of 1883, with the establishment of the Women's Medical College, Kingston.

During the previous winter and spring, liberal Toronto physicians had discussed the possibility of founding a women's medical college.[34] However, because of Kingston's experience, Dr Emily Stowe was unable to persuade the Toronto doctors to accept the two conditions attached to the offer of her young colleague, Dr Jennie Trout: she would donate $10,000 towards the foundation of a female medical college only if women were on the board of directors of any proposed medical school and women doctors were promoted to professorial rank as soon as their professional experience justified it. These conditions proved too much for the Toronto medical men and they continued to procrastinate.[35]

Kingston had no such inhibitions. Competent students and sympathetic faculty members already existed. When Principal Grant, Mr Knight, and other leading citizens called a public meeting at City Hall for the evening of Friday, 8 June 1883 to discuss various ways of setting up a women's medical college, they generated a successful crowd. After lengthy speeches, the following resolutions were received and accepted with enthusiasm:

i. That in the opinion of this meeting facilities should be given to females for obtaining a thorough medical education similar to those so abundantly provided for men; and that Canadian women should not be obliged to go to the United States or Britain to obtain such education.

Mover and seconder: Mr. A.P. Knight and Mr. Henry M. Folger.

ii. Whereas Kingston offers special advantages for successful working of a Women's School of Medicine. Resolved, that in the opinion of this meeting it is right and fitting to establish in Kingston, such a Medical College.

Mover and seconder: Mr. C.F. Gildersleeve and Mr. R.M. Horsey.

iii. That as the Royal College has resolved not to admit women to its classes in future, and as the session of any new institution must open not later than the month of October, it is desirable that immediate action be taken.

Mover and seconder: Sir Richard Cartwright and Principal G.M. Grant.[36]

Thus was founded on that warm summer's evening the first institution of higher professional education for women in Canada. This rare academic achievement was accomplished, not by church or state, or by professors or students, but simply through the will of educated citizens.

The evening's work was not finished, however, with the simple expression of uplifting sentiments. Principal Grant reported Dr Jennie Trout's offer of $200 a year for five years to support the college. Pragmatic as ever, Grant assured the assembly of the feasibility of setting up such a college in Kingston and of its continued viability: competition from Toronto was unlikely – or so he had been informed. Had there been even the slightest positive indication from Toronto, he would not have advocated founding a women's college in Kingston. As soon as Principal Grant sat down, the Honourable G.A. Kirkpatrick, seconded by Mr J.B. Carruthers, moved the opening of a subscription list – $2,000 a year for five years was thought to be sufficient to open the college. These gentlemen, along with a number of other prominent citizens – W. Harty, E. Chown, B. Robertson, R.V. Rodgers, R.M. Horsey, J. McKervey, George Macdonnell, J.M. Machar and James Swift – were promptly nominated as a campaign committee. They set a target of $1,500 per year. The other necessary $500 was anticipated to come from the student fees. The enthusiasm of the evening produced $750 towards the target.

News of the meeting reached Toronto almost immediately. Jealous of their city's provincial pre-eminence, procrastinating and conservative academics were jolted out of their indecision. The Toronto medical men attended a meeting organized by the Women's Suffrage Club in Shaftesbury Hall on Tuesday evening, 12 June. They withdrew their objections to women being on the board of management and acting as professors, and the majority then agreed to the immediate establishment of a Toronto Woman's Medical College.[37] Few dissented. The stupidity and inappropriateness of having two similar colleges in Ontario was plain. Edward Trout, Dr Jennie's husband, aptly described the actions of his fellow Torontonians:

... to call a meeting at this date was an act of discourtesy to the Kingston people. They had waited patiently until there seemed no prospect of the school in Toronto succeeding. Then they worked vigorously and established their college on a liberal and substantial basis.[38]

Those words appear to have fallen on deaf ears because, when they learned that Kingston's college was to open on Tuesday, 2 October 1883, courtesy and self-respect came in a poor second to civic chauvinism, and the Torontonians scrambled to open their college on Monday, 1 October.

The summer was one of careful and deliberate progress in Kingston. A meeting of the citizen subscribers on 25 June elected a board of trustees by ballot: A.P. Knight, J. Carruthers, E.J.B. Pense, H. Folger, Hon. G.A. Kirkpatrick, Sir R.I. Cartwright, W. Harty, A. Gunn, R.V. Rodgers, Mrs Edward Trout (Dr Jennie), Mrs Britton, Mrs W. Harty, Mrs Dickson, and Miss Gildersleeve.[39] The board of trustees immediately elected Sir Richard Cartwright chairman and Mr William Harty vice-chairman. Mr A.P. Knight, who had been the initiator a few years earlier of women's higher medical education in Kingston (and continued to be its guiding spirit), was the obvious choice as registrar. His statutory duties as registrar were to collect fees, register names of students, collect subscriptions, pay salaries of officials at stated times, conduct correspondence, and to write the minutes of the board.[40]

The college now had an administration, but no students or professors. The board asked Dr Michael Lavell to become full-time president and dean of the Women's Medical College for an annual salary of $300. But Lavell did not wish to sever his connections with the Royal (in fact he could not afford to) – at that time he was its representative on the Ontario Medical Council. The board of the Women's Medical College then gracefully conceded that Dr Lavell should retain his relationship with the Royal and appointed him the first president and dean of the women's college as well. Thus this first Canadian attempt to establish what has come to be called a geographic full-time appointment failed.

Within a week of his election, Dr Lavell submitted the names of his faculty for approval to the board. He put forward himself as professor of obstetrics and diseases of women and children. He recommended Dr Michael Sullivan as professor of surgery, Dr C. Irwin, professor of anatomy, Dr A.S. Oliver, professor of *materia medica*, Dr H.I. Saunders, professor of the theory and practice of medicine, and Dr. Thomas M. Fenwick professor of medical jurisprudence and sanitary science. The chair of the institutes of medicine and histology was left temporarily unfilled. The salary for each chair was $150 a year except for medical jurisprudence, which was denoted a "half chair" at $75 per annum. Also, not unexpectedly, the chair of surgery was to be worth $200 per annum while it was filled by Dr Sullivan, then the senior surgeon in town.

A deputation from the board of trustees waited on the Kingston City Council to seek classroom accommodation for the new college. At its 6 August meeting, the council voted to donate to the college the lease of Ontario Hall – considered to be the finest lecture hall in the province – and several convenient anterooms.[41]

D.D. Calvin wrote, when discussing Kingston's women's college, that "the dissecting room is said to have been high up, near the base of the dome structure."[42] It has been very difficult to produce corroborative evidence of this statement apart from the following piece of verse from *Queen's College Journal*, which was written some years after the founding of the college, when the women were hoping to move into better quarters. It provides a glimpse of the facilities available in City Hall, which were unique in Canadian medical education:

A WAIL FROM THE LADY MEDS

We are told to press onward and upward,
    This is just what we do every day,
Rising nearer, still nearer, the town clock,
    Looking forth o'er the city gray.

With our hearts beating high – we can't help it,
    And gasping for breath as we go,
We climb up that long winding stairway,
    Which has seventy-two steps as you know.

Yet we try very hard to enjoy it;
    Our complainings are seldom and few;
The seniors train freshies to love it,
    And tell them how they used to do.

The second and third years speak loudly
   In praise of improvements just made:
The blocks, shelves, and three ventilators,
   For which they'd so earnestly prayed.

Yet if the stove smokes very badly,
   When the wind doesn't blow the right way,
If the gas doesn't burn very brightly,
   And its odor will not let us stay,

We take up our note-books and ink-stands.
   And the Juniors say, 'Freshies, don't mind,
Tho' we're all going down to the P'lice Court,
   for Timmerman uses us kind.'

Oh, 'tis then we have such ardent longings
   To be nearer the Principal's care,
To have of his generous protection
   a somewhat more bountiful share.

And now, who will blame us for asking
   If the Toronto lady Med.
Has as tiresome a walk to her college,
   And such a steep stairway to tread –

If she's sent to the P'lice Court for lectures
   When the gas in her college won't burn,
If she's subject to such severe trials,
   When an M.D. she's striving to earn.

But our professors and methods
   Comparison need never fear,
Had we but a convenient building
   We'd invite the Toronto Meds. here.

We're desirous our college should prosper,
   That it should be second to none,
And be known throughout the Dominion
   As the College 'A' No. 1.

So we hope through the summer vacation –
   E'er the fall term of college draws nigh –
That our worthy trustees will locate us

In a place not perched quite so high![43]

Before classes opened in October 1883 the trustees spent $250 on various furnishings and appliances necessary to adapt the municipal offices to their new use. Dr Jennie Trout was so pleased with the evident progress in Kingston that she offered an annual scholarship of $50 on the condition that two more scholarships be donated. They were promptly forthcoming. Mrs Macnee donated $45 for four years, while other women of Kingston joined together to provide a Kingston scholarship of $60.

During the summer, Dr Lavell and Mr Knight issued a prospectus or calendar for the college. Nothing more clearly expressed the confidence of the new medical school than the following extracts from its opening pages:

Opening Session

The Session will be opened Tuesday, October 2nd, 1883, and continue for six months.

The course of Lectures will be equivalent in all respects to the ordinary winter course delivered in other Medical Colleges, and as such will be accepted in proceeding to the degree of M.D. in Queen's University.

The requirements for graduation will in no sense differ from what is required for the other sex, and the facilities for study will also be the same.

By the regulations of the University, the Matriculation examination of the College may be passed at any time before undergoing examination for the degree. The Medical Council Matriculation, which is the intermediate examination of the High Schools with Latin, will be accepted by the University.

The ladies lately in attendance upon the Medical Classes in the Royal College have signified their intention of continuing their studies in the Women's College, thus forming a nucleus for the various classes. Judging by the many letters received, the number of entrants will be by no means small.

The success of the lady students in the Royal College, and in Queen's University (where a lady won first place in a class of 20 in Chemistry), and at the primary examinations of the Medical Council (where some of them attained the highest percentage), is the best endorsement the city can offer of the value of its College instruction.

Local Advantages

The city possess boarding houses in plenty and asking reasonable rates; it is also a most orderly city. A lady can walk the streets at all hours without receiving any offence.

The Faculty have apparatus and appliances required for imparting a sound medical education. Through the abundant supply of dissecting material furnished by the Penitentiary, Gaol, Hospital, and other public institutions in the neighbourhood, the school will afford exceptional advantages for the study of Practical Anatomy, while it will not be second to any other Medical school in advantages for the prosecution of all other branches of medical knowledge. The Kingston General Hospital alone has accommodation for 150 beds, and contains in the 'Watkins Wing,' an operating amphitheatre, enabling all the students to witness operations; the other institutions referred to have a large number of patients constantly under treatment.[44]

In keeping with its promise of sexual equality, the board of trustees set the same fees for the medical course as those charged by the Royal. No overall fee was charged because students who had attended a similar course elsewhere, in an approved school, could request an exemption. The sessional fee for each of the major clinical and preclinical courses was $12.00, while courses of lesser importance usually cost $6.00. For purposes of comparison, in Kingston during the 1880s a student could obtain full board and lodging in private boarding houses for $2.75 - $4.00 per week and rent a telephone for $35.00 a year, and that the salary of Principal Grant was $2,750 a year.

The Women's Medical College, Kingston opened its doors on 2 October. Eleven women students were registered: three in the fourth year, two in the third, three in the second, and three "freshies" in the first year.

Regularization of its legal status was the first business attended to by the board after the college opened in October. When the board approached the provincial council, it advised them to procure a public or private act of the legislature, as the Royal had done seventeen years earlier. It also advised the registrar to see if the college could have the same affiliation with Queen's University as the Royal. This would allow its students, following matriculation, to sit the university M.D., C.M. degree examinations to become eligible for the Medical Council examinations and a licence to practise. The essential legal difference between the two medical schools was that graduates of the Royal did not have to have a Queen's M.D. to be eligible for a licence to practise, but the women of Women's Medical College needed the degree before they could sit the Medical Council's examinations.

At its meeting, 16 October 1883, the university's board of trustees set up a committee of resident trustees to consider the matter of affiliation. During the following April's annual meeting, the committee recommended regulations that the women's college students would be required to meet if affiliation was to be effected. The trustees accepted the regulations after a meeting between the principal and Mr Knight, who submitted the charter of the Kingston Ladies Medical College [sic] which was to be legalized under the Act respecting the Incorporation of Joint Stock Companies by Letters Patent.[45] This action probably accounts for the Women's Medical College never bothering to acquire a parliamentary act of incorporation.

Regulations drawn up for the College were similar to those for the Royal wherever they referred to students. In order to graduate, a woman student was required to show she was at least twenty-one years old, that she had received a certificate of good character from a clergyman, and that she had attended all classes; she had also to show that she had compounded medicines for two periods of six months or one period of twelve months in the office of a qualified medical practitioner and had attended six cases of midwifery.

Dr Michael Lavell taught midwifery – the subject considered most appropriate in a women's medical school. For many years he had been the leader of the medical community in urging the establishment of women's professional education. He taught the young ladies a full course of obstetrics and all the current major and minor gynaecological operations, and gave a series of lectures on diseases specific to women and children. To make this aspect of medicine more relevant and practical, the board of trustees of the women's college set up a dispensary on Princess Street, in a building provided by Miss Gildersleeve, for the treatment of women and children. Students were permitted to attend confinements in the city to gain practical experience in midwifery and meet the academic regulations.

By the academic year 1885/86 the college was well financed and progressing effectively enough for the board to be able to accept Dr Lavell's resignation from the chair of obstetrics. He had that year been appointed medical superintendent of the federal penitentiary. Dr Alice McGillivray was appointed as professor of obstetrics and diseases of women. She was also asked to continue as lecturer in practical anatomy, and to remain in charge of the dissecting room (both of these junior appointments she had taken on immediately following graduation).

The meetings of the Women's Medical College board were held three or four times a year with Dr Lavell and Mr Knight always in attendance. The other male trustees attended when they could, but the women trustees were punctilious in their support, particularly Mrs Dickson, Mrs Harty, Mrs Macnèe, and Miss Gildersleeve. Their thoughtful concern for the community was exemplified when they joined together with Dr Alice McGillivray to organize a course of lectures for all the women of the city on health-related matters particularly affecting women and children.[46] At the fifth annual meeting of the subscribers, the finances were found in sound condition – $1,656.60 was then in the bank. The future prospects looked so rosy, with twenty-three students attending the college, that the question of establishing a separate hospital for women and children in Kingston was seriously considered.

Although the hospital idea never materialized, in December 1888 the faculty and trustees of the college began to discuss the necessity of relocating. The suggestion to relocate on Queen's campus in the west wing of Summerhill, then Professor Dupuis's residence, led nowhere and the college continued to operate out of its cramped City Hall quarters.

At this time, Dr Lavell, who was approaching sixty, and Dr Sullivan, who was busy with his senatorial duties in Ottawa, gradually handed over their teaching and administrative responsibilities to their junior colleagues. Within two years of graduating, Dr McGillivray carried a full teaching load. In the fall of 1888, Elizabeth Smith returned to Kingston as Mrs Adam Shortt, M.D. and was appointed to the chair of medical jurisprudence. The appointment in 1889 of Dr Alice McGillivray as subdean of the Women's Medical College indicates another significant step for the college. She held this position while still performing her duties as professor of obstetrics.[47]

Towards the end of the decade, the board of the women's college considered the revolutionary idea of opening its classes to nurses. In 1860, Florence Nightingale had established her nursing school at St Thomas's Hospital, London, while Elizabeth Blackwell and Marie Zakrzewska had founded the first training school for nurses in the United States in 1873.[48] The revolutionary aspect of the college's suggestion was the idea that medical students and nurses would share in the same classes. Unfortunately this idea proved to be ahead of its time.[49]

After the college had been in operation for about six years, certain faculty members of the women's college appear to have moved to take over the college corporation. A number of them met and drew up a memorandum suggesting certain changes in the constitution that would effectively put control of the women's college into the hands of the doctors (both male and female) and wrest it from the firm grip of Mr (now Dr, but unlicenced) Knight and the staunch lay board of trustees. The minutes of a special meeting of the trustees held late on Saturday afternoon, 8 June 1889 indicate that this incipient revolt was smothered effectively and unanimously:

A memorandum was read from part of the Faculty asking for certain changes in the constitution and management of the College. Resolved that the Trustees representing the Subscribers to the Women's Medical College feel they cannot part with the control of the College which is virtually asked for in the memorandum under consideration and therefore they cannot approve of the changes therein suggested. The meeting then adjourned.[50]

A month later another special meeting of the board received Dr Michael Sullivan's resignation from the chair of surgery. However, within a year a change of heart occurred either on the honourable doctor's part or that of the board. He was offered the deanship when Dr Lavell retired and accepted on 31 March 1890.

In the same year, the board purchased a large double-fronted house at 75 Union Street. Miss Gildersleeve spent considerable time and energy in finding the most appropriate site for the college. They paid $4,800 for it, half of which was a down payment. The trustees, the faculty, and the girls were all pleased with the new college building. *Queen's College Journal* commented: "There is ample room on the lot for extensions. It overlooks Queen's College grounds. Its future, as far as location is concerned, is well assured."[51] Certain alterations had to be made at once: for example, two new windows were needed for the dissecting room, and the governors of the Kingston General Hospital generously gave them. The students were particularly pleased at the closeness of the university and the fact that they no longer had to make the daily trek from downtown. They were also proud that they could "now conscientiously invite any girl who thinks of studying medicine to come to Kingston."[52] The gifts of a piano, a telephone, and rocking chairs proved to the young women that the trustees and faculty were possessed of wisdom, generosity, consideration, and also an appreciation of "girl nature!"[53]

When it moved to Union Street, the college seemed assured of academic success. This was not to be. It gradually declined in size and importance because the Toronto Woman's Medical College and the newly opened women's medical school in the University of Bishop's College, Montreal, were providing a comparable medical education in the much larger metropolitan centres. Unfortunately, after the move into the new buildings, the finances of the college were in such a poor state that the trustees had to ask the faculty to accept corporation stock, in lieu of cash, for half their salaries.[54] The board of trustees remained enthusiastic but began to have staffing problems. The most significant one followed the resignation of Dr Sullivan as dean in April 1892. Dr Thomas M. Fenwick succeeded him as the third and last dean of the Women's Medical College, while Dr "Mickey" became honorary president and emeritus professor of surgery.

"Made weak by time and fate, but strong in will," the Women's Medical College gradually acquiesced to the inevitable. it was left, in September 1893, to Principal Grant, Mr Pense (chairman of the board), Mr Rodgers, Mr Horsey, Drs Fenwick and Knight, Mrs Dickson, and the ever-faithful Miss Gildersleeve to accept graciously the following melancholy resolution:

That the object with which the Women's Medical College was started, of enabling Canadian women to obtain an education in medicine in their own country, having been accomplished through the starting of schools in Toronto and Montreal, subsequent to our initiative and it being evident that there are not a sufficient number of students to supply three schools and have them efficiently equipped, resolved that the Board do now close the Kingston Women's Medical College and recommend that their students to complete their course either in Toronto or Montreal.[55]

By the fall of 1894, all that remained was the winding up of the financial affairs of the college. Liabilities amounted to about $3,900; to retire these the board sold its property on Union Street to the Children's Aid Society for $4,000. In time, Queen's University took over the building as the centre for teaching commerce and eventually demolished it to erect a new sports' facility.

The closing of the account books of the Kingston Women's Medical College ended a short and glorious experiment in Canadian higher professional education of women. It would be difficult to improve on the assessment of the eminent Canadian historian Hilda Neatby:

Short as its history was, the Women's Medical College was a distinguished example of the cooperation of doctors, citizens of Kingston, and the faculty of Queen's, especially Grant, Watson, Dupuis, and Knight, in rebuking narrow prejudice and supporting the best liberal principles of the age.[56]

The city of Kingston, Queen's, and the Royal can be proud of their contribution to Canadian feminism. Although only a few students have been named, many attended the women's college during its short life, and each in their own separate way was a credit to the school. Of the total enrolment of fifty-six women, forty-two graduated as Doctors of Medicine, thirty-five of these received the Queen's M.D., C.M., five, the M.D. from Trinity, and two, the M.D. from Bishop's in Montreal.

What sort of women came to Kingston a hundred years ago for medical education? What was their social standing? And how did they fare after leaving the college and Queen's? The religious persuasion of the majority was, not unexpectedly, Presbyterian, followed by a medley of other denominations. Twenty-four was the average age of the women on admission.[57] In an 1899 letter, Elizabeth Smith wrote that at that time, of the thirty-five lady M.D.s who had graduated from Queen's, one-third had married. With one exception the others were practising their profession, six as missionaries. She felt that the majority came from well-to-do families and the teaching profession rather than from wealthy homes, and that only a few students continued to go into society to a certain extent while at college.[58]

With the graduation of these young women, medical coeducation ended at Queen's. On numerous occasions thereafter, particularly during World War I, women requested admission to the medical faculty. On each occasion they were rejected. Even their champion Dr Knight, shortly before retirement, chaired a committee which sympathetically denied them admission. Women had to wait until the middle of the Second World War, when, in 1943, medical coeducation was at last firmly reestablished at Queen's.

Reverend George Munro Grant, D.D., LL.D., C.M.G., principal, Queen's University 1877–1902

Men of the "New Century"

Dr A.E. Ross

Dr. J.C. Connell, dean 1903-1929

Dr W.T. Connell, professor of Pathology and Bacteriology

Major-General Henry E.M. Douglas, V.C., C.B., C.M.G., D.S.O., M.D., C.M.

Officers, No. 5 Stationary Hospital, Cairo, 1916

No. 5 Stationary Hospital (Queen's), "March-Out", 5 May 1915, Kingston Armouries

Queen's Campus, photographed by Billy Bishop, 1919

Colonel F. Etherington, C.M.G., M.D., C.M., C.O., No. 7
Canadian General Hospital

CHAPTER EIGHT

The Rebirth of Queen's Medical Faculty

Both the Royal and Queen's University recognized that a close academic association was necessary for their survival as national institutions. From the moment of his inaugural address, Principal Grant indicated that he was particularly interested in the education of young doctors. Time after time he attended their final examinations; repeatedly he took part in the Royal's faculty board meetings. In 1880 he brought the Royal back to Queen's campus, and shortly afterwards he was instrumental in establishing the Women's Medical College of Kingston. Grant knew that the students wanted an "organic union" of the Royal with Queen's and set out to accomplish it. His success was of the utmost significance to medical education in Ontario and to the continued development of scientific scholarship at Queen's.

REUNION WITH QUEEN'S

The coming together of the university and its erstwhile medical school was not easy to arrange. Slowly, through the late 1880s, Principal Grant turned the Royal away from affiliation with Trinity University and towards closer union with Queen's. Because the return of the medical school was fraught with potential hazards, Grant and Dr Fowler agreed early in 1892 to put the idea of an "organic union" before the university council. This action would permit informal discussion between the parties before official consideration by their respective corporations.

The Council of Queen's University is a unique body, established by an amendment of the university charter in 1874. It consists of all members of the board of trustees, all members of the senate, and an equal number of elected alumni. The election of the chancellor of the university has always been its prime function. The council's continuing and perhaps most valuable contribution to the university is its role as a reservoir of professional and mercantile expertise which may be drawn on by the university at any time. A problem vexing the university community may be brought before the annual meeting of council for discussion and debate in an informal manner before the board of trustees or university officers take official action. As such, it was an ideal forum for the principal's purpose.[1]

The decision of Grant and Fowler led to one of the most significant meetings in the history of the council. Held on the afternoon of 26 April 1892, it was almost entirely devoted to consideration of potential problems arising from the proposed reunion. Present at the meeting were Chancellor Sandford Fleming, Principal Grant, all the senators, most trustees, and a few alumni mostly local ministers, or doctors on staff at the Royal. At that time, a member of council was required to attend all meetings and pay for the privilege. A defaulter could only be reinstated on payment of the unpaid fee. The first business of the 1892 meeting reinstated Senator, the Honorable Michael Sullivan, M.D., who had paid his arrears, and subsequently declared Dr K.N. Fenwick's seat vacant for his refusal to pay. Council then dealt with three issues affecting the medical school. First, the standards required by the Ontario Medical Council for matriculation and the entry into medical school were discussed. Next a committee consisting of the principal and four medical men was set up "to defend the rights of the University in its representation on the Provincial Medical Council." Thirdly, Dr Knight was appointed the University Council's representative on the joint Queen's/Royal Board of Medical Studies.[2]

The council dedicated the rest of the afternoon and early evening to considering a letter from the Aesculapian Society urging action towards reunification. It is not known whether this letter was prompted by the principal or Dr Fowler. However, it led directly to Dr Grant's motion "that in the opinion of the University Council it would be in the interest of the University, of medical science and medical education in this part of the Country that Queen's should establish a Faculty of Medicine."[3]

The motion carried, and a committee, consisting of the principal, Drs Lavell, Moore, Gibson, Bell, and the Reverend Dr Williamson, was appointed to meet immediately with the Royal. The council reassembled at ten o'clock in the morning, 27 April, and the principal asked that the members of the Royal's faculty be permitted to join council for discussions towards a closer union. After some compromising, it was moved, "that the Faculty accept the proposal of organic union with Queen's University, subject to the maintenance of the independence of the medical faculty, on similar conditions to those in use at McGill University, Montreal."[4] This resolution became the basis for all future discussions about reunion.

Later that day, the principal reported to the board of trustees the desire of the medical students and the willingness of the Royal to enter into an "organic union" with the university. He then added his own unhesitating conviction "that the proposed step would be in the interest of the Medical Faculty as well as of the University and of Medical Science."[5]

Grant recapitulated for the board the resolutions on the substantive aspects of the organic union on which tentative agreement had been reached earlier in the day at the council meeting. The major commitment required from the trustees by the medical men was the institution of a chair of biology. In Grant's opinion, this could be done by dividing Professor James Fowler's chair of botany into a chair of animal biology and a chair of botany. The principal promised that he would meet, out of his own pocket, any unbudgeted expenses arising from the support of the new chair, and the chancellor offered to help defray any unforeseen costs. Dr Grant then nominated Dr A.P. Knight for the new chair of zoology, physiology, and histology, and recommended a salary of $1,000 per annum, on condition that he qualify within the next two or three years as a licenced practitioner in Ontario by passing the Medical Council's examinations. Dr Knight would then be able to sign the student's tickets, which were mandatory evidence of a student's eligibility to sit the council examinations, in physiology and histology. As Dr Knight never did pass the required examinations, Dr D. Cunningham was appointed as his teaching fellow to perform this chore.

The board of trustees, after dealing with the appointment of Dr Knight, returned to the main question and resolved, as the minutes of that momentous meeting record, "that there shall be and there is hereby established in the University of Queen's College a Faculty of Medicine which shall be known as 'The Medical Faculty of the University'."[6]

Fourteen paragraphs reestablishing the new medical faculty were accepted. They dealt with the appointment and responsibilities of the dean, the professors, associate professors (members of the Faculty of Arts) and lecturers, with the collection of fees and their division between the faculty (for the professors salaries) and the university (for the general maintenance of the faculty's building and equipment), and with regulations for the internal government of the faculty. The university's Finance and Estate Committee was given power to decide when the provisions should be implemented and Dr Fife Fowler was appointed the first dean of the reestablished medical faculty in the university.

THE FIRST YEAR

The summer of 1892 saw a feverish reversal of the work accomplished twenty-six years before. The board set up a special joint appointment committee on the recommendation of the university council and in response to a letter from Drs Fowler and Sullivan stressing the urgency of regularizing the appointment procedures if the university wished to reopen its Faculty of Medicine for the fall session. The professors appointed by the board were listed according to their discipline or department in the university calendar for the thirty-ninth session 1892/93. There were three professors of medicine, Drs Fowler, Henderson, and Herald; two, of surgery, Sullivan and Dupuis; two, of anatomy, Garrett and Mundell; K.N. Fenwick was listed as professor of obstetrics and gynaecology; Saunders, Anglin, and Clarke, as professors of medical jurisprudence, pathology, and mental diseases respectively; Dr J.C. Connell, as lecturer in ophthalmology, otology, laryngology, and rhinology. The basic science chairs, funded fully by the university, were held by Dr James Fowler (botany), Dr A.P. Knight (zoology, physiology, and histology), Professors Goodwin and Nichol (chemistry).

Before the first session of the newly reestablished Queen's medical faculty opened, a faculty board meeting was held in the senate chamber on the evening of 13 September 1892. Principal Grant took the chair, Dean, Dr Fowler, and twelve faculty members attended. First they allotted the residue of the Royal College funds ($676) to the renovation of the Medical Building. They spent $500 at once on a new furnace, and $77 to clear the cellar and unclog its drain. At long last the doctors were able to install a much-needed water closet and two urinals in the basement and some new hemp matting in the corridors for the students' comfort. It was agreed that the old stoves could be disposed of, Tom Coffee being permitted to keep one for himself.[7]

The faculty then decided which standing committees to establish. These indicate, in an indefinable way, the subjects of most interest to medical educators almost a century ago. The committees in order of formation were: a committee to organize the faculty's opening ceremonies; a committee to frame by-laws under the board of trustees' enactment fourteen for the regulation of curriculum, examinations, admissions, fees, discipline, and internal government of the faculty; a salary committee; a committee to oversee financial administration of the faculty; a physiology and pathology committee to supervise the laboratories; a demonstrator of anatomy committee; and a timetable committee. An *ad hoc* committee was charged with drafting an expression of sorrow on learning of Dr Henderson's sudden death.

The official ceremonies marking the reopening of the medical faculty took place on Friday, 14 October 1892. The occasion was held in greater solemnity than when the faculty first assembled many years before at 75 Princess Street and listened to Dr Stewart's inaugural lecture. This time the ceremonies took place in Convocation Hall in the present Theology College. They opened with a prayer and were presided over by the university chancellor, Sir Sandford Fleming. Although only a small audience of notables attended downstairs, the students fairly filled the balcony. Of the speakers, only Principal Grant and Sir James Grant M.D., an arts alumnus, then recently elected to the board of trustees, were of interest to the medical students, some of whom slipped away during the tedious proceedings.

Principal Grant expressed the opinion that medicine should progress along three separate lines: "clinical investigation, practical anatomy and the study by means of the microscope of normal or diseased tissues and of bacteriology." These were presumably *avant garde* pedagogic ideas in the 1890s. He also strongly urged each medical student to watch his professor experimenting: the student "must handle the tools himself and become as familiar with test tubes as with the stethoscope."[8] His speech reflected his goal for the medical faculty at Queen's: a balanced education in medicine, characterized by excellence in both preclinical and clinical instruction.

Because many students had missed Principal Grant's speech at the opening ceremonies, they invited him a month later to address the Aesculapian Society. He made himself an instant favourite by explaining "what we were to expect from him as our Principal. He closed his remarks by telling us what he expected from us which might be included in the words – be gentlemen!" The part of his speech that seems to have most impressed the students was the often repeated admonition, "Pay your fees. Beg, borrow or – the money. It does not matter how you get it."[9] Rarely have such prudent words been heard from the principal and primarius professor of divinity at a Presbyterian university!

The minutes of the monthly meetings of the Faculty of Medicine contain the evidence of both the day-to-day business of running the medical faculty and the larger academic concerns of the late nineteenth century. Because Principal Grant hardly missed a meeting, he set the standard for attendance – and kept an official eye on the doctors.

Even during its first year of operation, the faculty board was troubled by government regulations. For example, at an early meeting, Senator Sullivan was asked to approach the federal government to allow the faculty to buy embalming alcohol free of excise. Equipment was a constant worry. New instruments for postmortems were bought for eighteen dollars, and the principal consulted the governors of the Kingston General Hospital in an attempt to convince them to share the cost. A number of microscopes disappeared and remained unaccounted for until Mr Walker, a local detective, was set on their trail. Through his efforts all the microscopes were back in the laboratory within the following months. In keeping with the tradition established at the Royal, the new Queen's medical faculty voted a hundred dollars towards the expenses of the Aesculapian Society's annual dinner.

From the time the faculty rejoined the university, a dean's report, including a financial audit, was made annually to the university board of trustees. Before he forwarded it to the trustees, the dean presented it to his colleagues. The auditor's first report, for the academic session 1892/93, showed that total receipts for the year were $5,965.63, of which $2,912.96 was placed in the expense account and $3,052.67 in the salary account. At the end of the financial year the faculty had $10.90 to its credit in the bank.

The report of the Curriculum and Examinations Committee, presented to faculty at its April meeting, describes the 1893 curriculum. When allowances are made for the advances in medical technology, it looks remarkably like that of today. The four-year programme previously offered in the Royal was continued, the major difference being the introduction of a pathology course in the third year. Before Dr W.T. Connell's appointment, Dr W.G. Anglin held the chair of pathology on a parttime basis. An examination in each subject had to be passed at the end of the year in which it was taken. Complete medical training cost approximately 300 dollars excluding board and lodging.[10] It was agreed that university medals, prizes, honours should be awarded. These included three house surgeoncies at the Kingston General Hospital of six months each, to be granted to those in the third session who earned the highest marks in the examinations. Anatomy demonstratorships and prosecting appointments were also open to competition. The last regular meeting of the faculty's first year of operation appointed Dr K.N. Fenwick as examiner in obstetrics to the Medical Council of Canada. A special meeting was sadly called on the afternoon 26 June 1893 to make arrangements for Dr T.R. Dupuis's funeral. Unfortunately, by this time the school had closed for the year, and the students, scattered across the province, could not take part in the procession.

Principal Grant's annual report to the board was the section of the minutes of the board of trustees of most interest to the medical faculty. It must have given him great pleasure to be able to announce financial as well as academic good news. At the meeting, Principal Grant reported a bequest of $40,000 from the estate of John Roberts of Ottawa. The board grasped the opportunity and used the money to ensure financial security for Dr Knight's chair of animal biology. The principal then reported on the restored Faculty of Medicine's first year of operation. He expressed his regret at the untimely death of Dr William Henderson, and announced his replacement, Dr T.M. Fenwick as professor of clinical medicine, who was then presiding over the declining Women's Medical College.

Grant's concept of organic union was far-reaching. In his report on the reconstituted faculty of medicine's first year, the principal proposed that eventually the university might have to take over total funding of all medical faculty salaries. The then current practice was that professors who taught full time received part of their income from their students and the rest from their clinical practice. After all, Grant realized that if the university funded salaries for medical chemistry, comparative anatomy, physiology, and histology, little reason remained for it to withhold such aid to the medical faculty if the school was to be truly an organic part of the university. He hoped that the university would "soon be able to undertake other subjects also. Pathology and bacteriology have claim only second to these subjects that have been so undertaken, and a professor should be appointed as soon as possible who would devote his whole time to them."[11]

Grant laid down the principles of medical education on which the medical faculty of Queen's was to develop over the next fifty years. He thought that talk alone could not bring about the "organic union" he had planned. "It can be done only by wisdom and liberality, and by all pulling together."[12] Friends, alumni, students and others, led by Chancellor Sandford Fleming and the principal himself, had started the conversion from the potential to the actual by paying some of the expenses of Dr Knight's chair of biology.

Not least among those who laid the foundation of the resurrected medical faculty were the city's hospitals, who so generously opened their doors to the medical students. The Kingston General Hospital erected its new postmortem room; it also promised a first-class theatre for operations and proposed a maternity wing to be built in the near future. Principal Grant also courteously acknowledged the contribution that "the new Hotel Dieu with its admirable equipment"[13] would make to the education of Queen's medical students.

"In modern parlance," the principal concluded, "the Medical Faculty has come to stay.[14]

PRINCIPAL GRANT'S MEDICAL SCHOOL

The chief credit for ensuring that the medical faculty had come to stay was undoubtedly Grant's. The last ten years of his life coincided almost exactly with the first decade of the faculty's return from the wilderness, and so in his declining years he could directly superintend that "peculiarly happy" relationship his inaugural address had instituted fifteen years earlier. During that decade, the Faculty Board held 103 regular and 5 special meetings. The principal presided over 86 of them and, with the aid of Dean Fowler, appears to have maintained harmony. The medical faculty had learnt its lesson, and did not repeat the petty squabbling of its early years at Queen's. A strong principal and a competent dean effectively limited the aberrant behaviour of individual medical men.

Dr Grant contributed to the improvement of clinical teaching through his presence on the Kingston General Hospital's board of governors. He was most influential during the fifteen years, 1885-1899, when the Kingston General Hospital underwent a "big expansion in buildings, facilities and services." Improvements in the hospital directly affected its relationship with the medical school. As Principal Grant said, "we cannot have a first class Medical Faculty without a first class hospital beside it, to which the students have free access."[15]

The Kingston General Hospital contained approximately 100 beds in 1892. A medical superintendent, Dr Ronald Kilborn, 7 attending consulting physicians, a house surgeon, Dr Isaac Wood, and Dr J.C. Connell, who restricted his practice to treating diseases of the eyes, ears, nose, and throat staffed the hospital. The attending staff taught 145 medical students. With the reorganization of the medical school, Drs Garrett, Saunders, and Anglin joined the hospital's clinicians, Drs T.R. Dupuis, K.N. Fenwick, W.H. Henderson, and A.S. Oliver to increase the teaching of medicine, surgery, and gynaecology in the new hospital facilities. The relatively modern Nickle wing, designed for infectious fever cases, and the Doran wing, for maternity beds, provided more clinical teaching areas. The faculty joined with the hospital in improving the facilities for performing autopsies in the newly renovated morgue.

An important new contribution of the Kingston General Hospital to clinical teaching followed in 1895 when Dr K.N. Fenwick offered $2,500 for the erection of a surgical operating theatre. The medical faculty added a further $500, which the board of the hospital matched. The Fenwick Operating Theatre, as it came to be called, was built in the rear of the main hospital block. It was a semicircular building covering over 1,500 square feet. The walls were lined with polished Italian marble. Surrounding the operating area were three rows of seats, meant to accommodate about 100 students. It was the pride, not only of the hospital, but of the university and the city as a whole.

On 15 October 1895, the medical school opened formally in the new operating amphitheatre. Dr Fenwick presented the building to the hospital's board of governors. The dean expressed the appreciation of the faculty. Dr Garrett, representing the surgical staff, spoke on antiseptics and aseptics. The principal brought the ceremony to a close with an address on the general state of the faculty and its relationship with the Kingston General Hospital. He concluded by pronouncing the theatre the most convenient, in Canada and surpassed by only one or two in the United States.[16] After many years of useful service as an operating room, the Fenwick theatre became the Medical Staff Room and is now the hospital coffee shop.

Clinical teaching also occurred in the wards, lecture room, and operating theatre of the Hotel Dieu Hospital, paralleling that done in the Kingston General Hospital, although on a smaller scale. For forty-six years the Hotel Dieu Hospital served Kingstonians in its original buildings on Brock Street. In 1891 it purchased Regiopolis College and its grounds, which covered the complete block from Sydenham Street down to Bagot Street between Johnson and Brock. With the consequent increase in hospital beds, Drs Sullivan and Ryan were able to hold their weekly clinics specifically for the benefit of the Queen's medical students. A student petition encouraged the faculty to use these extra facilities. It also included a request that Dr McKenzie of the Hotel Dieu Hospital be appointed a lecturer in Orthopedic Surgery. Apart from the outstanding work of the Honorable Dr Michael Sullivan, his son, Dr Vincent Sullivan, and Dr Ryan, little direct or overt cooperation between Queen's medical faculty and the Hotel Dieu Hospital occurred until many years later, when, about 1970, confessional and professional barriers were eventually surmounted.

At Queen's, although external influences, such as the Ontario College of Physicians and Surgeons, were impinging more and more on clinical and preclinical teaching, internal ideas began to shape the curriculum. After his appointment, Dr Knight ensured that advances in science and technology were incorporated into basic science teaching at Queen's. In the first volume of *Queen's Quarterly* (1893), Knight outlined the sweep of his discipline, which included the medical aspects of comparative anatomy, histology, embryology, and physiology. He thought animal biology should be taught along with pathology and bacteriology in the first two years of the M.D. programme. By 1896 Knight reached the conclusion that the proper preparation for entry to the clinical study of medicine was a full bachelor's degree in biology. He persuaded the faculty to establish a committee to meet with a similar one representing the arts faculty to draw up a common course of study that would lead to the granting of both a B.A. and an M.D. degree in six years, as was already being done at McGill.[17]

Dr Knight was unable to generate sufficient enthusiasm among his colleagues for the innovation. It may have occurred to the committee members that parents of the average medical student in eastern Ontario would be unwilling or unable to pay for an extra two years' tuition for the dubious advantage of a B.A. Five years later, however, he repeated his suggestion, this time making it more attractive by offering a truly combined B.Sc/M.D.,C.M. course and a rather liberally oriented curriculum, which included Latin, Greek, French, German, English, philosophy, and mathematics, followed by the usual preclinical and clinical disciplines of the regular M.D. course.[18]

When the senate and faculty finally agreed to the B.A./M.D.,C.M. (unfortunately, not until a month after Principal Grant's death in 1902), it had become necessary to acknowledge pathology, bacteriology, sanitary science, and mental diseases as courses which could legitimately be taught, or at least recognized for a degree, in the Faculty of Arts and Science. Clinical teachers had been aware for years of the inappropriateness of teaching these subjects in the medical school simply as addenda to courses in applied anatomy, physiology, and practical surgery and found it increasingly difficult to teach the new sciences of bacteriology and pathology while pursuing a full career as practising clinicians. The problem could only be permanently solved by instituting a professorship in pathology and bacteriology, as had been done when the chair of animal biology was established. The remuneration for the professor would have to be derived from students' fees, supplemented by university funds. However, such a salary would hardly have been attractive to an established clinician, however suitable he might have been. But

Queen's took an academic gamble. What may have seemed a stop-gap measure at the time turned out, by one of those fortunate accidents of history, to be a beneficial influence on medical education at Queen's for the next seventy-five years. The university appointed the newly graduated Dr Walter T. Connell as its first full-time, salaried medical professor to the chair of pathology and bacteriology.

The appointment was a classic example of the lucky coincidence of man and the occasion. Principal Grant, in his convocation address of 1894, reported that all Queen's final-year men, who had just gone up before the Medical Council for examination, had passed, but only Dr Connell had received honours in all subjects. The principal proudly announced that no Ontario medical college could claim such a record for that year. With these words of praise ringing in his ears, Dr W.T. Connell set off to do postgraduate work in the laboratories of St Bartholomew's Hospital in London. Back in Kingston, the senior medical faculty members, who were the faculty's subcommittee on physiology and pathology, advised Dr Fife Fowler, to write to Dr Connell

"that the Faculty desired a competent man to devote his whole time to Pathology and Bacteriology; that in the meantime the Faculty would provide $600 per annum in addition to fees from postgraduate students and fees from analyses from other practitioners and asking Dr Connell if he would accept such an appointment and take a course to fit him for the position.[19]

Within two months, Dr Connell had accepted the position on the conditions laid down by faculty. The faculty sent him an inventory of its laboratory equipment and a request that he submit his own needs for the conduct of his courses. He was asked to report, if convenient, for duty during September 1895. A faculty board meeting early that year more clearly defined Dr Connell's salary. He was to be paid $600 from faculty funds for the first year, $700 for the second, rising to $850 in the third. Moreover, "all fees for examination of pathological specimens other than those made for the University, which shall be made by him free of charge, and that at the end of the second year both parties of this agreement shall be free to make a new engagement beginning at the end of the third year."[20] The board of trustees ratified this agreement at its annual meeting in May 1895, but added the *caveat* "that he is not to practise his profession for three years."[21] Modern pathologists might see in this a nice semantic point.

In keeping with the terms of his appointment, Dr Connell set up a laboratory and performed the required analyses and tests for the university. By the end of the three years he offered a complete range of laboratory services to the practising medical profession in eastern Ontario. The following advertisement in the *Kingston Medical Quarterly* shows the spectrum of tests available and how they generated a small, but adequate income over and above Dr Connell's university salary:

DR. W. T. CONNELL

Desires to announce to the Profession that he is prepared to make Microscopical, Chemical, and Bacteriological Analyses, as may be required, of Morbid Tissues, Tumors, Serous or Purulent Effusions, Curettings, Sputum, Urine, Blood, Stomach Contents, Throat Membranes or Secretions, Urethral or Vaginal Discharges, etc. He is also prepared to apply Widal's method for diagnosis in Typhoid Fever, and to perform autopsies.

For information, methods of transmitting specimens, etc., address

Pathological Laboratory,
Queen's University, Kingston.[22]

The faculty approved this extension of health-care service to the community, and showed its appreciation of Dr Connell when they offered the young doctor of twenty-three an opportunity to give the inaugural address to the medical faculty at the opening of its 1896/97 session. His topic was "Some relations of Pathology to Modern Medicine." Those who had the privilege of listening to this young man could have had no doubt that Queen's medical curriculum was well in step with modern medicine, and for the next fifteen to twenty years readers of the *Queen's Quarterly* or the *Kingston (Queen's) Medical Quarterly* could not fail to keep abreast of scientific medicine if they read Dr Connell's regular contributions.

In addition, Connell published his *Practical Bacteriology* in 1899. This textbook and course guide must have been of inestimable value to the students, first in the laboratory classes and then in their private practice after graduation.

Shortly after the establishment of his bacteriology laboratory and a diagnostic service for the local practitioners, in 1895 the faculty gave Dr W.T. Connell permission to teach Dairy School students one hour per week. These young men were not members of the university, although perhaps in Principal Grant's private plans they were destined to become Queen's alumni. He had already established an affiliated School of Mining and Agriculture in 1893.[23] The principal did manage, however, through the help of Kingston's M.L.A., William Harty, and the provincial premier, Oliver Mowat, to establish a Dairy

School, located in the building and grounds of the old Kingston Collegiate. Although the government itself paid for the teachers in dairying and other subjects related to the profession, the university gave instruction in chemistry, and its medical faculty provided the services of Dr Connell to teach bacteriology, sanitation, and hygiene.

The Dairy School lasted only slightly longer than another of Principal Grant's imaginative schemes. If Dr Connell's abilities could be turned to wider academic pursuits, why not use the talents of the professor of animal biology? What fitter role could there be for Dr Knight than dean of a veterinary school at Queen's? This idea, with its hint of profit just over the horizon, led to the establishment of a new seat of academic learning in the same collegiate building that housed the Dairy School at the corner of Barrie and Clergy Streets.[24] Dr G.N. Bell, appointed in 1895, was the first principal of Queen's School of Veterinary Science. At that time, he was running Dr Bell's Veterinary Clinic, a very successful private practice, at 129 Brock Street. Dr (later Lt Col) W.J. Morgan, a military veterinarian who had fallen under Principal Grant's spell as a student, became the professor of practical anatomy, Dr Knight became, as was fitting, the professor of animal physiology and histology, Dr John Herald, at that time professor of *materia medica*, therapeutics and pharmacy in the medical faculty, presumably taught the same subjects in the Veterinary School, while Dr W.T. Connell taught pathology and bacteriology. *Queen's University Journal* in November 1895 good-humouredly welcomed the new venture: "the students of the Veterinary School attended lectures in the medical building. If they are as eager to obtain materials as some of the meds. are, according to the painting of the local papers, all glue factories will have to build steel vaults to preserve their subjects."[25]

During the four years of its existence, the Veterinary School admitted seven students in the first year, twelve in the second and five in the third. By that time there were more professors than students. But before the school closed in 1899, on the recommendation of Dr Knight as acting dean, it awarded three diplomas, and Queen's senate granted its one and only Doctor of Veterinary Medicine and Surgery degree to Mr W. Rowson of Frontenac. Queen's Veterinary School, one of Principal Grant's unfulfilled aspirations, has been called "a glorious failure."[26]

The students at the Dairy School and the Veterinary School, when added to the increasing numbers of medical students and biology honours students, exacerbated the already pressing problem of space. Lecture rooms were available in the Arts Building, and physics and chemistry laboratories in Carruther's Hall, but the teaching of the strictly medical subjects – physiology, histology, embryology, pathology, and bacteriology – required an increasing amount of laboratory space. The principal, at the request of the medical faculty, was repeatedly unsuccessful in his attempts to draw this matter to the attention of the board of trustees.

The faculty's widened teaching responsibilities and the expanding activities of Dr Connell in particular led, in 1897, to the establishment of a committee, composed of Drs Mundell, Ryan, W.T. Connell, Garrett, and Fowler, "to consider the advisability of erecting an anatomy building and report upon plans and finances." They commissioned Mr Newlands to design an extension to the Medical Building. After six months, the situation remained unchanged. The faculty continued to discuss the problem until in 1901 it agreed to the addition of a third story to the Medical Building, if the walls were found strong enough to support it. Mr. Ellis, a second architect, pronounced them sound, and presented new plans with an estimate of $9,250 for the addition.[28]

At its annual meeting in 1900, the board of trustees authorized, on the advice of the university council, an increase in accommodation for the medical faculty, and gave to its Finance and Estate Committee power to act on the matter of a new third floor for the Medical Building. The committee encouraged the medical faculty to proceed with its plans as quickly as possible. The university board of trustees was willing to lend $10,000 for the project. The debt was to be repaid at the annual rate of $800, which included interest of 4 percent. The medical faculty accepted the offer and immediately began to consider the various ways of paying back the principal and interest.[29]

During the summer of 1901, masons, carpenters, plumbers, and plasterers took over the faculty's building. On the ground floor a physiology and histology laboratory, a private laboratory for Dr Knight's research, a lecture room, and a students' cloakroom was constructed. The next floor, Dr Connell's domain, contained separate pathology and bacteriology laboratories and a preparation room. On the same level was a second lecture room, a library, a museum, a students' reading room, and a private retiring room for the professors. On the top floor was the dissecting laboratory, a smaller one for the demonstrators to conduct their "grind" classes, another private room for the professors, and two further lecture rooms.

The opening of the renovated building was set for 2 October 1901, and invitations were sent out across the country for the occasion. Unfortunately, the two foremost nonmedical members of Queen's community, Dr Grant and Sir Sandford Fleming could not be present. Dr Fife Fowler, however, who had served the faculty for forty-seven years was in his glory. He received a tumultuous ovation, his short speech of welcome being followed by a chorus of "long live the Dean."[30]

Everyone felt Principal Grant's absence from the festivities. From his sick-bed in the Kingston General Hospital, "in full view of the university to which he had devoted his life," he dictated a message "to my boys of the Medical Faculty," to be read at the celebrations by the Reverend Dr Barclay. It was "a message which thrilled the assembly, who reverently stood during its reading. The words were listened to in dead silence for they came as a voice from the Chamber of Sickness":[31]

Ten days ago, one of your professors told me to look into the kingdom of darkness. I did so steadily, and found nothing to terrify. But several old truths were impressed upon me, one or two of which I give to you:

Never was I so much impressed with the advantage of having distinct centres of medical education, or with the generosity of your professors. The old pagan idea that matter is evil and the body worthless is only now giving way to the Christian idea of the sacredness of the body and the high duty of understanding its mysteries. I pledge myself to do more for the faculty and for the hospital than ever before, and I hope that I may teach others their privilege in this regard. Your professors have earned the right to expect this.

As to yourselves – for the sake of all that is noble and worthy, take your profession seriously from the outset, quite as seriously as the students of divinity take theirs. If you cannot do that, drop it, and seek some honest way of making a living. It is awful to think that men, women and children should be at the mercy of irreverent and half-taught young doctors. I pledge myself that hereafter, for your own sakes, and for the sake of humanity, I shall try to let no such student pass our examinations. God help you to lay this word to your hearts.[32]

Prolonged and heartfelt cheers broke out for the absent principal. That evening, Senator Michael Sullivan excelled himself in an after-dinner speech when he expressed the love held by Queen's for its incomparable George Munro Grant.

Our chief thought to-night is with the man who lies on a bed of illness, and who was to have been the leading factor on this occasion. His message to us should be written in letters of gold on the walls of this University. Let us send to him to-night a bouquet which shall express our devotion, our admiration and our love for him. No man is held in more general esteem by the whole country. Protestants and Catholics, Jews and Gentiles, and those of no religion at all, pray earnestly for his restoration that he may be able to complete some of the grand projects he has in view.[33]

Lying in his hospital bed, the principal undoubtedly thought of those who had helped him convert his dream into reality and bring his university to national stature, the students and staff who had accepted the authority of their dying "King Geordie" and contributed to his school.

The medical students had taken the transition from the Royal to Queen's with the equanimity recently advocated by William Osler in his famous valedictory, as did the editor-in-chief of the *Queen's University Journal*, A.E. Ross. He reassured his reading public that he and the principal "are sure that good old Queen's will, in the future, have some no more loyal than those whose patron saint is Aesculapius."[34]

The union effected a few changes in the preclinical and clinical facilities, but established traditions continued unbroken. Principal Grant was "Our Geordie," who knew each student by name and gave them the M.D. degree. Generally the students liked to attend Principal Grant's Sunday afternoon talks in Convocation Hall. In the medical school, whether of the Royal or the university, only Dean Fife Fowler, was seen more frequently than the principal.

The students' courts or *concursuses* continued to function, with varying degrees of success. When the arts' court became the subject of some amusement among certain freshmen in November 1893, *Queen's University Journal* commented that "the Court is, or should be, an organization for maintaining the unwritten laws of college etiquette, breaches of which cannot for the most part be taken cognizance of by the Senate. In recognition of this the Faculty of Medicine is far ahead of Arts."[35]

In its early years occasional instances of cheating during examinations were the only serious disciplinary matters that came under the eye of the new faculty board. The faculty again employed Mr Walker, the detective, this time to supervise the examinations and assist the professors in keeping order. During the jurisprudence examination, Mr Walker and Dr Saunders spotted a student cheating. He was debarred from going up for any other examination that year. Another student, who refused to follow Mr Walker's directions during an examination, was denied his marks until he apologized to the detective. At the end of the year, faculty was so pleased with Walker's work that they voted him a bonus of five dollars.

The board also had to deal with students in trouble with the law. And, the students, of course, had to face a double jeopardy: if they ran into difficulties with the civil authorities they might find themselves answerable to the faculty as well. On the afternoon of 3 March 1894, the principal presided over a special meeting of the faculty called to consider "the case of the medical student who had been fined in the Police Court for using obscene language in the Opera House."[36]

The student and one of his companions were brought in and questioned. Both acknowledged that on the occasion in question they had been drinking and that the one who had pleaded guilty to the charge of using obscene language was not the guilty party. His companion acknowledged that he had used the language for which his fellow student had been summoned to the Police Court. The Principal then addressed them on the sin of drunkenness and the even greater sin of using obscene language. The students were then informed that the Faculty would consider this case. After the students had withdrawn it was decided that all the medical students should be notified to meet the Faculty in the General Lecture room of the Medical Building on Wednesday next at 2:30 p.m. – that the Faculty and the two students implicated should be specifically notified – that the Principal should before all reprimand the guilty students and intimate that in future similar conduct on the part of any student would be punished with rustication or expulsion as might seem best to the Faculty and that an account of the meeting should be supplied by the secretary to the Public Press omitting names.[37]

The common room popularly known as the "den" continued to be the locus of the medical students' less heinous activities and the subject of repeated entries in the *Queen's University Journal*. Such matters as the provision of a telephone, the installation of cuspidors, and the purchase of reading material generated either compliments or complaints from the students. These were not usually reported verbatim but moderated as became the delicacy of the *Queen's University Journal's* editorial policy. The student paper also noted, without comment, the gradual growth of the medical library and the faculty's attempt to set up a reference section, which was to be available each afternoon between two and three o'clock.[38]

From the earliest days of the Royal, the annual Medical Dinner has been a major event. In the first decade back at Queen's, the committee, set up by the Aesculapian Society to organize the dinner, was augmented by a member of the faculty, who kept an eye on the expenditure of the $100 annually contributed by faculty to the celebrations. Every year the society tried to outdo previous occasions, and each time everyone seemed satisfied that the goal had been accomplished. Other medical schools were invited to send representatives, and Kingston's leading citizens and medical men were always welcome to share the good company, fine food, elegant speeches and final sing-song. A short and witty speech by the Honorable Senator Sullivan was mandatory. He could be counted on to amuse the company and to express the loyalty and pride of those present, as he did, for example, when he declared at the 1896 dinner that "Father Adam was the first surgeon on record." To the obvious delight of all he continued, "it was one of the grandest triumphs of the medical profession in Canada to have a city like Kingston supplying other parts of the world with cultured and able physicians."[39]

The annual convocation was the other major event in the medical school year and it remained essentially unchanged by the reunion with Queen's. The chosen valedictorian expressed, as tradition dictated, the thanks of the graduating class to its Alma Mater and the faculty for the education they had received and the ideals with which they had been imbued, and to the citizens of Kingston for the graciousness of their hospitality. In 1898, Dr William Moffatt of Carleton Place spoke for all:

we have now reached what at one time seemed the goal of our ambition, that is graduation, and now it seems as if the foot of our rainbow is nearly as far off as ever, but thanks to our teaching there is still a rainbow ahead of us, apparently stretching from the Klondyke to the distant East. To some it may appear that to find the mythical pot of gold at the rainbow's foot is the greatest thing to be desired, but to most of us this must ever be but a part of life's scheme, not the real inspiration, not the true teaching of our Alma Mater.[40]

The faculty as a whole matured under the principal's leadership, and in 1896 the academic medical society which had been in existence from September 1880 to May 1881 and from September 1888 to May 1889 as the Cataraqui Medical Society (Association) was reborn. Faculty members on the medical staffs of the Kingston General Hospital and Rockwood Hospital met in the office of the General Hospital on Monday, 1 June 1896; Drs Oliver, Herald, Garrett, Anglin, Webster, W.T. Connell, Mundell, Cunningham, and Third were present, while Drs T.M. Fenwick, J.C. Connell, Wood, Clarke and Forster sent their apologies. Motions were presented and carried establishing the Kingston Medical and Surgical Society. The society aimed to introduce and discuss medical cases, and to read papers and discuss matters relating to the welfare of society. By-laws were drawn up and Dr Oliver was elected president and Dr J.C. Connell vice-president. Members were required to contribute a scientific paper and attend meetings. Dr Mundell presented the first paper, "Remarks on Diseases of Bone." A short while later the house surgeon at Kingston General Hospital requested permission to attend, but the society decided that "it would not be in the best interest of the

Society for students to be present at the meeting."[41]

Queen's University Journal in January 1897 commented on the activities of the society adversely enough to cause Drs Garrett and Connell to move a motion of censure against the *Journal*. The society never explicitly mentioned the exact bone of contention which may, of course, have been the exclusion of the student house-surgeon from the society's meetings.

The minutes describe the meetings of the Kingston Medical and Surgical Society for the next six years. The society's publication, the *Kingston Medical Quarterly* established within six months after the first paper was presented, reported the faculty's views on medical and academic matters. The journal continued under the faculty's wing, supported from its funds until 1908 when it ceased publication because the "funds had to be reassigned to maintain the New Medical Building."[42]

Since Kingston's gradual decline in importance as a military fortress, and the North West Rebellion (1885) the staff and students of Queen's medical school appear to have taken little notice of the geopolitical forces shaping the world for its entry into the twentieth century. The perennial anti-British outpourings of American politicians and soldiers caused hardly a ripple of concern. But in the late 1890s, the problem of imperial defence and the possibility of sending Canadian contingents overseas faced the Canadian public.

Queen's men made a very real contribution to the South African or Boer War of 1899-1902. As far as actual participation in the war is concerned, the most active members of the Queen's community were the students and staff of the medical faculty.[43] The *Kingston Medical Quarterly* and *Queen's University Journal* reported the activities of the medical alumni who served in the field with the imperial forces in South Africa.

Surgeon-Major H. Ramsay Duff (Meds '86) was appointed the senior medical officer of the Canadian Mounted Rifles.[44] Ramsay Duff graduated in arts, enrolled in medicine at the Royal, and received his L.R.C.P.S.(K) and M.D.,C.M. from Queen's. While a student he had served as a trooper in the 4th Hussars, Kingston's own militia cavalry unit, which was established in 1875. On graduation, he was commissioned as the unit's surgeon-major. Apart from his military appointment, which lasted ten years, he carried on a general practice, first in Newburgh and then in Kingston until he went overseas with his regiment.

Dr R.R. (Bob) Robinson, who received his M.D. with the last class to graduate from the Royal, joined up as a private in Surgeon-Major Duff's unit just before it embarked for the Transvaal. He had been a very popular student, a football player, a champion sprinter and vice-president of the Alma Mater Society. After graduation, he had served as a ship's surgeon on a C.P.R. liner and as a surgeon on a US Revenue cutter in the Bering Sea. When prospecting for gold in the Klondike proved unsuccessful, he returned to his original profession and developed a lucrative practice as assistant physician at St Mary's Hospital in Dawson City, which he left to join the second contingent of the Canadian Mounted Rifles.

The "Strongman" of Meds '92, as he was popularly known, Dr J. Alton Harris, was another of the Queen's boys caught in the fever of war. He was en route to London, presumably for postgraduate study, when he heard that the Americans were outfitting the hospital ship *Maine* for the South African theatre. He applied for a position and was accepted. On arrival in England, however, he changed his mind and joined the 18th Bearer Company, 15th Brigade, 7th Division of the field forces.

A Queen's man who served with special distinction was Lt Harry Edward Manning Douglas (M.D. 1897), who went to Edinburgh and immediately joined the Black Watch as their M.O. On 11 December 1899, he found himself at the battle of Magersfontein under heavy fire with all his regimental officers wounded:

Lieutenant Douglas showed great gallantry and devotion, under a very severe fire, in advancing in the open and attending to Captain Gordon, Gordon Highlanders, who was wounded, and also attending to Major Robinson and other wounded men under a fearful fire. Many similar acts of devotion and gallantry were performed by Lieutenant Douglas on the same day.[45]

Towards the end of this hectic day, Douglas, in the role of infantry officer, rallied the scattered ranks of the Gordons. He was awarded the Victoria Cross for those heroic actions. Six days later, Douglas wrote to his parents from hospital describing, with good humour, the battle. He explained that at the end of the day's action a shell had burst just above his head, "and down I went like a thousand bricks by a piece of shell hitting me on my left cheek. . . . I consoled myself that I got off cheap with only a stellate scar that a penny will cover about an inch below the eye and one and a half inch from my nose, a broken upper jaw, a few loose teeth and a most glorious black eye that does one good to look at."[46] By March he was invalided back to England, well established on the military career that saw him become Maj. Gen. Henry E.M. Douglas V.C., C.B., C.M.G., D.S.O.

Dr A.E. Ross was one of the most popular of all the Queen's men who went off to the Boer War. He had been editor of the *Queen's*

University Journal, president of the Alma Mater Society and a tackle on Captain Curtis's famous football team. After obtaining his B.A., he entered medical school, although he continued as a tutor in Greek in the classics department. In 1897 he became an assistant to Dr T.M. Fenwick in Kingston.

In the fall of 1899 Ross received an anatomy demonstratorship, but in January 1900 he was given leave of absence to go to South Africa as an assistant to Surgeon-Major Duff in the rank of Hospital Sergeant. Assembled students sent him off from the anatomy department with an impromptu concert and a case of surgical instruments with the inscription "Presented to A.E. Ross, B.A., M.D., by Queen's Medical Students." Within a week of leaving Queen's, Arthur Ross, who was destined for a brilliant military and civilian professional career, was acting as war correspondent to the *Queen's University Journal,* first from Stanley Barracks in Toronto, and then from the front in South Africa.[47]

Some of the medical students who remained to complete their studies were moved by reports of the formation of militia units of volunteers from every part of the country. They imitated a movement in December 1899 to establish Field Hospital companies in Montreal, Toronto, and Kingston. At first the government reacted cooly to the suggestion, but after the "Black Week" of British reverses at Stormberg, Magersfontein, and Colenso, they accepted and allowed the establishment of the No. 2 Field Hospital Corps in Kingston.

The major (perhaps the only) military operation of the No. 2 Field Hospital was its summer camp, held for ten days at Barriefield. Although the commanding officer, Surgeon-Major Abbott, was not a militia man, the other two officers, Surgeon-Lt. Kilborn, Kingston General Hospital's medical superintendent, and Surgeon-Lt. Mundell, Queen's professor of the principles and practice of surgery, both were. They "were as good a trio of officers as any Red Cross Tommy could wish to serve under."[48] Of the ten medical students in camp, three were sergeants, one, a corporal, and six, privates. Master Sergeant Tyner and Sergeant Compounder Porteous were in charge of the dispensary. The contingent's guests seem to have remembered the social activities of the corps while in camp better than anything else, but the corpsmen thought that they received worthwhile "dressing" experience and clinical work.

When the Boer War ended and the heroes welcomed home, they found Principal Grant's medical school well equipped and well staffed, but missing its guiding spirit – the principal himself.

CHAPTER NINE

Toward Higher Ideals in the New Century

The twentieth century brought new men and new ideas in medical education to Queen's. The faculty decided to celebrate its fiftieth anniversary, 14-16 October 1903, at the time of the Reverend Dr Daniel Miner Gordon's installation as principal of the university. For the medical school this was a bittersweet occasion. Principal Grant, whom it had taken to its heart, and Dr Fife Fowler, the last of its founding fathers, were both absent. Two months before the combined celebrations, Dr Fowler died quietly at his home on the corner of Brock and Clergy Streets. He would have rejoiced to hear Dr Geike, Trinity Medical College's famous dean's words, "I earnestly hope that your Medical Department may become year by year so strongly and so permanently established – and do not its past five successive decades fully warrant that hope – that it may see many Jubilee celebrations." That Queen's medical school was celebrating its fiftieth anniversary was without doubt a monument to Dr Fowler, who was, as the faculty wrote to his wife, "an example to all of everything high and noble in the Medical Profession."[1]

The Jubilee events included congratulatory speeches by Professor R. Ramsay Wright of Toronto, Dr McMurrich of Ann Arbor, Michigan, and Sir William Higston of Laval. Dr John Herald, secretary of the faculty, gave an outline of the medical school's history. The speech is interesting today because it is a firsthand account of the second generation of Queen's medical teachers, men whom Dr Herald knew personally. Dr Alex Richardson, managing editor of *Queen's Medical Quarterly*, after reporting Herald's reminiscences, described the Jubilee events and, with pardonable pride, included these two paragraphs of academic minutiae:

We note with pleasure that Dr. H.H. Chown '80, is the efficient Dean of the

growing Medical Faculty of Manitoba University and Dr. Reeve of the Class
of '65 occupies a similar position in the new federated Medical School of
Toronto and Trinity.

Any of the Universities of North America or the· Islands of the Sea
requiring Deans for their Medical Faculties may communicate with Dr. W.T.
Connell. (All communications will be considered strictly confidential. Man'g
Ed.).[2]

The Jubilee over, the faculty turned towards its new management
and the future. The changes that occurred in the constitution, the
buildings, and the curriculum of the medical school at Queen's
between 1903 and the Great War inevitably affected its evolution.

Following Principal Grant's death in May 1902, an interregnum of
eight short months followed. Nathan Dupuis presided over the
medical faculty meetings as acting principal until Gordon took over.
He, like his predecessor, presided over almost every medical faculty
meeting during his principalship, assuming the role of an elder
statesman helping the faculty to actualize its potential

THE CONSTITUTION OF THE
MEDICAL FACULTY

The board of trustees received the first intimation that the medical
men wished to amend the 1892 agreement of "organic union" when it
received a report from the University Council on 23 April 1903. The
board postponed consideration of it *sine die*, perhaps hoping that the
doctors might not be serious. Meanwhile, it dealt so effectively with
another constitutional problem, a request from some medical men in
Vancouver, British Columbia for possible affiliation with Queen's by a
proposed medical college, that the problem never returned. The
board's minutes state that "it was resolved on motion of Dr Rogers
that they be communicated with stating that when the College is
established this University will take the matter into favourable
consideration if suitable arrangements can be made."[3]

Local problems could not so easily be disposed of. On 19 May 1903,
the medical faculty sought and obtained a meeting with the board to
discuss the proposed constitutional changes. The board listened to
the views of the doctors, discussed them and accepted, without
objection, an amendment to the 1892 constitution. This action
immediately alleviated some of the faculty's grievances. It was agreed
that the trustees would appoint the dean from among members of the
medical faculty – an amendment designed to set the faculty's fears at
rest in the light of Dr Fowler's increasing infirmity and the possibility

of an outsider, who might be insensitive to the Queen's way of doing things, presiding over them in the absence of the principal. Secondly, a secretary-treasurer was constitutionally appointed. Thirdly, the five-year limitation on the medical professors' appointments was lifted; they were granted the same terms as the other academic staff, subject to ratification by a special appointments committee. The major addition to the constitution seems to have been the establishment of a faculty finance committee, which was to control the disbursement of all moneys derived from fees and elsewhere, apart from those allocated to the salary fund. The faculty were generally pleased with the new constitution, and lived with it until 1913. It satisfied the medical men because, although a compromise, it allowed them to retain their autonomy and at the same time be an integral part of the university.[4]

The new provisions concerning the appointment of a dean came into effect very soon. The university and the faculty were in the midst of their Jubilee festivities when the principal called an urgent special faculty meeting. The board of trustees needed immediately "the opinion of the Faculty regarding the most suitable person to be appointed Dean of the Faculty."[5] The thirteen faculty members present at the meeting thanked the board for its courtesy. Dr Knight moved and Dr Ryan seconded that each member write down the name of the person he thought most suitable for the post on a piece of paper. The principal collected the slips and the result was divulged only to the board of trustees. The faculty minutes simply record that the ballot was conducted; but the minutes of the board of trustees show that eight members voted for Dr Connell – J.C. that is, not the young and unrelated W.T. – while four were in favour of another unnamed candidate. With this mind, the Queen's board of trustees immediately and unanimously appointed Dr James Cameron Connell as the university's fifth dean of medicine.[6]

The next constitutional crisis occurred almost a decade later, when Queen's University broke irrevocably with its own roots and sectarian past. In 1912 it successfully petitioned the Parliament of Canada to decree An Act respecting Queen's College at Kingston and to change its name to "Queen's University at Kingston." The act removed the Presbyterian denominational restrictions, with the proviso that "the University shall continue distinctly Christian and the trustees of the University shall satisfy themselves of the Christian character of those appointed to the teaching staff."[7] This restriction not unnaturally offended Canadian Jews. The Jewish Legislative Committee influenced Parliament to withhold "national" status from Queen's University.[8] In the course of history, common sense and courtesy have led the trustees to accept Principal Gordon's concept of Queens religious status as "Christian without being sectarian,"[9] in the broadest possible way.

The act preserved all existing rights and privileges of the medical faculty but unfortunately failed to solve the constitutional difficulties which still plagued it. When the dust had settled, the Faculty of Medicine's position was no better than before the secularization of the university. The doctors decided to take drastic action to change this state of affairs.

Early in February 1913, Dr Etherington, who was then a lecturer in surgery, gave notice of motion regarding the formation of a committee to study the relation of the medical faculty to the university. The dean was not present at the next meeting, later in the month, but he sent a letter pointing out that lecturers were not allowed to vote at faculty meetings. To solve the problem, other faculty members moved and seconded Dr Etherington's motion. The motion was declared lost by majority vote. Immediately following this event, the principal read another letter from Dr J.C. Connell, in which he tendered his resignation as dean of the faculty. The fat was properly in the fire; a committee was immediately struck "to interview the Dean at once and to inform him that it was the unanimous wish of the Faculty that he should withdraw his resignation.[10] As if this were not sufficient for one faculty board meeting, a further committee was appointed to interview Dr W.T. Connell, who was considering whether or not to accept a position elsewhere. Whether this latter threat was real, a rumour or just a manoeuvre to improve his standing in the faculty cannot be stated for sure.

In any event, on Wednesday 12 March 1913, the dean withdrew his resignation explaining that he had held lengthy discussions with the principal and others regarding the faculty and its connection with the reorganized university. The doctors at once prepared a memo for the board of trustees on the constitutional position of the faculty. After some minor disagreements and subsequent amendments a revised Constitution of the Medical Faculty as Amended 1913 was presented to and accepted by the board of trustees at its annual meeting that April. At the same time, the board accepted the division of duties and functions appropriate to the senate and the Faculties of Arts and Medicine and the School of Mining.[11] The new constitution offered a number of improvements for the medical men. The medical professors were to have proportionate representation on the university council and to hold office on the same terms as professors in other faculties. The dean and three faculty members would represent the faculty in the senate. The university would pay half of the dean's salary, the other half would be paid by the faculty. A library fund was set up equal to $5.00 for each registered student from year to year. The university relieved the faculty of the remainder of the $10,000 debt incurred in refurbishing the Old Medical Building. From the date of acceptance of the new constitution, the medical faculty was to share equitably in all university funds and grants. The twenty-third clause eliminated any lack of clarity in the status of the medical faculty: "the purpose of the present amendment to the constitution of the Medical Faculty is that the Medical Faculty shall become as integral a part of the University as any other Faculty."[12]

The new constitution of the medical faculty weathered the vicissitudes of time and temper for the next fifty years. The functions of the faculty board set out in the current calendar are almost word for word those recorded in the minutes of the faculty meeting of Thursday 17 April 1913 - only the power "to determine the amount of fees and manner of payment"[13] was withdrawn from the faculty in the 1960s.

THE NEW MEDICAL BUILDING

Both the faculty's functions and its constitution have remained undisturbed longer than its buildings, which have grown with the faculty members' aspirations and the burgeoning student population. As mentioned previously, the old Medical Building was refurbished. But even then the expanded facilities were strained.

Dr W.T. Connell's work for the Dairy School and his laboratory investigations brought him into close contact with the Ontario government. During 1903, the faculty asked the provincial Board of Health to recognize his university laboratory as the provincial public health branch laboratory for eastern Ontario. The Board of Health refused the application, allegedly for administrative reasons, although local opinion held that it was refused because other parts of the province would demand similar laboratories. Premier Ross wrote in January 1904 that "he could not sanction such a scheme."[14] In May, however, the government officially appointed Dr Connell its special provincial health officer (assistant provincial bacteriologist) in Kingston, at an annual salary of $500.

As the appointment was a personal matter between the doctor and the government, Queen's was only concerned that it receive a reasonable fee for the use of its laboratory for Connell's provincially generated tests. The faculty effectively, although unofficially, instituted a provincial branch laboratory by charging Dr Connell $200 annually, which he paid into the faculty's laboratory fund. Dr Connell retained the rest of his government salary. During the first ten months of the laboratory's operation, he examined 815 specimens. Faculty soon asked the government for a further $1,500 to put the operation on a sound financial basis (at that time the Toronto laboratory was receiving $7,000 per year and examining only about 3,000 specimens).

But it was some time after Dr Connell's appointment before faculty saw any improvement in its teaching facilities. The first indication that change was in the air became apparent when Premier Ross announced early in 1905 that the government had granted $150,000 to the University of Toronto for the improvement of medical education and the modernization of the Toronto General Hospital. During the same year, Queen's medical faculty set about milking the same cow. A committee consisting of the principal and the dean travelled to Toronto, met the leading members of the government, and came away reassured by Premier Whitney of financial help, but still empty-handed.[15] After a further deputation and a repetition of the premier's promise, the faculty heard on 19 May 1906 that it had been granted $50,000 to aid medical education. This amount was considered quite satisfactory since the faculty had only asked for $75,000. The grant seems to have been common knowledge during the spring because the April issue of *Queen's Medical Quarterly* carried an editorial, "Government Aid to Medical Education at Queen's." The editor, Dr W.T. Connell, announced with undisguised pleasure that the amounted voted would at once be applied "to the erection of a new Laboratory Building to house the departments of Physiology, Pathology, Bacteriology and Public Health"[16] (he, of course, had a vested interest in the last three). Dr Connell prophesied that the site would be chosen, the plans selected and the first sod turned within a few weeks. His hopes ran ahead of events, but at least a Faculty Building Committee was appointed before the end of spring.

At its June meeting the University Board of Trustees took the advice of its Finance and Estate Committee and accepted its recommendations:

1. That as the Ontario Government has passed a vote of $50,000 for the Medical Faculty of Queen's College for the promotion of Medical education it is proposed to expend this sum on a building suitable for laboratories and on their equipment.

2. That the Building Committee consist of two members of the Medical Faculty selected by the Faculty and two members of the Board of Trustees of the University.

3. That the Trustees of the University shall provide a site for the building.

4. That the provision of this site shall be regarded as an engagement that the building to be erected thereon shall be held in perpetuity for medical education.

5. That provision shall be made in the proposed building for the following subjects: (1) Pathology, (2) Bacteriology (Medical and dairy), (3) Pharmacology, (4) Physiology, (5) Histology, (6) Animal Biology, (7) Public Health, and such other subjects in addition to or in substitution for any of the foregoing as shall hereafter be determined by the Trustees of the University with the Concurrence of the Medical Faculty.

6. That the question of the relation of the Department of Biology be considered by the Board of Trustees of the University at its regular annual meeting in April next and the Medical Faculty have an opportunity of presenting their views upon that question.[17]

The faculty agreed to spend $35,000 on the construction of a building and the remainder on furnishings and equipment. It had been hoped that the external structure would be of stone secured from the penitentiary quarries, but as the federal Department of Justice refused permission, it had to substitute Roman stone to keep within the masonary budget. His Honour William Mortimer Clark, lieutenant-governor of Ontario laid the cornerstone on 24 April 1907.

Tuesday, 14 January 1908, was a bright, sunny, winter day, ideal for the opening of the medical laboratories. At two o'clock the building was ready for inspection. At three o'clock the principal, dean, and assembled dignitaries moved to Convocation Hall and listened to the Honourable Dr Pyne, minister of education, and L.F. Barker, Sir William Osler's successor as professor of medicine at Johns Hopkins University, who congratulated the university on its wisdom in erecting such a first-class basic medical science building. Drs Reeve and McCallum of Toronto and Adami of McGill also added lustre to the occasion. In the evening, the Aesculapian Society held a banquet in Grant Hall for 250 guests. The Grand Opera House orchestra performed during the meal. At half past eight the Grant Hall Galleries were opened to the public, and light-hearted entertainment and oratory was provided. Everybody, including the reporter from the *Daily British Whig*, appeared to enjoy the evening.[18]

The New Medical Building provided every modern facility for the teaching of pathology, bacteriology, physiology, and the whole range of paraclinical disciplines previously shoehorned into the original Old Medical Building. The new building had three floors of teaching laboratories, professors' offices with private laboratories, storerooms, and a commodious lecture theatre. It served the purpose of medical education until 1982, when, notwithstanding its being held in perpetuity for medical education, it was restructured to house the university archives and renamed the Kathryn Ryan Building after a generous benefactor.

EARLY TWENTIETH-CENTURY MEDICAL CURRICULUM AT QUEEN'S

Changes in curriculum occurred primarily because the new faculty men understood the importance of the new laboratory sciences and supported the changes demanded in medical teaching by the Provincial Medical Council. Because each legislatively recognized medical school had a seat on the council, Drs Fowler and Sullivan were unwilling to accept the legal disestablishment of the Royal at the time of the "organic union" with Queen's. Although the Royal was *de facto* moribund as a medical school, it was still legally entitled to a seat on the Medical Council of Ontario (i.e. the College of Physicians and Surgeons). With Dr H.V. Moore and then Dr Herald representing Queen's, Dr Spankie of Wolfe Island as the territorial representative and Dr Sullivan the Royal's, the Kingston medical community had, in fact, a disproportionately loud voice at the college and in the curricular changes being introduced throughout the province during the first decade of the century.

The subjects taught and the teaching methods in the faculty today have their roots in the curriculum of the Edwardian era, which remained a more than adequate preparation for the practice of medicine until new therapeutic advances and technology were introduced after World War II. The four-year curriculum, with a five-week summer course between the third and fourth years, had been accepted by the Provincial Medical Council as a compromise to meet, on the one hand the academic standards of the university faculties, and, on the other, the financial constraints of students from the country. Students who had entered medicine after a year or two in the arts faculty were given equivalent standing, up to one year off the programme, but only if they had taken the appropriate courses, usually those which formed the bulk of the first medical year or session.

Timetables published in the university calendars at the beginning of this century probably fairly indicate the emphasis placed by the faculty on each subject. During the first session, Mr Carmichael lectured on physics for three hours a week before Christmas. Professor Edward Ryan, the faculty's first full-time professor of anatomy, gave two lectures a week and supervised twenty hours' work in the dissecting laboratory. Chemistry and biology were also taught in the first session. In the second session, the lectures in anatomy increased to three, while time devoted to dissection decreased to fifteen hours. In the second session, the curriculum emphasized more clinically oriented disciplines: physiology, histology with embryology and *materia medica*. Professor J.W. Campbell gave 125 lectures on the art of dispensing prescriptions and held practical pharmacy classes every Saturday afternoon for the whole of the second session. Expertise in practical pharmacy was extremely important for physicians who would practise outside the larger urban areas, where no pharmacists existed. Even in towns, the doctor was often expected to dispense his own medicines, compound the powders and roll the pills he prescribed.

A significant improvement in the preclinical departments complemented the strength of the clinical subjects. Instruction in anatomy followed the strong tradition handed down from Dr John Stewart by way of Drs Sullivan, Dupuis, Irwin, and Ryan. Dissection and didactic lectures in regional anatomy occupied the first and second years, while surgeons performed demonstrations in operative anatomy during the senior years. Because almost every senior staffman had spent at least a year or two as a junior demonstrator in anatomy, clinical teaching was naturally strongly influenced by morphological principles.

The provision of cadavers – "subs" or (more euphemistically) "dissecting material" – proved a constant worry. In 1895 the faculty sent out some of its members across eastern Ontario to remind the local inspectors of anatomy of their duty to meet the university's legal need for cadavers.[19] The inspector of anatomy at Belleville reassured Drs Campbell and Gibson that he would be only too pleased to send the bodies to Queen's on the same terms that he had previously sent them elsewhere, presumably Toronto, at twenty-five dollars for each "sub." In addition, the faculty asked Dr Anglin to write his brother, Dr J.V. Anglin of Montreal, while Dr W.T. Connell wrote to Prescott for any available bodies. The whole exercise appears to have been successful, as we hear no more of a shortage of cadavers for some years. Even though most stories of students "resurrecting" bodies are apocryphal, some evidence of illicit traffic in "the lately deceased" from Hay Bay to Kingston disguised as shipments of apple barrels does exist.[20]

Before the faculty returned to Queen's, prosecutors in anatomy were allowed a rebate of fees for their work in preparing the cadavers.

However, the privilege was cancelled in 1899. Senior to the prosecutors were the demonstrators. In that year, Dr D.V. Sullivan (Dr Michael's son) was given sick leave from his position as demonstrator. Dr Gordon Mylks and Dr A.E. Ross were appointed as senior and junior anatomy demonstrators respectively in his place. Two years later, Drs Morrison and Richardson joined Dr Ryan, professor of anatomy, as his assistants. Their salaries were: Mylks – $100.00; Ross – $50.00; Morrison – $25.00; Richardson – $25.00.

The examples of Drs Connell and Knight brought home to the faculty the advantage to be gained by the appointment of a full-time senior teacher of anatomy (tutor). The dean stated in his report to faculty on 25 February 1904, that he had held conversations with the university board of trustees on the feasibility of such an appointment, and that if the right person were found, then the board "might find it possible to appropriate $600 or $700 for the purpose."[21] Two months later its finance committee pushed this back to $375, but permitted faculty to charge the remainder to the general expense account if the right man became available.

The dean and Dr Ryan considered for the position young Dr Frederick Etherington. During the spring of 1904, he was sent to Edinburgh University to learn how to run a department along the lines of the most famous of British anatomy schools. After he was appointed, he divided his time between teaching and preparing anatomical specimens for the museum. By April 1905, fifty permanent specimens were already on show, and when he presented his annual report to the trustees, Dean Connell's support for Dr Etherington's appointment was unequivocal: "If we are able to retain the services of Dr. Etherington, I firmly believe that in a few years our department of Anatomy will be second to none in this country."[22]

With some further encouragement from the faculty, the board increased its contribution to Dr Etherington's salary to $500. In total, he received $625 per year. Dr Ryan assumed the clinical teaching post as professor of medical and surgical anatomy, while taking charge of the surgical clinics at the Hotel Dieu Hospital. Dr Mylks was nominated professor of anatomy with Etherington as his lecturer and chief demonstrator.

The idea of appointing a full-time senior anatomist to occupy an endowed chair, although unusual, continued to be taken seriously. The board of trustees authorized the opening of a subscription list for the sole purpose of endowing a chair of anatomy; anyone subscribing $500 became the owner of a foundation scholarship in perpetuity in the arts faculty, while donors of lessor sums received less extensive scholarships.[23] Unfortunately few donors appeared; the small amounts actually subscribed were presumably taken into the general endowment fund of the university. A named chair of anatomy never materialized, and when Dr Etherington was promoted to professor in 1905, his salary continued to be funded from the operating budgets of both the faculty and the university. During the summer of 1906 he was paid an extra $200 to help with his expenses while studying embryology in the United Kingdom in the hope that he would be able to take over the teaching of this subject from Dr Knight. In fact he did so on his return.

Over the years, pathology gradually replaced anatomy as the discipline crucial to the understanding of medicine. Dr W.T. Connell taught two lectures per week on general pathology and morbid anatomy during the third and fourth sessions, followed by a series of lectures and demonstrations on specialized morbid anatomy. The study of morbid histology consisted of examining four to six sections of diseased tissues per class. Each student had to spend three or four weeks in the pathology laboratory assisting in the preparation, staining, and mounting of microscopic specimens for general class use. During the fourth year the students took turns in assisting in postmortem examinations and writing up the autopsy reports. Students had to assist at six autopsies at least, which were held in the mortuaries of the Kingston General and Rockwood Hospitals.

From two to three o'clock each Tuesday and Thursday during the final session until Christmas, Dr W.T. Connell gave a series of lectures and demonstrations in bacteriology. Each student was taught how to make cultures and perform bacteriological examinations of secretions and excretions. These classes were kept strictly relevant to the needs of the practising doctor. From 1899 to 1913, Dr Connell's laboratory guide or textbook in practical bacteriology went through three editions. The book was interleaved throughout for the students to record their own observations and divided into four parts: 1) practical bacteriology, consisting of twenty-four lessons ranging from simple microscopy to Noguchi's modifications of the Wassermann reaction; 2) preparation of media; 3) bacteriological analysis of water, sewage, and milk; 4) clinical microscopy and diagnosis of urine, blood, gastric contents, faeces, exudates, and transudates. The straightforward, practical presentation of material in the book reflects Dr W.T.'s excellence as a teacher.[24]

In his commitment to the welfare of Queen's medical faculty, Connell was a jack-of-all trades, not only as a teacher but also as an administrator. For the first eight years of the century he was faculty librarian and from 1904 until 1907, the faculty secretary. Dr Connell also became the faculty's expert on sanitary science, a discipline which in those days was more practical than theoretical, particularly when every general practitioner had to be the unpaid unofficial public health medical officer for his community. The nature, methods of spreading, and means of prevention of infectious diseases were particularly important before the era of sulfa drugs and antibiotics. Matters of isolation, disinfection, quarantine, and disposal of the dead not infrequently became the concern of the local G.P. Initially, he gave the lectures only during the summer session. They covered food, water, air, ventilation, sewage disposal, hospitals, the climate, and soil, with emphasis on their special importance to public health.

Dr A.R.B. Williamson, who started out as Dr Connell's demonstrator in pathology, took over his lectures in medical jurisprudence and toxicology in 1904. Again, these subjects had practical as well as theoretical importance. In the days before wholesale prescription of potentially poisonous drugs, toxicology was more appropriately taught with medical jurisprudence than pharmacology. The medical jurisprudence course introduced the students to the legal implications of their future actions as doctors. It included study of real and apparent death, appearances of wounds, effects of suffocation, drowning, evidence of rape, criminal abortion, impotence, sterility, medical toxicology, life insurance examinations, detection of blood stains, legitimacy, concealment of pregnancy, and infanticide, as well as types of medical malpractice and the subsequent penalties.

In 1904 it was suggested that a legal man should give at least some of the lectures in medical jurisprudence. Mr John McIntyre K.C. assumed that responsibility from 1905 until 1914, when he was succeeded by Mr J.M. Farrell, then the police magistrate for Kingston.

Even before J.C. Connell was appointed dean of the faculty in 1903 he had evinced a strong personal interest in medical ethics, a subject closely allied to medical jurisprudence. In 1897 he began a series of short articles in the *Kingston Medical Quarterly*, which in 1906, became the basis of a booklet printed by the faculty and issues to every student. The three chapters of Connell's *Principles of Medical Ethics* dealt with the duties of physicians to their patients, the duties of physicians to each other and to the profession at large, and the profession's duty to the public. The same booklet, with slight amendments, was still being issued in the 1920s.

Dr J.C. Connell, early in his tenure of office, suggested that a course in the history of medicine be introduced into the curriculum. Faculty voted to leave the details of organizing the course in his hands. He appears to have given most of the lectures himself, but coopted Dr Knight and Dr W.T. Connell to lecture on William Harvey and Louis Pasteur respectively.[25]

As usual during the senior undergraduate years, obstetrics and gynaecology with paediatrics, surgery, and medicine were the major clinical disciplines. The final hour of every day for the last two years of the curriculum was devoted to obstetrics and alternately gynaecology or paediatrics. Professor Garrett did most of the teaching after he took over the chair from Dr K.N. Fenwick. The course consisted of one hundred lectures, and embraced the theory and practice of both obstetrics and gynaecology. These lectures became the foundation of Dr Garrett's *Textbook of Medical and Surgical Gynaecology*, published in 1897.[26] The class was sectioned so that each group of students could attend deliveries in the labour room and maternity wards in the Doran Wing of the Kingston General Hospital. Dr Isaac Woods placed special emphasis on the postnatal care of the mother, and the care of the newborn. After Wood's death in 1910, Dr Gordon Mylks (senior) became professor of paediatrics and associate professor of obstetrics and gynaecology.

Surgery was divided into the principles and practice of surgery and clinical surgery. As the university senior surgeon, the Honourable Dr Michael Sullivan was expected to give one hundred lectures on the more theoretical aspects of surgery, either in the classroom or at the Hotel Dieu Hospital. The lectures included a course of surgical anatomy and surgical pathology. For almost forty years Dr Sullivan had taught, with an enthusiasm approaching religious fervour, that complete knowledge of anatomy was necessary if the surgeon was to be even minimally competent, or even moral. Sullivan also taught the proper use of surgical instruments and apparatus and performed routine surgical procedures on the cadavers. Unfortunately, after the return of the medical school to the university in 1892, he began to lose interest in the day-to-day teaching of his specialty. His lectures were not as well organized, sometimes he did not even show up for lectures, and if he did, he regularly went over his time. In 1899, when he became ill and could not continue his lectures, Dr Mundell, professor of applied anatomy, and Dr Anglin, professor of clinical surgery, took over his duties. The following year, Sullivan asked for an associate professor to lighten his duties – he would also have right of succession. Although faculty complied with his request, matters did not greatly improve; in 1904 the new dean, J.C. Connell forced Dr Sullivan's resignation from the active faculty and his acceptance of an emeritus professorship.[27] Dr D.E. Mundell became Sullivan's associate and in 1905 his successor as professor of the principles and practice of surgery, a position he retained for the next twenty years.

Medical and surgical anatomy was the only mandatory basic science course in the final two years of the programme. The third year placed emphasis on anatomical relations, ligation of arteries, fractures, and dislocations; The fourth, on topographical anatomy of the thorax, abdomen, and brain. Dr Mundell's textbook, published in 1903, *Anatomy Applied to Medicine and Surgery*, covered the entire course. Today, although dated, it is interesting reading because of the light it sheds on clinical teaching at the beginning of the century.[28]

Clinical surgery occupied an hour every morning five days a week in both the third and fourth year. Taught at the bedside and in the theatres of either the Kingston General Hospital or the Hotel Dieu Hospital, it was an earlier version of surgical grand rounds. Professor Anglin chose patients who exhibited particular pathological signs or symptoms and presented their case histories, diagnosis, treatment, natural course of the disease, and prognosis. Operations thought to have pedagogical value were performed, when possible, in front of the students. Dr McKenzie offered clinics in orthopaedic surgery at the Hotel Dieu as early as 1893.

Seven years later, an attempt was made to formalize the clinical teaching at the Hotel Dieu Hospital in relation to the university. The principal and secretary of the faculty were authorized to request the Kingston General Hospital to pay the Hotel Dieu $75 per session, from the moneys it received from the university, to pay for the students' admission to Dr Ryan's clinic at the Hotel Dieu Hospital. No evidence exists that the Kingston General Hospital complied, but by 1905 the faculty was paying the Kingston General $604 and the Hotel Dieu $120 for hospital fees per annum.[29]

One area of surgery that would today be recognized as a distinct specialty was that of the eye, ear, nose, and throat. Dr J.C. Connell gave the course during the summer session; the students rotated through his office to learn the use of the ophthalmoscope and laryngoscope.

When the faculty was reestablished at Queen's in 1892, Dr Fife Fowler was the professor of the principles and practice of medicine. Following his illness in 1900, he became the emeritus professor and handed over the bulk of the teaching to his juniors, Drs John Herald, J.W. Campbell, and James Third, who together formed a rather loosely organized Department of Medicine. Dr Third taught the theory and practice of medicine twice a week at a junior and senior level. Both courses embraced the following divisions: the general principles of medicine; the nature, cause and classification of disease; the symptoms, natural course and the various means of the prevention and cure of diseases, and general hygiene.

Dr Herald's course in clinical medicine covered the same topics, but in relation to patients. It consisted of lectures about the clinical study of diseases, with reports of cases, the instruments employed in the diagnosis of disease, the physical diagnosis of medical diseases, and the diagnostic importance of the chemical and microscopic examination of blood, expectoration, vomited matters, gastric contents, urine, and serous effusions. Patients in the wards of the Kingston General and Hotel Dieu Hospitals illustrated the lectures. As with clinical surgery, an hour a day, five days a week, was allotted to clinical medicine for two years.[30]

In keeping with the curricular requirements of the College of Physicians and Surgeons of Ontario, Queen's medical faculty had for years provided a strong course on mental diseases. After Dr C.K. Clarke came to Kingston from Hamilton to replace Dr Dewhurst as superintendent of Rockwood Hospital for the Insane, he offered a course in his subject each summer. Dr Clarke gave his lectures and demonstrations at Rockwood, rather than on the university campus, to give the students direct experience with mental patients. Each year the faculty voted a special appropriation for his salary. Earlier in the decade, Drs W.C. Barber and W.C. Herriman, both on staff of Rockwood Hospital, became clinical assistants and helped with the undergraduate teaching. Shortly after Dr Clarke moved to Toronto in 1904, Queen's awarded him an honorary LL.D. on the recommendation of the medical faculty. He was succeeded as superintendent of Rockwood by Dr Edward Ryan, who had been the professor of systematic anatomy, associate professor of surgery, professor of clinical medicine, and now became professor of psychiatry.

As early as August, 1895, Dr Knight had suggested that the faculty should initiate a postgraduate medical course. A committee was established consisting of Drs Knight, Saunders, Anglin, K.N. Fenwick, and Garrett and commissioned to report as soon as convenient. Two years later, Dr Knight outlined a postgraduate programme to consist of chemical physiological (i.e. biochemical and pathological) laboratory work and clinical training. Little progress, apart from the continuation of demonstratorships in anatomy and *materia medica*, occurred until 1903 when the faculty accepted in principle a postgraduate scheme which it hoped to run on a system similar to that of the New York Polyclinic.[31] This was one of the proprietary schools looked on with disfavour by Flexner[32] a few years later because it lacked a university affiliation.

It was only after the Medical Council of the Ontario College of Physicians and Surgeons instituted a mandatory fifth year in the medical curriculum that the Faculty Committee on the Fifth Year and Higher Degrees officially reported to Faculty Board, in December 1907, the following recommendations:

1. That the options permitted by the Ontario Council be opted for the fifth year of study. These are –
    (a) a year in a recognized hospital as House Surgeon
    (b) six months with a qualified practitioner and six months at a recognized hospital attending clinical lectures
    (c) six months with a qualified practitioner and six months in a medical school.

2. That fifth year students inform the Secretary not later than Oct. 16th how the year is being spent and that certificates presented at the end of the fifth year be accompanied by a declaration as to the work done.

3. That the degree of M.B. be granted on the completion of the work of four years. Fee $30.00.[33]

4. That the examinations at the end of the fifth year be oral, practical and clinical.

5. That the degrees of M.D., C.M. be granted on the completion of the fifth year examination. Fee $30.00.[34]

These recommendation were received and accepted; the five-year curriculum had come to stay.

Faculty then decided to take the academic step towards instituting a higher research degree. The faculty's committee recommended:

That a degree of D.Sc. be established, with the following requirements:

(a) The period of three years must elapse between graduation as M.D. and the completion of the course.
(b) Original and independent research in some subject of importance to medical science must be undertaken.
(c) The candidate must submit a thesis embodying the results of his research. The literary as well as the scientific quality of the thesis is to be taken into account in judging the candidate's fitness to proceed to the examination.
(d) The candidate must apply in writing to the Secretary at least two years before he proposes to present himself for final examination and must submit the subject of his research for approval.
(e) The examination will be upon subjects cognate to that of the thesis and will be assigned by the Faculty. They will include a reading knowledge of either French or German.
(f) Fee $50.00.[35]

The committee also suggested that a diploma postgraduate course in public health and sanitary science be established, with details to be submitted later. Once the committee's recommendation had been accepted, everyone seems to have been content to let a sleeping dog lie, particularly as no candidates were forthcoming.

The attempts by medical faculties to raise their own standards and to meet the requirements of the Educational Council of the Ontario College of Physicians and Surgeons were not always appreciated by educated laymen or the medical press. At the time these changes were being instituted at Queen's, the *Montreal Medical Journal* and the *Canada Lancet* were engaged in a war of words over academic standards in the medical schools of Halifax and Kingston as compared with those at Toronto and McGill.[36] But the opinions of these journals were about to be overshadowed by the publication of the *Flexner Report*, which has since then been seen as the benchmark for North American medical education.

THE FLEXNER REPORT AND QUEEN'S

The Carnegie Foundation for the Advancement of Teaching issued in 1910 a report by Abraham Flexner[37] *Medical Education in the United States and Canada.* Its publication had such a profound effect, for good or for ill, on medical education in North America that seventy years later the general pedagogical principles identified and the specific recommendations enunciated still influence day-to-day instruction in our medical schools.

During 1908 and 1909 Flexner visited 155 institutions claiming to be medical schools, whether "allopath, homeopath, eclectic, osteopath, or whatnot."[38] Eight of these schools, all attached to universities, were located in Canada: Halifax Medical College, Laval University Medical Department, McGill University Medical Faculty, Medical Department of Queen's University, University of Toronto Faculty of Medicine, Western Medical Department, and Manitoba Medical College.

Flexner, a member of a distinguished scholarly American family, was particularly well prepared for this one-man commission. Even though he was not a physician, he had studied philosophy and psychology at Harvard and in Germany and he had broad experience in teaching at the secondary and university levels. As he began the study of American medical education, he discovered that the central question concerned how modern science and technology relate to medicine and, in consequence, to medical education, the organization of medical schools, and their admission requirements. He recognized clearly the perennial problem medical school administrators have to face – research versus teaching: "Practitioners of modern medicine must be alert, systematic, thorough, critically open minded; they will get no such training from perfunctory teachers. Educationally, then, research is required of the medical faculty because only research will keep the teachers in condition. A non-productive school, conceivably up to date today, would be out of date tomorrow; its dead atmosphere would soon breed a careless and unenlightened dogmatism."[39]

The early chapters of the *Flexner Report* outline the development of medical education in the United States. There new scientific disciplines were gradually included into preclinical teaching, extending a curriculum already heavily loaded with anatomical subjects. Flexner identified three types of medical schools that provided education in the laboratory disciplines. The best schools were "those that by careful selection of students and extraordinary pains in teaching make the very most of the situation."[40] Among those in this group he thought McGill and Toronto deserved special mention, whose five-year curriculums – the same as Queen's – put them in this category, along with Minnesota and Michigan. The two other types of school either operated "on a lower plane" or were "frankly mercenary."

Among Flexner's broad recommendations for reconstruction of North American medical education are some observations specifically related to the Canadian situation:

In Canada the existing ratio of physicians to population is 1:1030. The estimated increase of population last year was 239,516, requiring 160 new physicians; losses by death are estimated at 90. As the country is thinly settled and doctors much less abundant than in the United States, let us suppose these replaced man for man: 250 more doctors would be annually required. The task of supplying them could be for the moment safely left to the Universities of Toronto and Manitoba, to McGill and to Laval at Quebec. At some future time doubtless Dalhousie University at Halifax will need to create a medical department. The future of Queen's depends on its ability to develop halfway between Toronto and Montreal, despite comparative inaccessibility, the Ann Arbor type of school. As for the rest, the great northwestern territory will, as it develops, create whatever additional facilities it may require.[41]

The university and the medical school at Queen's had always accepted the geographic shortcomings of Kingston as a fact of life. The question was whether Kingston could develop "an Ann Arbor type of school" in spite of them.

The University of Michigan Department of Medicine and Surgery was organized at Ann Arbor in 1850. It had, for years before the *Flexner Report*, a first-class reputation. Elizabeth Smith hoped to attend this school before her matriculation examiner, Dr (then Mr) Knight, persuaded her in 1879 to attend the Royal and Queen's. Ten years later, Dr Maclean, professor of surgery at Ann Arbor, and founding member of the Royal in Kingston, resigned his chair because of the smallness of the town of Ann Arbor itself and consequent relative paucity of surgical patients. At the time of Abraham Flexner's visit, Ann Arbor's population was 14,734; Kingston's was approximately 20,000. Ann Arbor's medical school was eminent for two reasons: first, the resources available for its maintenance consisted of income from fees of $34,903 and an endowment of $175,000 (Queen's Medical Faculty's income was approximately $20,000 per annum; it had no endowment); secondly – and this was the envy of all medical educators of the time – the medical school at Ann Arbor had its own hospital, every bed of which was available for teaching purposes.

The detailed description of Queen's Medical Faculty in Flexner's report – the raw data on which his conclusions were based – shows how it appeared to a qualified, disinterested contemporary in the first decade of this century.

KINGSTON: *Population,* 20,000

MEDICAL DEPARTMENT OF QUEEN'S UNIVERSITY. Organized 1854. The relation of the medical department to the University is anomalous, marking a period of transition that is likely soon to result in complete integration.

Entrance requirement: Heretofore somewhat below that of the arts department of the University, though students must comply with the requirements of the Province in which they expect to practise. The medical course covers five years.

Attendance: 208, 71 percent from Ontario

Teaching staff: 38, 16 being professors

Resource available for maintenance: Income in fees, $19,978. A fixed percentage of fees is annually expended on buildings, equipment, and maintenance. The remainder belongs to and is disbursed by the medical faculty.

Laboratory facilities: The laboratory building is new and the equipment is adequate to intelligent routine work. At present, physics, chemistry, and physiology are taught in the University, in return for which the University receives a part of the fees of the students instructed. Full-time professors in anatomy and pathology are provided by the medical school. A museum is in process of formation. There is a small collection of books and periodicals in the faculty room, open to students.

Clinical facilities: The clinical facilities are limited. The school relies mainly on the adjoining Kingston General Hospital, in which its faculty practically constitutes the staff. The average number of beds available is 80, but they are well used. In addition to ward work, students are required to work up individual cases in correct form, including the clinical laboratory aspects. There is a ward for infectious diseases. Obstetrical cases are too few. Post-mortems are secured mainly at the Rockwood Insane Asylum. Two supplementary hospitals provide additional illustrative clinical material. The opportunities for out patient work are slight.

Date of visit: October, 1909./42

Flexner concluded his report to the Carnegie Foundation with the following observations:

In the matter of medical schools, Canada reproduces the United States on a greatly reduced scale. Western University (London) is as bad as anything to be found on this side [sic] the line; Laval and Halifax Medical College are feeble; Winnipeg and Kingston represent a distinct effort toward higher ideals; McGill and Toronto are excellent. The eight schools of the Dominion thus belong to three different types, the best adding a fifth year to their advantages of superior equipment and instruction.

At this moment the needs of the Dominion could be met by the four better English schools and the Laval department at Quebec. Toronto has practically reached the limits of efficiency in point of size; McGill and Manitoba are capable of considerable expansion. The future of Kingston is at least doubtful. It could certainly maintain a two-year school; for the Kingston General Hospital would afford pathological and clinical material amply sufficient up to that point. But the clinical years require much more than the town now supplies. Its location – halfway between Montreal and Toronto, on an inconvenient branch-line – greatly aggravates the difficulties due to the smallness of the community.

. . . Our trouble in the United States has been at bottom not less one of low ideals than of low standards. Indeed, where ideals are low, there are no standards; and where ideals are high, the standard, even though low, is at any rate so definite that it furnishes a sure starting-point towards a clearly apprehended goal.[43]

Queen's had always claimed high ideals. Flexner's report focussed on its chronic difficulties: lack of endowment, inconvenient location, and a limited number of hospital patients for clinical teaching. At the same time, Flexner's observations implied that it was possible for Queen's Medical School to attain the level of Ann Arbor, where "liberal policy has largely overcome the disadvantages of location in a small town"[44] and where "the thoroughness and continuity with which the cases can be used to train the student in the technique of modern methods go far to offset defects due to limitations in their number and variety."[45]

The faculty minutes do not mention Flexner's visit to Kingston or how he was entertained while in town. In his annual report of 1910, the dean mentioned this and another visit:

In October last our school was inspected by Mr. Flexner, representing the Carnegie Foundation, and Dr Colwell, representing the American Medical Association. The report of Dr. Colwell has been received, and it must be gratifying to our friends to know that Queen's is one of the four schools in Canada in Class 'A' or acceptable to the Association. The other three are Toronto, McGill, and Manitoba. The reports of the Association and of the Carnegie Institute are to be made public and will be available for all examining and licensing boards.[46]

The following year the dean attempted to allay the apprehensions that had arisen from the published *Flexner Report* and to reassure the board:

The report of the Carnegie Foundation relating to Medical Education, published last summer, contained some statements and criticisms which are unfavourable to our school. As these were manifestly based on inadequate knowledge of the actual conditions, they have not been taken very seriously by the Faculty.[47]

Notwithstanding this confident assertion, the faculty was compelled to take Flexner's observations seriously, over the years, and slowly changes were made. The growth of Kingston's population and its hinterland, along with an increase of hospital beds over the last seventy years, has hardly altered the major difficulty facing Queen's medical school: the student-hospital bed ratio problem has continued to bedevil the faculty's development.

PREWAR OPTIMISM

Between the faculty's Jubilee celebrations and the beginning of the Great War, Dean Connell had led his faculty from insecurity to a state of self-satisfaction based on the belief that the twentieth century really did belong to Canadian medicine. The *Flexner Report* had erased the possible stigma of being a proprietary school and with the institution of the 1913 constitution, the faculty was fully integrated into the university. Scientific medicine was being taught in the medical school's new laboratories, and no great doctrinal or political issues had disrupted its growth. The curriculum, the buildings, and the organization of the faculty were in place and, apart from minor alterations, persisted for the next half century. Under Dean Connell the faculty lived a life that was never to return – in a mood of optimism which has, nonetheless, been justified in spite of two wars, a depression, and decades of discontent.

Queen's University Journal, the students' perennial voice, reflects the tranquility of the decade before the Great War. Its reports of the Aesculapian Society offer a good example of the decade's mood. The Aesculapian Society, following the example of its seniors, periodically adjusted its constitution. In 1911, a general meeting of the society accepted the report of a committee which practically recast the constitution it had lived with since the return of the Royal to Queen's. The main changes related to the expenditure of the society's funds, the function and procedure of the medical court, the *Concursus*, and the regular meetings of the executive.

The Aesculapian Society occasionally invited speakers to address the students. In view of the relative lack of interest in military matters, the appearance of Dr Jones, director of the Medical Army Corps, before the medical students is noteworthy. His object was to interest medical students in the militia. To this end, he suggested that Canadian medical schools institute a series of lectures leading to an examination on the Canadian Army Medical Corps (C.A.M.C.). He anticipated that such a programme would prepare doctors for the contingency of a war.[48] Members of the medical faculty were also invited to give Aesculapian Society lectures, and the honorary president of the society was selected from among the faculty. The favorites were Drs Sullivan, the Connells, (both J.C. and W.T.), Herald, Knight, and Etherington.

Each issue of *Queen's University Journal* provided a column of gossipy minutiae. These are usually of only passing interest, although occasionally a few paragraphs tell of students who caught the imagination of their peers.

Dr Samuel Eshoo graduated in 1902. He did a year of postgraduate work before returning to Urumia in Persia, his homeland. Within two weeks of setting up practice, he treated twenty-five patients for a total remuneration of forty cents. Queen's University Missionary Association adopted Dr Eshoo and for the next few years managed to supply him with money. In 1904 Principal Gordon, the chancellor and Dean Connell all contributed to the fund; $180 was sent. The following year the fund sent $200 for cholera patients, $125 for Dr Eshoo's room and board, and $10 for the hire of his horse. The initial enthusiastic support for Dr Eshoo's missionary activities soon waned. After his letter of thanks was published in the May 1906 issue, he disappeared from the pages of the *Journal*, although the faculty was assured – through Dr Eshoo's work – that its influence continued to be felt in the small Muslim villages of northern Iran, half a world away.[49]

At the other end of the student spectrum, G.L. Hagen-Burger entered the university's history in a small item in a column of facetious comment in the *Journal*: "Drs. H-g-n-B-g-r and Mc-C-b-, having secured certificates on "Mental Diseases," ... at last report they had secured a case – of Labatts."[50] Unfortunately, however, Hagen-Burger caused the university far more trouble than the *Journal* could have foreseen.

It is rare for a medical school faculty or a university senate to be faced with a situation like the one created by G.L. Hagen-Burger. On the recommendation of a well-respected alumnus, he was admitted to Queen's fourth-year class during December 1902. He attended the rest of the session but failed to pass the final examinations. In September 1904, he returned to Queen's, passed the supplemental examinations, and was grated the M.D.,C.M. During the interval he had practised in Boston, Massachusetts.

Shortly afterwards, the secretary of Queen's medical faculty received a specimen of Hagen-Burger's handwriting from the State Board of Medical Examiners of Colorado and an enquiry asking whether he had a Queen's degree. Hagen-Burger had presented what was thought to be a forged degree from Kiel University to the Colorado authorities. At the same time, a criminal action was pending against him in Denver. In order to clear his name he was granted, through political influence, permission to visit Germany in 1902 to obtain a copy of his degree. Instead he came to Queen's.

When the letter from Colorado arrived, Dr Herald was no longer the faculty secretary, but he remembered that Hagen-Burger had presented a degree from Kiel and licences to practice in Montana and Colorado. In December 1905 Hagen-Burger appeared before Queen's senate with his counsel. He denied allegations of impropriety or forgery. His defence must have been sufficiently plausible for the senate to reserve judgment. It sent Professor Patchett to Kiel during the summer to investigate the situation. However, even before he left for Germany, Dr Van Meter of Colorado attacked Queen's in the *Journal of the American Medical Association*. In reply, Dr Connell wrote that "once a degree had been awarded by Queen's senate, it is no light matter to cancel it, and requires evidence that will hold in any court of law."[51] When Professor Patchett returned, he reported a series of events that, when taken together, suggested that not only had Hagen-Burger fabricated the Kiel degree entirely on his own, but also that no one at Kiel was implicated in the forgery.

The senate and medical faculty met in December 1906. They considered Patchett's report carefully and with great solemnity stated that "in view of the findings, the Senate of Queen's University declare and adjudge that the degrees of M.D. and C.M., obtained by Mr Hagen-Burger from Queen's University, were founded on documents which are invalid, and they do hereby cancel these degrees and withdraw from Mr Hagen-Burger all right to use them."[52]

The faculty was allotted the unpleasant duty of notifying the State Boards of Massachusetts, Montana, and Colorado, and the editor of the *Journal of the American Medical Association* of the Senate's action. The faculty was relieved to hear the last of Mr Hagen-Burger, when in April 1907, he withdrew his suit from the courts for the restitution of his degree.

Dr Eshoo and Hagen-Burger were unusual examples – for the most part the medical students at Queen's were content with their world, which was geared to the annual examinations in May and punctuated by the ritual medical dinner or Oyster Supper. An occasional "At Home" might be hosted by a senior faculty member and his wife. Principal Gordon continued the Sunday afternoon sermons in Convocation Hall that had been instituted by his predecessor. They were attended by the more religiously inclined students who gradually, along with their Sunday lie-a-bed colleagues, took the new principal to their hearts.

Medical students also played their part in the parties and parades of the football season, and the faculty prudently looked the other way on the infrequent occasions when celebrations became boisterous. After one particularly rowdy Saturday football game in 1908, however, a drunken mob scene was rapidly developing in the marketplace when the chief of police called on the mayor, the city's chief magistrate, to quell the incipient riot. The luckless mayor was none other than the professor of pharmacology and *materia medica*, Dr A.E. Ross. With superb tactical judgment, the doctor-mayor and the chief of police waded into the fray and apprehended two innocent divinity students whom they promptly clapped in jail for the night. Through this action they set an example to all Queen's students not to fall into the temptation of Demon Drink, and retained the loyalty of the medical students.[53]

Neither staff nor students were immune from the ills suffered by the general populace. Fortunately, during the prewar period there was apparently less illness than in previous decades. In early 1903, Dr W.T. Connell was confined to his house for a few weeks with typhoid fever, and the *Queen's University Journal* advised all students to boil all drinking water and abstain from drinking milk. Although many appear to have been laid up with typhoid, all seem to have recovered by the summer. A year or two later, Fred Cays, a third year student, asked for *aegrotat* standing because illness had deprived him of eight months of study. His request led to the faculty setting up a committee specifically to deal with "students in arrears with work."[54]

The Aesculapian Society during the 1906/07 session became very worried because a shack behind the Kingston General Hospital, which was set aside for tubercular patients, was that year solely occupied by Queen's students. The society formed a committee to investigate the feasibility of the Alma Mater Society building a Queen's tubercular "shack" on the lower campus opposite the hospital just for the students' use. It was thought this would lead to a further cooperative venture between the hospital governors and the university trustees for the benefit of the students. Unfortunately, nothing came of this particular Aesculapian initiative apart from a heated debate in the *Daily British Whig* between Dr Third, professor of medicine, and P.G.C. Campbell, professor of French, who lived close by and did not wish to see a decline in the value of his property.[55]

Between the death of Dean Fowler in 1903 and the beginning of the Great War, the faculty changed very little. Drs John Herald and Isaac Wood died, Dr Sullivan retired, and Dr C.K. Clarke was transferred from Rockwood Hospital to Toronto where he became superintendent of the Christie St Asylum. Younger men were promoted or appointed to fill the vacancies. These men formed, in the main, Dr Connell's team until the 1920s, and together with a new constitution new building, and a new curriculum, they probably ensured Kingston's survival as a major health-care and education centre in the province of Ontario.

CHAPTER TEN

Queen's Medicine Goes to War

Queen's sent the first of its men on to active service within two weeks of the declaration of War World I on 4 August 1914. Apart from a few individuals who enlisted separately, the 5th Field Company of Engineers under the command of Maj. Alexander Macphail, professor of civil engineering, was the first Queen's unit to be called up. It was detailed to prepare Camp Valcartier for the thousands of recruits who were even then volunteering. *Queen's University Journal* reported as early as November 1914 that over forty engineers were already overseas with Major Macphail, 1st Field Company Canadian Engineers. While at Valcartier, Macphail himself was spoken of by Rudyard Kipling as "the man who builds bridges with one hand and writes poetry with the other."[1]

During the early days of Valcartier, Lt Col A.E. Ross was president of the Standing Medical Board, and at the same time he assembled his own No. 1 Field Ambulance in preparation for its embarkation overseas with the First Canadian Contingent.[2] Other Queen's men were among Ross's medical officers: Captains Graham, Stone, Ruttan, Cockburn, and McConnell and Lieutenant Hubbell.[3] For the initial draft, 32,000 physically fit men and 7,500 horses were assembled at Valcartier. The Assistant Director of Medical Services, H.R. Lt Col Duff of Queen's supervised the camp's health. He had served with distinction in South Africa (the Queen's Medal with four clasps) and was A.D.M.S. of the 3rd (Kingston) Division at the beginning of the war. Unfortunately he was thrown from his horse and badly hurt. When he recovered, however, from this injury and the subsequent chest complications, he joined No. 5 Stationary Hospital in Cairo as second in command to Lieutenant-Colonel Etherington.[4]

Dr W.A. Kennedy (Meds '12) was overseas at the declaration of the war and had his postgraduate studies interrupted. Following graduation and a short time at Columbia University, he was appointed Queen's first Douglas Lecturer in pharmacology, but after two years he resigned and left Kingston with every intention of settling in Constantinople. On the outbreak of war he immediately joined the Red Cross in France where he served with Dr H. Gray, another 1912 alumnus. Also by early October, Dr Harry Harty was serving on a hospital ship off the coast of Scotland.[5] Later he became a Royal Naval Surgeon on H.M.S. *Marlborough* with the Grand Fleet.

While the first contingent was *en route* for France, back at Queen's, Principal Gordon steadfastly maintained the almost Christian duty of students to take "drill and musketry instructions throughout the session,. . . . because we are part and parcel of the British Empire, and the Empire has not faced such a crisis since the days of Napoleon, if even then."[6]

But patriotism did not solve practising physicians' problems with the politics of medical reciprocity. The faculty resolved at one of its meetings early in the war that "whereas a number of Physicians registered in Ontario have volunteered for imperial army service and have not been accepted because the Ontario qualification is not recognized in Great Britain ... in the opinion of the medical faculty of Queen's University the time is opportune to establish reciprocal relations between the General Medical Council of Great Britain and the Medical Council of Ontario."[7] For some inexplicable reason the time for reciprocity has not yet become opportune seventy years later. The exigencies of war, however, eventually led to the recruitment of many Ontario graduates into the Royal Army Medical Corps (R.A.M.C.).

The medical students had to decide whether to finish their studies or march off to the trenches and dubious glory. The regular meeting of the Aesculapian Society discussed, late in October 1914, military training and the formation of an ambulance corps. The compromise suggested was that the medical students should regularly devote two hours a week to ambulance corps drill, and, if willing, could take regular infantry drill with the arts and divinity men.

It was about this time that the convalescent Lieutenant-Colonel Duff, returning from Valcartier, gave a stimulating address to the faculty on the need for experienced men to take charge of military base hospitals. Rising to the challenge, Dr W.G. Anglin immediately volunteered his services. *Queen's University Journal* thought that although the professor of clinical surgery would be greatly missed by the people and students of Kingston, he would be a great gain to the Militia Department.[8] Further insight into the medical problems of modern warfare was given by the honorary president of the Aesculapian Society, Dr G.E. Kidd, professor of anatomy. Having spent the summer in Europe at the time of the declaration of war and the opening of hostilities, he talked to them about "The Attitude of England Toward the War and Mortality of Modern Warfare." He compared the types and causes of casualties in ancient and modern battles and concluded that "much of the success of the Japs was due to the fact that their sanitation and medical service on the field of battle was very much superior to that of the Russians (during the war of 1904/05)."[9]

The Aesculapian Society supported the war effort with patriotic songs and a suggestion that the second verse in "Queen's College Colours" be changed to

The Kaiser's not invincible,
He trembles at the news
Of Queen's College Colours, and
He's shaking in his shoes.[10]

However, the German thrust to the Channel ports during the fall of 1914, although not completely successful, drove facetiousness of the front pages of *Queen's University Journal*. Everyone came to realize that the war would not be over by Christmas. Dr Etherington suggested to the Militia Department that he would recruit a stationary hospital accommodating 200 patients, with senior personnel drawn from the medical faculty and other ranks from among Queen's students. Apart from the nursing sisters, it was to be entirely a Queen's unit. The government immediately responded that the imperial authorities had not up to that time evinced any interest in receiving either a stationary or a general hospital from the Dominions. The Canadian Militia Department did promise, however, to contact Dr Etherington as soon as a contingency should arise.

When Etherington, who some years earlier had resigned his chair of anatomy and later returned to the faculty as a junior surgeon, reported officially to faculty the military's response to his offer, Dean Connell moved and Dr Mundell seconded the following motion, which was carried unanimously:

Resolved that the medical faculty approves the formation of a Hospital unit for military service abroad to be composed of professors, graduates and students of the University; commends to the students immediate training for this purpose, enlistment to take place if the proposal is finally accepted by the Government, and resolved that the faculty facilitate the completion of classes and examinations so that students enlisting in this or any other unit, will not be delayed in graduating.[11]

Adding his own considerable reputation to Etherington's, the chairman of Queen's board of trustees, Hamilton Cassels, wrote to the government repeating the offer of its facilities. Sam Hughes, minister of militia, replied by forwarding a copy of a telegram from Lord Harcourt on behalf of the Army Council declining the university's offer. He expressed his own warm appreciation but regretted the refusal of the offer by the imperial government.

At about the same time a letter from Capt. (Professor) Lindsay Malcolm of No. 6 Field Company, Canadian Engineers, thanked the faculty for allowing the medical students in his unit "the privilege of completing their examinations before leaving for active service.[12] The concern shown by faculty for the welfare of individual students during the early days of the war is also indicated by its response to A.W. Trefry's request. Trefry was a sergeant in the Clearing Hospital of the Canadian Expeditionary Force. He asked faculty for permission to write off his final year examinations while he was in France.[13] Faculty decided to examine Trefry extra-murally for his degree. Dr A.E. Ross was asked to give the examinations when opportune and as he saw fit. Ross's report would then be forwarded by the faculty to the senate along with those third and fourth year medical students who had volunteered for overseas service. Queen's held a special convocation on 18 February 1915, at which the degree of Bachelor of Medicine was bestowed on twenty fourth-year enlisted students. They and third-year students left Kingston the next day. After three weeks of training in Ottawa they embarked at Halifax and arrived in Liverpool on 24 March. They were immediately posted as "dressers" to the Duchess of Connaught's Canadian Base Hospital on the Astor estate at Cliveden in Maidenhead. The Queen's volunteers treated mud-splattered patients fresh from the trenches at Ypres and casualties returning from the Dardanelles. While they were there, one of their fellow students, Sapper Buchanan, died following amputation of his gangrenous leg. He was given a special military funeral with Queen's men as the pallbearers. The alumni then serving in England sent a huge floral Q in tribute.[14] Early in May the fourth-year M.B.s were granted commissions in the R.A.M.C. and dispersed throughout the corps, either to field ambulances or regimental work. The third-year dressers returned to Canada and Queen's on the C.P.R. liner, *Metagama*, to complete their medical training – they were almost immediately recalled to active service with the Canadian Army Medical Corps.

QUEEN'S UNIVERSITY HOSPITAL

While individual students were answering the call in their own ways, Dr Etherington was not satisfied to let matters take their course in the university. Through the good offices of Principal Gordon's son-in-law, W.F. Nickle, M.P. for Kingston, Etherington obtained an interview with the minister of militia, Sam Hughes. As a result, a second cable was sent to the War Office in London reiterating Queen's offer. This time the grim realities of the Western Front forced London to accept with alacrity. Orders arrived in Kingston at one o'clock on the morning of 26 March 1915; Dr Etherington began recruiting eight hours later. Mobilization of No. 5 Stationary Hospital was well under way by the time of the next faculty meeting, when the dean moved and Dr Anglin seconded a motion "that students who are enlisted in Queen's Stationary Hospital for Overseas Service be granted their year's standing, and that those who are in the fourth year be recommended to the Senate as worthy to receive the degree of M.D."[15] A short while later the faculty recommended that some enlisted M.B.s who had been working in hospitals be converted to M.D.s.

The medical faculty, under the active leadership of the dean, discussed the best way to outfit No. 5 Stationary, which soon became known as Queen's Hospital. Dr W.T. Connell was authorized to give the hospital any equipment that could possibly be spared from the New Medical Building. Faculty decided to send a circular to its graduates and issue press notices to the public appealing for $5,000 for the initial equipment of the hospital and $300 per month for its upkeep. It was also suggested that the advertisements include a note ensuring the public that a subscription of $25 would entitle the donor to have a bed named after him.[16] Almost every social organization, fraternity, sorority, or religious society in Kingston and eastern Ontario joined Queen's faculties, classes, and other groups, such as Levana (the women's branch of the Queen's Alma Mater Society), to underwrite one or more hospital beds. Numerous individuals, alumni, and companies sent money to help support the hospital either in response to the dean's informative begging letters or as part of the Red Cross's major war effort in Kingston. In 1916 the dean reported that $20,000 had been subscribed to the local Red Cross, all of whose efforts went to the support of No. 5 Stationary and then, when it was upgraded in 1916 to No. 7 Canadian General Hospital.

Students from all of Queen's faculties volunteered for duty with the hospital. Great care was taken in the selection of these recruits.

"In addition to the ordinary tests for military service, every man chosen was required to have a clear academic record and be of good character."[17] Eighty-nine other ranks volunteered: of these, eight were Queen's medical students or graduates, seven were M.D.s. These seven were later commissioned and transferred to other Canadian or British units.

Initially the commissioned complement of No. 5 Stationary Hospital was placed at ten: eight medical officers, one dental officer, and the quartermaster. The eight medical officers, released members of the medical faculty, included: Dr W.G. Anglin (professor of clinical surgery), Dr W.T. Connell (professor of pathology), Dr G.E. Kidd (professor of anatomy), Dr F. Etherington (assistant professor of surgery), Dr S.M. Polson (clinical assistant in eye and ear), and Dr J.P. Quigley (clinical assistant in medicine). The necessary thirty-five nursing sisters were recruited from all across eastern Ontario. Within two weeks everyone was mobilized and periods of feverish training activity and kit inspections alternated with periods of boredom during which rumour chased rumour concerning date of embarkation until at last orders were received. – the hospital was given twenty-four hours notice to entrain. There were no overseas embarkation leaves, only brief farewells for those who lived in Kingston. The send-off was magnificent. The entire hospital was assembled in a general muster of officers, sisters, and men on the university campus in front of Fleming Hall on the afternoon of 5 May 1915. The farewell tea provided by the ladies of Kingston in Grant Hall was followed immediately by the march-out. The only delay en route to the outer station was a short halt called at the armouries on Montreal Street, where the hospital was joined by an eastern Ontario battalion also proceeding overseas. After short addresses of bon voyage by the mayor and Mr Nickle, M.P., and a photograph, the two units marched up Montreal Street to the Kingston junction. Next morning the Queen's No. 5 Stationary Hospital, along with McGill's No. 3 General Hospital and No. 4 Stationary Hospital, boarded the CPR liner S.S. *Metagama* in Montreal. The trip down the St Lawrence and across the Atlantic was calm and pleasurable apart from a rumour about the sinking of the *Lusitania*.[18]

Ten days after leaving Kingston, on the morning of 15 May the *Metagama* docked in Plymouth harbour. The nurses were immediately disembarked and sent off to London and then to France for urgent duty. The remainder of the hospital unit took one of those meandering British troop trains which brought them, tired and hungry, to Shorncliffe just outside Folkestone on the south coast of

England at four o'clock in the morning. Moore Barracks provided temporary quarters, until a few days later the unit was transferred to St Martin's Plain.

Here the Queen's men were first put in charge of a tent hospital for venereal diseases. They treated 800 patients in a two-month period and had 150 on sick parade each day. Once the Canadians became accustomed to running the hospital, the number of beds was raised from its initial complement of 200 to 400 beds. Almost immediately a further 200 were added and the 600 beds were filled with wounded from the front.

By the time orders had arrived and No. 5 embarked for Egypt on 1 August 1915, over 1,000 patients had been treated. When the director general of Medical Services visited the hospital and expressed his satisfaction, the faculty at home was understandably proud.[19]

The order to proceed overseas brought the unit back to a 400-bed hospital. The doctors had already been recalled, and the nurses, who had been scattered across England and France, were reunited with the unit. Just before embarking, reinforcements of forty-five officers and men arrived from Kingston. A significant addition to No. 5 Stationary Hospital at this time was nursing sister B. Willoughby, who was appointed matron. She came with six months' experience in military hospitals in France and three or more years as a matron in Kingston General Hospital before the war.

Another new member of the unit, Walter McCree, M.A., who had been editor-in-chief of the *Queen's University Journal* during the previous academic session, wrote back to Kingston as soon as possible describing his experiences. The voyage to England "was a veritable pleasure trip." The "delightful" troop train journey brought him to Shorncliffe at half past two in the morning (predictably), but this time the newcomers were welcomed by their fellow Queen's men. They were marched up to the tent hospital and provided with a warm meal, blankets, mattresses, and news that they were leaving for the Mediterranean the next day.[20]

Two other Canadian stationary hospitals, Nos. 1 and 3, joined Queen's No. 5 Stationary hospital on the H.M.S. *Asturias*. The descriptions of the outward voyage are interesting. The commanding officer (C.O.), Colonel Etherington, reported that "the voyage eastward with the exception of a day in the Bay of Biscay, was enjoyed by everybody"[21] – an officer's opinion. The other ranks viewed it a little differently. H. Nicol wrote: "we sailed from Southampton and the first day and a half's sailing was pretty rough . . . and passed Gibraltar on the following Wednesday morning about three o'clock. We couldn't see anything but a big searchlight playing over the water."[22] Anyone who has lounged on the deck of a troop ship will feel with Walter McCree:

We embarked that Sunday afternoon and had a pleasant voyage to Alexandria. The food was good, the quarters passable, but owing to some absurd restrictions we were limited to a very narrow area of the deck and many of the boys suffered somewhat in health from sheer lack of exercise. A few of us played innumerable games of bridge and any devotee will tell you that that is an efficient way to make any place, time or company agreeable.[23]

After arriving in Alexandria, the authorities decided that Stationary hospitals Nos. 1 and 3 would proceed to Lemnos to care for the Gallipoli wounded, while Queen's No. 5 would move on to Cairo. This decision was considered by the C.O. to have been arrived at by the authorities because "we held the lucky card." Except for McCree and the fatigue party in charge of the baggage, they all followed the order to proceed to Cairo at once. He, for some unknown reason, was more or less on the sick list and was "volunteered" to check off the stores as they came off the ship's hold. He reported, "I had my first experience also of army methods. Get all your own and as much as possible of the other fellows equipment' seems to be the favourite motto."[24] McCree was to remain with the hospital for the rest of the war. Eventually he was commissioned as the unit's paymaster just before the armistice. Because of his obvious administrative ability, No. 5 Stationary Hospital arrived at the cavalry barracks at Abbassia more than sufficiently equipped and began accepting its first patients within two weeks. The Abbassia barracks were alleged to be "very large, spacious, comfortable ... The second best in the world – built under Kitchiner's [sic] instructions when he was Kedive here" according to Sgt Maj. Alvin Crawford (Meds '17).[25] They were close to Heliopolis and the pyramids and, what impressed the C.O. most was "the boundless Libyan Desert."

The hospital consisted of three large, three-storied, balconied buildings. The two upper floors of each building were converted into wards. The lower floors served as offices, storerooms, an operating room, an X-ray room, a pathology laboratory, and a pharmacy. Each ward consisted of 4 rooms, each with 20 beds. The total available beds was 480. The wide, open balconies were also used for extra beds whenever needed. Colonel Etherington named the wards Gordon (Queen's principal), Connell (Queen's dean of medicine), Bermingham (a leading Kingston citizen), Davis (a Kingston donor of $1,000 and an ambulance), Douglas (Queen's newly elected chancellor), and Martin (Mrs Iva Martin, president of the Kingston Red Cross Society).

When No. 5 Stationary Hospital opened on 27 August 1915, Dean Connell sent a circularized letter and illustrated booklet to the "Subscribers to Queen's University Hospital" describing the duties of the staff. The C.O. had organized his personnel as follows:

Block I	Officer in Charge	– Lieut.-Col. E. Kidd
	Gordon Ward	– Capt. S.M. Polson
	Connell Ward	– Capt. G.E. Kidd
	Operating Room	– Col. F. Etherington
Block II	Officer in Charge	– Lieut.-Col. W.G. Anglin
	Davis Ward	– Capt. W.H. Ballantyne
	Bermingham Ward	– Capt. G.A. Platt
Block III	Officer in Charge	– Lieut.-Col. W.T. Connell
	Martin Ward	– Capt. K.E. Hollis
	Douglas Ward	– Capt. John Tower

Anaesthetics – Capt. Platt, X-ray Dept. – Capt. J.P. Quigley, Pathological Laboratory – Capt. F.X. O'Connor, Dental Dept. Capt. E.B. Sparkes, Quartermaster – Capt. J. Wallace, Chaplains – Major F.C. Piper, Major J.T. Thompson.[26]

The hospital treated mainly Australians, New Zealanders, and other imperial troops from the Gallipoli fiasco. However, soldiers stationed nearby were also sent to the hospital from regimental sick parades, and emergency work often arose from cavalry injuries in the local Remount Depots, from tramway accidents in Cairo or occasionally from camel bites. Gradually the number of patients and beds increased until January 1916, when the hospital was upgraded to become No. 7 Canadian General Hospital, it could boast of 1,040 beds.

Life in the hospital had by that time settled into a regular routine. The Christmas festivities – carols, decorations, and a special dinner – had that particular poignancy which comes from a combination of service and hospital life. All members of No. 5 Stationary Hospital sent home a simple but specially designed Christmas card. Two unhappy events marked the stay in Cairo: W.T. Connell's recall to Queen's to continue his war work teaching pathology in Kingston and Lt Col. H.R. Duff's death on 8 February 1916. Colonel Duff was the hospital's second-in-command at the time. He had joined No. 5 in October 1915 while it was in Cairo and died suddenly four months later while on active duty. He was quietly laid to rest in the British cemetery. When asked why he had not remained at home in Canada, when he was offered the chairmanship of the Pensions Board, he replied: "Being an officer in the Permanent Army, I would rather die overseas than live in comfort at home when my country is at war."[27]

McCree's letter to the *Queen's University Journal* gave a sympathetic vignette of Lieutenant-Colonel Duff during his last few weeks of life.

Lieut.-Col. Duff is somewhat deaf. He was orderly officer for the day and the sick parade came up before him. Up stept Woodside, Meds '17. This was the first time he had paraded sick since joining. His arm was numb and painful. What's the matter with you my boy? Slept on my wrist, sir, and its very painful. What – stept on your wrist? How did you do that? Duty![28]

While the students were doing their practical work in the wards, operating room, laboratory, and pharmacy, they were also required to attend lectures twice a day, one at half past six in the morning, the other at half past seven in the evening. It was anticipated that examinations would be conducted in a number of subjects for which credit would be obtained back at Queen's. Unfortunately, because of the relocation of No. 7 General Hospital in April 1916, they were never held.

Word came from middle east headquarters to close the hospital and prepare for immediate embarkation. The hospital had, during its stay in Cairo, treated over 10,000 patients. On 10 April 1916, after all the remaining patients had been evacuated, the unit left Cairo for Alexandria. A few days later it sailed on H.M.S. *Delta*. The return journey through the Mediterranean and the Bay of Biscay was pleasant and calm. This time the troops were allowed ashore at Gibraltar for a day's sightseeing. Hopes were high that shore leave would be granted to everyone in England when the *Delta* steamed into Southampton Roads. Unfortunately, they only spent two hours in the harbour before setting off into a Channel gale for Le Havre, where the war really changed for them.

When the personnel of No. 7 Canadian General Hospital arrived at Le Havre, they had no inkling of their immediate duty or destination. After a spate of rumours and the inevitable train ride "shrouded in darkness and permeated with cold," they arrived at Le Treport, a small fishing village huddled at the base of high cliffs on top of which were modern suburbs. Three military hospitals has been established in the immediate area. The site allocated to the Queen's contingent had absolutely no buildings but possessed, in the words of the C.O. "extraordinary advantages of beauty and wholesomeness in surroundings, its landward boundaries being the limits of neighbouring hospitals and the pleasant stretches of a golf course."[29]

Lieutenant-Colonel Etherington and his men were ordered to establish a tent hospital of 1,040 beds. They set about converting the equipment of the original 400-bed Stationary hospital, they had brought from Egypt, into a full general hospital. Experience gained in England and Egypt proved invaluable. Within a week the hospital was laid out and the first tents put up. By early May, the hospital was completely set up and by 5 June, ready to accept patients. Large tents arranged end to end in threes' formed the wards. There were 27 wards with 36 beds each, row on row. The other ranks, orderlies, stretcher bearers, cooks, etc., lived in bell tents; the medical officers (M.O.s) and nursing sisters were assigned permanent huts on the periphery of the hospital. A larger hut, similar to one used in Cairo, was adapted for the X-ray Department, the operating theatre, and the laboratories. Every department was running smoothly in time to receive the wounded from the Battle of the Somme which soon erased any remaining illusion that war was not stupid and wicked. As Etherington wrote:

This was a period of pressure felt in all departments. Three or four convoys a day, composed of men fresh from the horrors and glories of battle would be brought to us ... Not infrequently the hardened mud of the trenches clung to their uniforms, and evidences of a fresh, uncared for wound were obvious.[30]

The hospital was presented with every kind of war wound. Fifty operations a day, sometimes seventy X-ray examinations and even more laboratory investigations were routine during July 1916. A separate hut housed postoperative surgical cases, where forty patients received special nursing and medical care. This was in effect an early intensive care unit, another example of military medicine setting an example for postwar civilian practice.

Gradually all aspects of the hospital's work became more efficient and more pleasant. Huts slowly replaced tents, particularly as living quarters for the noncommissioned officers (N.C.O.s) and men. The high morale throughout No. 7 Canadian General Hospital showed in the generally neat appearance of paths and roadways. After the professional aspects of the military hospital had been fully taken care of, permanent quarters provided an area for recreational and cultural activities. Social activities were instituted for both patients and staff. The hospital enthusiastically supported its baseball team, and was very proud of its twenty-four piece orchestra.

During the summer of 1916 the hospital treated over 5,000 patients.

Many were returned to duty, others, sent home or to England for convalescence. Just as the load was lightening in August 1916 the staff was brought up to establishment for a general hospital by the arrival of a further 12 medical officers, 36 nursing sisters and 43 men from Kingston.

With the fall came new rumours of a move, and soon the complete unit entrained for Etaples, a well-known hospital centre established by the British army early in the war. The British Tommy's "Eatables" was situated on the sluggish Canche estuary in Picardy, about fifteen miles south of Boulogne. It had a long military association. Here Julius Caesar assembled his legions to invade England. Napoleon and Hitler assembled troops in the same area for the same reason but without the same success. The town of Etaples was a flourishing trading port during the Middle Ages and was consequently looted alternately by the French and the English – the last time just after the Battle of Crecy.[31]

The hospital's new location was a great contrast to its previous one at Le Treport. The hospital was situated on the low-lying beach area within half a mile of the high water mark. The facilities had initially been organized before the United States entered the war by the famous Chicago surgeon, John B. Murphy. When the United States went to war, the British took them over as a general hospital. When the Queen's contingent arrived, they found a substantial institution of thirty-five wooden huts, each accommodating thirty beds, fully equipped and functioning operating rooms, an X-ray department, and a corrugated iron administration building with office space, pharmacy rooms, and pathological laboratory. The hospital had 500 patients on its roster when No. 7 took over on 15 November 1916. The same evening a further 200 wounded and sick arrived, and Colonel Etherington and his unit were back in business from that day until hostilities ceased two years later.

The first winter in France was worse then they had expected. Fortunately by spring everyone was acclimatized, although many had suffered transient illnesses. The whole unit was upset, however, when Nursing Sister Etta Sparks, one of the original nurses who joined No. 5 Stationary Hospital when it was first mobilized two years earlier, died after being evacuated back to England with an unspecified illness.

During 1917 the hospital more than doubled its complement of beds to 2,290 and became the largest Canadian general hospital to be established during the war. Extra tents had to be erected, but they were only used for light surgical cases. The staff was increased to forty medical officers, mostly Queen's men, and a comparable number of nursing sisters.

From the hospital's earliest days in Cairo, periodic changes in personnel occurred. As most of the original N.C.O.s and men were Queen's University graduates or undergraduates, they were pressured to take further medical training and then accept commissions as medical officers. As soon as No. 5 Stationary arrived in England, Sgt Maj. C.A. Briscoe, Sgts C.A. Kidd, P.M. McLachlan, R.W. McQuay, and Cpl C.W. Coulter, who were also M.D.s, were transferred to the British Army and commissioned in the R.A.M.C. At the same time, Sgt F.X. O'Connor and Cpl H.W. Whytock were promoted to captains in the Canadian Army Medical Corps and remained in the Canadian army. O'Connor, one of Queen's stalwarts, stayed faithful to No. 5 Stationary and subsequently No. 7 General.

In his 1917 published report on No. 7 Canadian General Hospital, Colonel Etherington listed other personnel changes which affected the medical faculty:

For almost a year no further changes were made. Then in March, 1916, just before the close of our Egyptian service, an order from London to the effect that all Medical Students of final year standing should return to Canada to complete their studies, recalled home the following men: Sergeant-Major E.C.A. Crawford, S. – Sergeants L.D. Stevenson and A.B. Whytock, Sergeants H. Barnes, D.R. Fletcher, K.M. Shorney and R.J. Tucker, Corporal J.B. Willoughby, Privates G.F. Denyes, G.F. McLaughlan, F.H. O'Reilly, J.R. Patterson, G.S. Purvis and G.L. Sills. These men attended the Summer Session at Queen's University. Twelve of them received Commissions in November 1916, and ten are again serving Overseas.

In March, 1917, the order regarding the return of Medical Students was amended to include those men who had completed the third year of the five-year Course. Thirty of the men of the unit came under this category and left for Canada to resume their studies. Their names are as follows: Sergeants L.H. Appleby, G.L. Bell, F.H. Barry, W.D.S. Cross, C.S. Dunning, G.F. Goodfellow, J.E. Hammett, J. Kearney, A.J. McIntyre, R.M. Parker, H.A. Pelton, Corporals G.M. Campbell, H.W. Leahy, D.H. Nicol and D. Nicholson, Privates L.S. Fallis, G.F. Guest, A.B. Haffner, J.C. McGregor, F.E. Price, C. Reist, G.J. Rutledge, R.C. Shaver, E.C. Topliffe, H.A. Woodside, G. Baggs, R.W. Kirkby, P.R. Urie, C.F. Abbott and K.R. Maitland.[32]

Both the men and women who stayed with the contingent and those who returned to Queen's were proud of the accolade bestowed on the hospital by senior professional soldiers. When it left Egypt, Surgeon-

General R.W. Ford, D.S.O., Director of Medical Services (D.M.S.) Egypt, wrote to Lt Col. J.C. Connell, dean of medicine:

... The hospital has been excellently organized ... The administration too is in the hands of a most capable Commanding Officer (Lieut.-Col. Etherington) to whom it owes very largely the reputation it has justly earned. Indeed I consider this Unit a credit to Queen's University and to Canada. I shall feel honored if these few words of appreciation from me find a place in the records of the University, so that future generations of students may see what has been achieved in the past by their predecessors, and this should stimulate them to similar efforts shall the 'call' to duty sound again.[33]

Though he was not directly associated with it, Brigadier General Ross, C.B., C.M.G., D.M.S. (France) clearly believed that the university should continue its association with No. 7 Canadian General Hospital during the postwar period. This was not to be. At home, although interest was maintained in Queen's and Kingston's own military hospital, naturally enthusiasm seemed to wane as time passed. Although, as Kathryn Bindon has written, "the Queen's Hospital was in all respects a success,"[34] many other demands assumed precedence on the concern and pockets of Kingstonians and Queen's alumni.

A smaller and less publicized effort by Queen's medical faculty and one not recognized by the major Canadian war histories was the Depot Field Ambulance No. 3, founded in May 1916. During that summer the depot was based at Barriefield camp, but with the onset of winter it moved into the old Kingston Collegiate building on Clergy Street. Locally, of course, it was known as Queen's Field Ambulance. The officers on staff, with the exception of the quartermaster (Q.M.), were all medical faculty graduates: Capt. R.F. Filson was the C.O., Capt. J.F. Houston, adjutant, Capt. P.J. McIlroy, paymaster. The other officers were Capts. W.H. Jacks, R.C. MacGregor, O.E. Kennedy and Morrison (Q.M.). Also attached to the ambulance were Capts. D. Byers, W.A. Jones, J.H. Moxley, D.A. Coon, and M.J. Moler, most of whom were also Queen's men.[35]

Early in 1917, Queen's No. 3 Field Ambulance went overseas as a unit – No. 15 Field Ambulance with the 5th Division of Canadians in France. Major Filson was in command, but at the front two more senior Queen's men with longer service, Lieutenant-Colonel Stone and Major Graham, were nominated by the dean and appointed by the director of medical services in France (our Col A.E. Ross, formerly professor of pharmacology), to assume command.

The men who stayed in Kingston remained as the depot ambulance to train reinforcements for other units. The C.O. was James Kenneth Mundell who, before taking up medicine and going overseas with the No. 1 Field Ambulance in 1914, had been a cadet at the Royal Military College. He graduated in medicine during December 1916, reenlisted for active service, but continued to serve in Kingston at the request of the faculty in order to train the continually needed orderlies for hospitals at home and in France.[36] The orderlies and others who performed the routine barrack work in local military hospitals – Queen Street, Ongwanada, and Mowat Memorial Hospitals – were drawn from different trades, businesses and professions in the city, including even four "theologues" from the university.

QUEEN'S MILITARY CONVALESCENT HOSPITAL

Students and staff of the medical faculty individually volunteered to serve king and country overseas from the earliest days of the war. However, not until the spring of 1917 was the full horror of battle casualties brought home to Kingston. On 29 November 1916 the Finance and Estate Committee of the board of trustees met with representatives of the Board of Trade and Colonel Gardiner, chief medical officer of the 3rd Military District (Kingston). Mr Nickle, M.P. moved and was seconded by the Reverend Dr Macgillivray "that being confident of the co-operation and sympathy of the arts faculty and students, this committee is of the opinion that every effort should be made to meet the urgent requirements of the Hospital Commission and is prepared to place the New Arts Building and Grant Hall at the disposal of the Government upon terms and conditions to be arranged, and desire a conference with representatives of the arts faculty to perfect other accommodation for classes." *Carried.*[37]

Within two days, the senior professors of the arts faculty committed Queen's to war on the home front. Grant Hall and Kingston Hall were given over to the Military Hospital Commission. Carruthers Hall provided space for teaching English, philosophy, Latin, French, and public speaking. Greek was to be taught in Fleming Hall, with politics and mathematics in Ontario Hall in the space previously used as a military kitchen for the 72nd Battery and the 5th Company of Engineers. They immediately made special insurance arrangements to allow alterations to the buildings to be started at once. By the end of December 1916 a lease, at $4,000 a year, had been signed by the chairman of Queen's board and sent to Ottawa. Senator Lougheed, chairman of the Hospital Commission, expressed the commission's warm appreciation for Queen's generosity.[38]

Grant Hall, the student memorial to the man who personified the Queen's spirit during his lifetime, is the university's Convocation Hall. The New Arts Building or Kingston Hall had been erected a short time earlier following city council's munificent gift of $50,000 in 1900. Both buildings, which are joined by a stairway, were altered during the early months of 1917 to receive convalescent veterans. Charlotte Whitton, editor of *Queen's University Journal*, wrote: "The transformation in Grant Hall is startling. The gallery has disappeared – not removed, but swallowed up; railing and all, by a second floor."[39] Widening the gallery allowed two rows of beds to be installed along either side. Sturdy beams supported the gallery and all columns and walls were protected by beaverboard; Grant Hall's stained glass windows were replaced by clear glass. With these alterations, 400 patients could be accommodated on the two adequately lighted and well-ventilated floors. The New Arts Building needed little alteration to afford office accommodations for the C.O. and M.O.s, Interns used the club room, while the office of John Watson, professor of philosophy, became the admission and discharge room. Every member of the graduating class of medical students had to spend two periods, each of at least a month's duration, on duty as hospital interns in these wards and offices. A large wooden hut was quickly erected and attached to the east end of Kingston Hall to be used as a kitchen and eating hall for both patients and staff.

The C.O. of the Queen's Military Hospital was Lt Col. W.T. Connell, professor of pathology, who had been recalled late in 1915 from active service in Egypt. He integrated this appointment with his continuing responsibility for the 3rd Military District Laboratories and his professorship of pathology. Connell was assisted in running the hospital by two of No. 7 Canadian General's original medical officers, Maj. J.P. Quigley and Capt. F.X. O'Connor, who had returned from France and joined the teaching staff of the medical faculty. By the time it was closed, the hospital had cared for almost 5,000 patients.[40]

Towards the end of 1917, a Vocational Training Department for returned soldiers was established in connection with Queen's Military Hospital in the hope that Kingston would become a major centre for rehabilitation of the wounded. Unfortunately, the Department of Soldiers Civil Reestablishment saw fit to support established centres elsewhere. For a short while, however, Major Quigley's Electrotherapeutic Department in the Queen's Hospital was considered second to none in its equipment and results.[41]

In all, over 1500 Queen's staff, graduates and students served in all branches of the fighting forces. Some gave their lives, some returned with wounds, some with decorations for gallantry, but most with just campaign medals and memories.

According to Dean Connell, Etherington, promoted to colonel near the end of the war, was the only Canadian officer to command a unit from the day he recruited it until it disbanded six months after the Armistice. On 31 May 1919, No. 7 Canadian General Hospital was the last Canadian hospital to leave France.[42] After the war, Etherington continued his civilian practice as a surgeon. He reentered the mainstream of Queen's academic life in the twenties and eventually succeeded Dr J.C. Connell as dean.

CHAPTER ELEVEN

Queen's Medicine on the "Home Front"

While Drs Ross and Etherington and their faculty colleagues and students were serving in Canada or overseas during the war, the medical school was having its own less dramatic problems on the home front. The shortage of senior staff and the exigencies of war, as well as political circumstances beyond the control of faculty created other difficulties for the faculty.

INTERNAL PROBLEMS

Dean Connell's annual report to the board of trustees in April 1913 was a statement of quiet confidence in the faculty's future. Over the twenty-one years since its reestablishment in the University, the faculty had increased from ten professors, one lecturer, and one demonstrator to fourteen professors, four associate professors, five assistant professors, six lecturers, and eight clinical assistants or demonstrators. It had graduated about 750 doctors. The dean was particularly proud of Dr W.T. Connell's research – his public health laboratory had helped the local cheese producers when their manufacturing process had become bacteriologically contaminated, and ensured the continuation of the cheese industry in eastern Ontario.[1] The medical library was growing. It was well-funded from student fees and contained all the recent medical books and periodicals. A new acquisition policy permitted the addition of 200 books that year and a further 238 in the following year. During 1913 the university received one of its treasures. On the advice of Sir William Osler, Mr C. Bermingham gave the university a copy of Vesalius's *De Fabrica Humani Corporis*,[2] the famous textbook and atlas of anatomy which ushered in the modern era of medicine when it was first published in 1543.

But the war introduced problems to this relatively calm atmosphere. Staffing became the dean's major difficulty on the home front during World War I. Shortly after the beginning of the war, a freeze was placed on new appointments. Luckily, by that time, Dr A.H. Lothrop of Columbia had been appointed to teach chemistry in the medical faculty;[3] in 1916 he was promoted to professor of biological and medical chemistry and stayed with the faculty until after the war, when he moved on to Oberlin. In 1914 Dr Garrett was forced to give up both teaching and consulting practice because of ill health; Drs Williamson and Mylks took over his responsibilities in obstetrics and gynaecology. Professor A.E. Ross was replaced as senior pharmacology teacher by the Douglas Lecturer in Pharmacology, first Dr Kennedy, then Dr S.M. Asseltine.[4]

During 1916, as a wartime measure, faculty decided to keep the school open continuously until the end of hostilities. A new session began on 1 May 1916 and full instruction continued until 30 November, with the next session beginning the following day, 1 December in the anticipation that fifty extra students would graduate every year and be able to apply for military commissions. The standard of tuition was maintained by the appointment of Mr T.L. Patterson as assistant professor of physiology, Mr J.D. Halverson as lecturer in biological chemistry, Dr E.C.D. MacCallum as assistant professor in medicine, and Drs R.J. Gardiner, H.E. Day, H.A. Boyce, Robert Hanley and H.E. Bell as clinical assistants. Dr S.J. Keyes was appointed lecturer in anaesthetics in addition to assisting Dr Sparkes in teaching anatomy, while Dr W.T. Connell on his return from Egypt resumed control of the department of pathology and bacteriology, from Dr Gibson, who had run it very competently in Connell's absence.[5] Very few other changes occurred in the staff of the medical school until after the war, when a massive transfusion of new staff took place at both senior and junior levels.

Two short vacations, one in August, the other at Christmas, interrupted the continuous classes. The majority of those taking part in the war sessions were servicemen, either from the Queen's hospital overseas or from other units, who had returned to complete their medical education.

Little change was made in the five-session curriculum apart from a tightening up of the anatomy course. After Dr Kidd, professor of anatomy, left with the 5th Stationary Hospital, the teaching was in the hands of junior staff men and became disorganized. Dr D.C. Matheson was a recent graduate who at the same time that he was teaching anatomy, was also a part-time clinical fellow in anaesthetics at the Kingston General Hospital. In addition, towards the end of the war, he acted as medical superintendent of the entire hospital.[6] This state of affairs was not satisfactory, and, in September 1916, Dr W.T. Connell was appointed to chair a committee to investigate the teaching of anatomy at Queen's. The committee laid down a tight set of guidelines for the course, which was still to be taught in the first and second years. Seven systems were to be taught regionally: bones, joints, muscles, blood vessels, lymph drainage, nerves, and viscera. The senior students were to continue studying applied anatomy from Dr Mundell's *Clinical Aspects of Anatomy*.[7]

Radiology was the only other course reassessed during the war. Since it had come of age and proved its importance on the battlefield, the discipline had to be integrated into the curriculum as a separate academic medical course. X-radiation was no longer an option or a confirmatory adjunct to practice, but an essential part of the diagnostic armamentarium. Dr Third, chairman of the Committee on X-ray and Electro-Therapy, recommended to faculty board on 5 October 1917 that the course be given to fifth-year medical students by Queen's physics department. The committee also hoped that the students would have access to the diagnostic and therapeutic apparatus in local hospitals. The proposed course was divided into three parts: X-rays and high frequency apparatus, radioactivity and the different types of radiation including ultra-violet light. The faculty board agreed that the course be included in the timetable at once.[8]

Many students went off to war after graduating as M.D.s. Some volunteered for noncommissioned or nonmedical service before graduation. Early in the war, the senate very sensibly suggested that students should complete their medical studies before they enlisted and should not be encouraged to rush off to join the combatant ranks. When the board of trustees heard this, it construed senate's suggestion as unpatriotic and passed a motion to that effect.[9] Nine days later the senate reconsidered its position and adopted the resolution, a compromise: "that as a general rule the training of Medical students shall be for medical service."[10] As the war developed, many students who had enlisted in nonmedical units were returned to Queen's for further training for medical service. This procedure followed the government's early objections, which were initially on the grounds of the general public policy, that medical students at the front should not receive preferential treatment by being allowed to return home to complete their education while their colleagues remained in the trenches.

In 1917, faculty was affected by the conscription crisis, when the Military Service Act came into effect. The Department of Militia and Defence announced that all medical students in good standing on 1 November were permitted to continue their studies, subject to joining the reserves and undergoing Officer Training Corps (O.T.C.) training; in addition, every new graduate had to enlist in the C.A.M.C. or R.A.M.C. Unfortunately, this exemption from military service was summarily withdrawn from eight students enrolled in the first year of medicine at Queen's. Even though the local military authorities had granted them leave from January to June in order to complete their year's study, army headquarters cancelled it, and they were unceremoniously packed off for the last few months of the war. Faculty nevertheless, as was usual, granted them academic standing for the year.[11]

In the very last month of the war, the medical faculty, like the rest of the world, was faced with the devastating effects of the Spanish influenza. This pandemic killed 22 million people around the world – 50,000 in Canada and 145 in Kingston. Dr A.R.B. Williamson, faculty's secretary, who was also Kingston's medical health officer, directed the battle on what was truly a home front. His chief advice to the citizens was to keep their mouths shut, be cheerful, and avoid public places.[12] Dr Guilford Reed, assistant professor of bacteriology, tried to isolate the causal organism by attempting to cultivate it in a culture of pigeon's blood. When he felt he had prepared an effective vaccine, he innoculated 200 of the medical staff and soldiers in Grant Hall Hospital. The therapeutic benefit was perhaps more psychological than medical, although everyone was content with this particular application of science to medicine.[13] For the first and only time, Queen's suspended classes for a medical reason and on Wednesday, 16 October 1918, the following notice appeared around the university:

On account of the prevalence of Spanish Influenza, all classes will close at 12 o'clock today (Wednesday) until further notice.

R. Bruce Taylor, Principal

Although many students immediately left town for their homes, the medical students were sent across the province to assist in local hospitals, while many women students stayed in Kingston to serve as volunteer nurses. Fortunately, within two weeks the epidemic was over and classes were resumed. During the next week the armistice was signed and the *Ottawa Citizen* expressed its appreciation for the services of "ten medical men from Queen's University." The editorial indicated that a letter of thanks was being sent to the dean of medicine from the mayor of Ottawa for the students' help during the epidemic.[15]

The faculty's major social convulsion was unrelated to the war, and arose from outside pressures that caused faculty to act in an understandable but reprehensible manner: it stopped admitting black students and asked those already in the school to withdraw from Queen's and finish their medical education elsewhere.

The university had for many years sent out into the professions and business a steady stream of black students. Possibly because former faculty member, Dr Neish, spread the word on behalf of the Royal and Queen's after his emigration to Jamaica, a number of students – both white and black – from the Caribbean appear in the yearly register of the medical faculty. After graduation, these young doctors either returned to the British West Indies or settled down to practise in Canada or the United States. Before the Great War, coloured students were tolerated, if not fully accepted, by the Kingston citizenry. Unfortunately towards the end of the war an antiblack sentiment arose and, perhaps fuelled by soldiers returning from the front, spread rapidly through the city.

Throughout 1917, the antagonism of the Kingston General Hospital's patients against black medical students grew to such proportions that the faculty was forced to take notice of it. At the same time, the continuous clinical courses meant that there were not even enough patients for all the white students, including the extra students in the wartime sessions. It was a classic case in which vicious expediency could claim academic necessity.

The forms of propriety had to be maintained – the dean was authorized to prepare a paper for the university senate on "certain difficulties which have arisen in connection with the instruction of negro students."[16] The memorandum prepared for senate by Dr Connell suggested that many people, particularly convalescing soldiers in Queen's Grant Hall Military Hospital (by implication non-Kingstonians) absolutely refused to allow blacks to attend them. The dean also pointed out in his paper to the senate that neither Toronto's medical faculty nor McGill were going to continue the clinical instruction of coloured students, even though their respective cities had much larger negro populations than Kingston. Dalhousie, on the other hand, was the ideal university for the medical education of negroes, in Connell's opinion, because Halifax had a large black population. At its January 1918 meeting the senate accepted the dean of medicine's position paper without dissent and told the faculty "to deal with the whole question along the lines suggested in his memorandum."[17] No recommendations had been made to the contrary, so the medical faculty managed to relocate its fifteen black students in other medical schools. The problem was forgotten until well after World War II, when black students were readmitted. In its 5

February 1918 issue, *Queen's University Journal* gave a fair, but brief, resumé of the situation and reprimanded *The Toronto Varsity* for not looking to the beam in its own medical faculty's eye while assiduously poking around for the mote in that of Queen's medical school.

EXTERNALLY GENERATED PROBLEMS

In addition to the strictly local convulsions arising from racial prejudice during 1917/18, Queen's medical faculty was faced, during the war years, with a recurrence of prejudice emanating from the provincial capital and its university.

As early as 1910, the governors of the University of Toronto made representations to the Ontario legislature for an amendment to the Provincial Medical Act. Toronto's medical faculty requested that students who had passed its examinations should be exempted from examination by the Ontario Medical Council. This meant that, in effect, a degree in medicine from Toronto University would carry with it the right to practise medicine throughout the province without further constraint. Following submissions from Queen's, the premier, Sir James Whitney, had the amendment withdrawn.[18]

During the years that followed, the legislature received applications for incorporation from several healthcare groups, the osteopaths, chiropractors, drugless physicians, and manotherapists. To place these requests in perspective, the legislative assembly appointed a Royal Commission in September 1915 to report specifically on licensing procedures, and to study medical education and practice across the province.

The commissioner, Mr Justice Frank E. Hodgins of the Ontario Supreme Court, heard a number of submissions in Toronto. He then visited Hamilton and London. On Monday and Tuesday, 10 and 11 April 1916, he was in Kingston.[19]

On the first morning, he was escorted through the teaching facilities available to Queen's medical faculty: the Old Medical Building, the New Medical Laboratories Building, the chemical laboratory in Gordon Hall (the newest in Canada for teaching and research), and the physics laboratory. In the afternoon the commissioner was shown the faculty's main clinical facilities: the Kingston General Hospital and the Hotel Dieu Hospital. Also presented as sources of patients for clinical teaching were Rockwood Hospital for the Insane and the Mowat Memorial (T.B.) Hospital, along with orphanages and military hospitals.[20]

On Monday evening and Tuesday morning, Mr Justice Hodgins held open meetings for the presentation of briefs. The principal, the dean, Drs W.T. Connell and Knight appeared on behalf of the university. Dr Third spoke for the Kingston Medical and Surgical Society, while Dr William Gibson spoke on behalf of Regiopolis College Corporation.[21]

Almost two years passed before the commissioner laid his findings before the assembly in January 1918. Particularly of interest to Queen's was the part of the report related to Toronto medical faculty's repeated claim for privileged licensing status for its diploma in medicine. The commissioner recommended "the continuance of the present system of examinations which avoids much of the duplication yet maintains the quality of independence and stimulation so necessary to the maintenance of a proper standard."[22] This recommendation was much to the liking of Queen's medical faculty.

The only other recommendation of immediate concern to the faculty and the Kingston General Hospital was the suggestion that an institution or department of physical therapy be established to provide various forms of manipulative care. A considerable amount of this type of work was already being done at Queen's Military Hospital in Grant Hall and the faculty agreed it should be extended.[23]

Unfortunately, the Royal Commission's report did not end Queen's troubles. In 1916, at the same time that the Royal Commission was conducting its investigation, the desire for excellence (or American students) prompted McGill and the University of Toronto to change their standards for admission to their medical courses. Representatives from the universities of Toronto and McGill medical faculties met together privately and, without consultation with other university medical schools in Canada, decided to introduce into their universities a premedical year of study before the normal five-year medical course.

Dean Connell and Queen's university senate were officially notified of this action when Dean C.K. Clarke of Toronto (formerly Queen's professor of psychiatry) sent the full text of a resolution which had already been accepted by his senate. It authorized the institution of a mandatory postmatriculation premedical year, which was to be devoted to physics, chemistry, biology, and one literary subject, before one could embark on an undergraduate medical career at Toronto.[24]

The Kingston medical faculty, on being apprised of this situation, immediately convened its own "Committee on the Six-year Course." On 3 November 1916, the dean and Drs Third, W.T. Connell, and Knight were appointed to consider and report on the Toronto *fait accompli*. Six weeks later, on 15 December 1916, the dean submitted to faculty, for onward transmission to senate, a memorandum which covers five and one-half foolscap pages in the faculty minute book.

The memorandum condemned the Toronto and McGill position outright, first in general and then on specific points. It rejected the reasons for the proposed change, namely, the alleged need for more time in the preliminary sciences which lead to medicine, and an attempt to gain an American Class A Plus standard, as academically unnecessary and, in the circumstances of 1916, more than slightly unpatriotic. The committee argued that the hasty introduction of a lengthened course at Queen's would serve no immediate, useful purpose for Canadian medicine – it would only place the poorer students, whom Queen's habitually attracted, in grave financial difficulties. Queen's senate accepted completely the rationalizations of its medical faculty, approved the memorandum, and ordered it to be circulated widely to other universities, provincial medical councils, and the public press.[25]

As might have been foreseen, the pressures of war put a stop to the planned changes at Toronto and McGill until October 1919. Even then, they were not to be applied to returning servicemen. Queen's medical faculty tried to call a conference of representatives from all medical schools to discuss the lengthened programme and other important matters; unfortunately Toronto and McGill did not approve and nothing materialized.[26] In September 1920, Queen's medical faculty, bowing to the inevitable, adopted the six-year course. At the same time, for full measure, it introduced a seven-year course in arts and medicine, the B.A. to be granted at the end of five years and the M.D., after seven.

ATTEMPTS TO TRANSFER
QUEEN'S MEDICAL FACULTY TO
OTTAWA

Between the signing of the armistice in November 1918 and the disestablishment of No. 7 Canadian General Hospital at the end of May 1919, the first job of the Queen's medical officers was the repatriation of the sick and wounded. When they were not caring for their patients or breaking camp, and while waiting impatiently for their own return to Civvy Street, the military doctors often discussed among themselves in the Officers' Mess the problem plaguing Queen's medical faculty since 1854: the appropriateness of persisting in the education of medical students in Kingston. The *Flexner Report* considered Queen's viability as a five-year medical school questionable simply because Kingston was not a large metropolitan centre. The city, and hence Queen's medical school, lacked what is today called an adequate "patient base." In other words, not enough of the sick people in Kingston's hospitals would allow themselves to be used for clinical teaching.

Kingston's shortcoming as a medical centre became particularly evident to the numerous Queen's military graduates who had seen for themselves the comprehensive teaching facilities in Britain and on the continent. It seemed that Kingston could not, in the foreseeable future, support a modern medical school of the stature of the Toronto and Montreal schools, and that although Queen's could conduct a preclinical medical school, it might be more appropriate to move its clinical teaching to a centre with large municipal hospitals. Indeed, such a place was relatively close at hand.

Ottawa's suitability as a site for a Canadian national university and major medical centre had been discussed before. A November 1899 editorial in the *Queen's University Journal* was headed "Medical College – Time For A Change?" After considering the run-down condition of the Medical Building and the advisability of the whole university changing its location to a larger and wealthier city than Kingston, the article implied that the students and their seniors were thinking along the same lines:

And if it be true, as they say, that some of the wealthy and generous men of Ottawa are willing to aid munificently the establishment of a University in that city, it would perhaps be of mutual benefit to combine our experience with their capital – forming a National University including all the various branches of education, Medicine, Science, Arts and Divinity.[27]

For the next twenty years little was heard of relocating Queen's or its medical school. Internally, the medical professoriate was concerned with putting its house in order. The old guard was passing away, the new, busy with curricular changes, new buildings and responding, as we have seen, to constitutional imperatives and to Flexner's criticisms. Externally, the Great War thrust all academic problems into the shade.

Faculty members who had remained in Kingston during the war or who had returned to teach or care for the sick in the local military hospitals were well aware of the need to upgrade the teaching and clinical facilities in Kingston and worked to this end rather than accept the easy solution to the problem and relocate to Ottawa. The primary task, in the view of the dean and others, was to improve the facilities available at the Kingston General Hospital.

In the 1917 annual report of the medical faculty to the university board of trustees, Dr Connell reported that during the year ending 30 September 1916 the Kingston General Hospital had cared for 4,300 indoor patients in the same plant and facilities which had housed only 1,300 patients during 1903, the year the dean had taken office. He continued:

During this period there has been a complete reorganization of the clinical teaching but it is carried on under great disadvantages. The wards are totally inadequate and, owing to structural defects in the old main building, it is impossible to renovate them to advantage. The accommodation for infectious diseases is also unsatisfactory and, indeed, the whole institution needs extension and reorganization. Chancellor Douglas has interested himself in this matter and has subscribed $100,000 towards a fund which will be used to make the hospital modern in every respect. A joint committee of the Faculty and Board of Governors of the Hospital, with Mr. J.M. Farrell representing the Board of Trustees of the University, has engaged a firm of architects who are specialists in hospital construction to study the problems and to submit general plans and estimates. The successful completion of this project will place the clinical facilities of the medical school on a very high level and will round out the reorganization of the school which began fifteen years ago.[28]

Dean Connell apparently believed that the generosity of the university's chancellor and others would solve the faculty's clinical teaching problems. Unfortunately he had not taken account of the returning soldiers' opinions or of Ottawa's "fifth column" – Dr Adam Shortt and Dr Elizabeth Smith Shortt – on the Queen's board of trustees.

Because an Ottawa mandarin's words are often more powerful than the actions of soldiers or the writings of professors, the effect of the political scientist, Dr Adam Shortt, on the possible development of Queen's medical faculty is interesting. With their move to Ottawa, Dr Adam Shortt, a trustee elected by Queen's graduates, and his wife, the former Dr Elizabeth Smith of Women's College fame, must have shifted their loyalty in matters of medical education from Kingston to the capital. At a meeting of the Queen's Board of Trustees on 25 April 1917, "Dr Shortt spoke on the possibilities of the University availing itself of the clinical facilities and possibilities for research available at Ottawa and moved, seconded by Mr Henderson, that the Principal name a Committee to consider the matter and report."[29] The motion carried, but circumstances beyond the board's control – the resignation of Principal Gordon and the appointment of the Reverend Dr Bruce Taylor to replace him – led to delay. The committee was not appointed until October 1919, and by the time it submitted its report to the board, the medical faculty had weathered the storm and for all practical purposes had found its own solution – before either the soldiers or the trustees could effect a relocation, the medical staff had initiated appropriate changes at the Kingston General Hospital.

The facilities for teaching undergraduate medical students at the Kingston General Hospital, described by Dr Connell in his 1917 annual report, were deplorable. The report forced the hospital governors and the citizens of Kingston to recognize the need to improve their hospital – an action which would not only provide better treatment and accommodation for the patients, but would also help attract first-class men to the teaching staff of the medical faculty. The visit of Drs N.P. Colwell and W.J. Means, an American Medical Association accreditation team, during May 1918, and the subsequent upgrading of the school from Category C to B gave special impetus to the planning process, as did the fact that Toronto and McGill were the only Category A schools in Canada, Queen's and the Kingston General Hospital pushed forward as quickly as possible with the planned improvements.[30]

The combined efforts of the hospital governors, the university trustees, and the municipal and provincial governments that followed Chancellor Douglas's generous gift led to physical improvements that enabled fourth- and fifth-year clinical teaching to be continued satisfactorily in Kingston. At the same time, a new agreement between Queen's University and Kingston General Hospital was ratified in October 1918 which in effect, recognized the Kingston General Hospital as a major teaching unit, autonomous but affiliated with Queen's University. It also gave an internal organization to the hospital that encouraged and reflected the best trends in modern medicine. All parties interested in the continued growth of medicine in Kingston were gratified when the board of the Faculty of Medicine approved the agreement on 30 October 1918. The complete agreement reproduced below, represents an important constitutional step in the future development of the medical faculty:

Agreement between Queen's University and the Kingston General Hospital Ratified October 1918.

1. Appointments to the Visiting Staff of the Hospital shall be made by the Board of Governors on the recommendation of the Board of Trustees of the University.

2. The appointments of Interns to the Hospital shall be made by the Board of Governors on the recommendation of the Medical Faculty.

3. The number and duration of service and the numbers and rank of the personnel of the Visiting Staff shall be determined by the Board of Governors upon the recommendation of the Medical Faculty.

4. All appointments to the Visiting Staff shall terminate on the 30th of June in each year.

5. There shall be no remuneration to members of the Visiting Staff.

6. All public ward patients shall be entered under the care of the Heads of the Services and at the discretion of such head shall be available for the clinical instruction of students.

7. Medical Students of Queen's University shall be permitted to visit the wards, clinics and operating rooms of the Hospital for the purpose of receiving instruction from members of the Visiting Staff, upon payment of such fees and under such regulations and restrictions as the Board of Governors shall by by-laws or resolutions from time to time appoint.

8. Subject to the regulation of the Board of Governors, members of the Medical profession of the city of Kingston who are not on the Staff of the Hospital, shall have the privilege of attending patients in private and semi-private rooms.

9. The Medical Board shall consist of the Heads of the various services.

10. The services shall be organized so as to include both indoor and outdoor patients, and the Heads of the Services shall be responsible for the treatment of all such patients.

11. The following shall be the services in the several departments of the Hospital: –

    (a) In Medicine, one service to be increased to two or more co-ordinate services as the necessity arises.
    (b) In Surgery, two co-ordinate services to be increased to three or more as the necessity arises.
    (c) In Obstetrics, one service.
    (d) In Gynaecology, one service.
    (e) In Eye, Ear, Nose and Throat, one service.
    (f) In Pathology, one service.
    (g) In Anaesthetics, one service.

12. Each service shall be under a head with such assistants as may be necessary.[31]

But even the agreement with the Kingston General Hospital and soundly-financed building plans did not put an end to the attempts to relocate the last two clinical years to Ottawa. With Colonel Etherington in France and Professor Adam Shortt and his wife in Ottawa advocating the move, Principal Bruce Taylor's loyalties were tested to the utmost.

In January 1919 Colonel Etherington wrote on behalf of his colleagues and himself to Principal Taylor, whom he had never met. He explained that he had "come definitely to the conclusion that it is not in the interests of the University, to continue to attempt to conduct a full medical course in the city of Kingston." Etherington stated that he was not alone in this opinion, but it was "almost unanimously held by the profession, and Queen's graduates outside the city." To substantiate his contention, Etherington sent Principal Taylor a copy of a resolution passed at a meeting of all Queen's medical graduates on staff of No. 7 Canadian General Hospital.[32]

Principal Taylor replied that he fully understood the colonel's worries, and agreed that the situation "must either be ended or mended." He pointed out, however, that the Ottawa scheme, which appealed to him at first, was not progressing with any speed, and wondered whether it might not be sensible to send the senior medical students to McGill. He continued, in the philosophical vein which has ever been Queen's refuge in adversity, "that, of course, is a suggestion that affects our pride, but if Oxford and Cambridge find similar methods convenient, I do not see that Queen's should be beyond considering it."[33]

Colonel Etherington seems to have been encouraged initially in his seccessionist ideas by Dr W.T. Connell, who in March felt that clinical teaching had no future in Kingston "in our generation."[34] But in September, after Colonel Etherington's return from France, Dr W.T. Connell assumed a more statesmanlike position, urging the principal to set up a committee to study the conflicting claims of Ottawa, with a new Civic Hospital about to be built, and Kingston, with its extended and refurbished Kingston General Hospital.[35]

The Faculty of Medicine, supporting Dr W.T. Connell, asked the board of trustees to organize, as soon as possible, "a Special Committee on the Future of Medical Education in the University."[36] At its October 1919 meeting, the board established the committee under the chairmanship of the new university chancellor, Mr E.W. Beatty, K.C., president of the Canadian Pacific Railway (Chancellor Douglas had died not long before). The members of the committee were: Dr Wm. Rankin of Brooklyn, New York, George Henderson, K.C., Ottawa, Mr W.F. Nickle, K.C., M.P., Kingston, and the principal. In two months. they effectively established and saved the future of the medical school for Queen's.

The principal and Mr Henderson interviewed the mayor and controllers of the city of Ottawa, and afterwards the board of governors of the Civic Hospital. They drew up a tentative set of recommendations concerning the appointment of teaching staff and the clinical facilities which would be provided by the hospital as a basis of agreement between the hospital and Queen's University.[37] The medical faculty was interviewed and Dr M.P. Colwell, secretary of the American Medical Association, was asked whether he could come to Kingston and give his expert opinion on the matter. Unfortunately, he was too busy and could not come.

In Kingston, the full committee met first with the medical faculty, then with the Board of Trade and other interested groups of citizens. Among the medical men, perhaps the two most influential at the time were the dean, Dr J.C. Connell and Dr Edward Ryan, who had been the professor of anatomy, a mayor of Kingston, and was then the incumbent superintendent of Rockwood Asylum. Connell, who had never wavered in his loyalty to Queen's and Kingston, sent a printed "Open Letter to the Board of Trustees of Queen's University."[38] It was a twelve-page, closely argued position paper on the correctness of retaining the medical school undivided in Kingston, close to its parent campus. He considered the arguments of those who wished to relocate the school one by one, and demolished them in favour of the Kingston position. His final appeal to the board was a suggestion that if Kingston was not an appropriate location for a medical school then neither was Ottawa. Dr Ryan's memorandum to the board, although just as cogent, was more emotional. Both papers were filled with loyalty and love of Queen's and Kingston, where their authors had spent the whole of their working lives.

The Kingston community also understood the consequences for the university and city should the clinical and then the basic science departments move to Ottawa. The citizens expressed their disapproval of the move at a number of public meetings and in the newspapers. A letter submitted to the university's Committee on Medical Education by the Kingston Board of Trade included this extract from a resolution passed by the members:

That it is the sense of this meeting of the members of the Board of Trade and citizens of Kingston that every effort should be made to retain Queen's medical college in Kingston for the full medical term, and that the citizens here present pledge themselves to render all possible assistance to assure this desired end, and urge upon City Council the necessity of extending such financial assistance as may be necessary to accomplish this purpose.[39]

By 3 February 1920, the evidence had all been collected. A meeting was held in Summerhill, and after a lengthy discussion the board of trustees' committee unanimously agreed on the following points:

(1) The University will do its utmost to re-organize the Medical School in Kingston and to continue its work in the city.

(2) Development of the organization with a full-time Dean and an adequate number of full-time Professors on the clinical as well as on the purely scientific side.

(3) The largest possible measure of University control in the Kingston General Hospital consistent with the public necessities of the community and the non-exclusion of the private practitioner from the private wards.

(4) Development of the Hospital Pathological Department with adequate investigation of each case on entrance to hospital together with a complete follow-through record, the present system of records to be completely overhauled and extended.

(5) A first-class hospital Superintendent who shall be responsible for the medical administration of the hospital under the supervision of the University.

(6) *The Estimated Expenditure*:
   (a) For re-building of the hospital ....$750,000.
   (b) Enlargement of the Staff by the addition of full-time clinical professors, additional expenditure $20,000 to 30,000 per annum.
   (c) Pathological Department, additional expenditure $10,000 per annum.

(7) *Money in Sight or in Estimation:*

   (1) *For re-building of the Hospital*

   (a) The Douglas Fund ....$100,000.
   (b) The Richardson Bequest (for Tuberculosis) ....100,000.
   (c) Corporation of the City of Kingston ....150,000.
   (d) Private Subscriptions ....100,000.
   (e) Ontario Government 100,000
         (a year, for three years)
   (f) Capital grants from adjoining municipalities; grants to be invited on condition that the Hospital treat free, for a period of years to be determined, the needy sick of these municipalities.

   (2) *For re-organization of the Medical School*:

   (a) Contribution from the general University Funds.
   (b) Contribution to be requested from the Rockefeller Foundation.[40]

The acceptance of these recommendations by Queen's University's board of trustees, the board of governors of the Kingston General Hospital, and the medical faculty expressed their traditional loyalty to the citizens of Kingston. Implementation of them allowed a radical reorganization of the medical school which has survived the vicissitudes of depressions, wars, and technological advances to reach for the higher ideals of exemplary patient care, devoted teaching, and scholarly research.

Postscript

After World War I, the return of the medical veterans and the retirement of senior faculty members initiated a radical reorganization of the Faculty of Medicine which gave validity to Queen's decision to continue teaching medicine in Kingston. The agreement between the Kingston General Hospital and the University, the foundation of the new Queen's Medical School, has stood the test of time. The physicians who succeeded Drs Knight, Third, Garrett, Mundell, and Connell have lived through the tempestuous years of depression, war, and technological advance. Drs Austin, Miller, and Melvin, the first successors, were brought over to Queen's at the end of the war to raise standards and reorganize the departments of surgery, pathology, and physiology. Dr W.T. Connell and G.B. Reed took over medicine and bacteriology respectively. These men and their juniors broadened the teaching and research within the faculty, enabling it to continue to send out into the community physicians imbued with the ideal that first class humanistic medicine depends on excellence in scientific research.

The further history of Queen's medical faculty will inevitably be the lives and work of teachers and students during the deanships of Drs Connell, Etherington, Melvin, Ettinger, Botterell, Waugh, Boag, and D.L. Wilson. Each with their colleagues has fully sustained Principal Grant's perceptive observation that Queen's University was fortunate to live in a "peculiarly happy relationship" with a loyal medical school and devoted alumni who continue to offer to the people of Kingston and elsewhere the same concerned patient care as did Dr James Sampson and his colleagues at the time of the medical school's foundation.

Notes

DBW   *Daily British Whig*
FMAR   Faculty of Medicine Annual Report
KMQ   *Kingston Medical Quarterly* which became *Queen's Medical Quarterly* in 1903
MBT   Minutes of the Board of Trustees of Queen's University
MCRCPSK   Minutes of the Corporation of the Royal College of Physicians and Surgeons, Kingston
MFM   Minutes of the Faculty of Medicine
MFRCPSK   Minutes of the Faculty Board of the Royal College of Physicians and Surgeons, Kingston
MUC   Minutes of the University Council
PAC   Public Archives Canada
QCJ   *Queen's College Journal* which became *Queen's University Journal* in 1893
QMQ   *Queen's Medical Quarterly*
QR   *Queen's Review*
QUA   Queen's University Archives
QUJ   *Queen's University Journal*
UWSC   University of Waterloo Special Collections
WMC   Women's Medical College

ACKNOWLEDGMENTS

1 A.A. Travill, *Queen's University at Kingston Faculty of Medicine, 1854–1979 One Hundred and Twenty-Five Years Dedicated to Education and Service* (Kingston: Queen's University Medical Faculty 1979), 48.

CHAPTER ONE

1 Edwin B. Horsey, "Care of the Sick and Hospitalization at Kingston,

Ontario, 1773-1938," (Queen's University, Special Collections, Douglas Library, 1939), 3.

2 John W. Spurr, "Kingston Garrison, 1815-1870," *Historic Kingston* 26 (1978): 14-34.

3 Margaret Angus, *Kingston General Hospital: A Social and Institutional History* (Montreal: McGill-Queen's University Press 1973), 7ff.

4 Walter Henry, *Surgeon Henry's Trifles*, ed. Pat Hayward (London: Chatto and Windus 1970), 229-230.

5 Col Alfred Peterkin and William Johnston, *Commissioned Officers in the Medical Services of the Britsh Army 1660-1960*, Vol. I (London: The Wellcome Historical Library 1968), 218.

6 *Dictionary of Canadian Biography*, s.v. "Sampson, James." This entry is the definitive biography of Dr Sampson to date. Dr Angus's "Doctor James Sampson: A Brief Biography," *Historic Kingston* 31 (1983): 3-17 provides interesting sidelights on Dr Sampson's life.

7 William Canniff, *The Medical Profession in Upper Canada, 1738-1850* (Toronto: William Briggs 1894, reprinted Toronto: Clarke, Irwin for the Hannah Institute for the History of Medicine 1981), 613.

8 Kevin F. Quinn, "Kingston's Mayors 1838-1850. Sketches of a Local Elite," *Historic Kingston* 26 (1978): 3-7.

9 Walter Henry, *Surgeon Henry's Trifles*, 231.

10 Elizabeth MacNab, *A Legal History of the Health Professions in Ontario* (Toronto: Queen's Printer 1970), 4-6.

11 Canniff, *The Medical Profession*, 61-62.

12 Murray L. Barr, *A Century of Medicine at Western* (London: University of Western Ontario 1977), 52-55.

13 John J. Haegerty, *Four Centuries of Medical History in Canada*, Vol. II (Toronto: Macmillan Co. Ltd. 1928), 76-84.

14 *Kingston Chronicle and Gazette*, 22 July 1834.

15 Angus, *Kingston General Hospital*, 190-192.

CHAPTER TWO

1 *Kingston Chronicle and Gazette*, 21 December 1839.

2 Ibid.

3 "Sir John A. Macdonald," *QCJ*, 15 January 1890. "I was struck dumb, my hair stood on end and my voice was caught in my throat," Virgil, *Aeneid* II, 774.

4 The Royal Charter establishing Queen's College in Kingston, paragraph 4, 16 October 1841.

5 Margaret Angus, *Kingston General Hospital: A Social and Institutional History* (Montreal: McGill-Queen's University Press 1973), 22.

6 "MBT, 2 July 1841," QUA. A fascinating biography of Dr William Dunlop may be found in Canniff, *The Medical Profession in Upper Canada* (Toronto: William Briggs 1894, reprinted Toronto: Clarke, Irwin for The Hannah Institute for the History of Medicine 1981), 352-361.

7 "MBT, 9 May 1842."

8 "MBT, 19 July 1853."

9 This kind of action inspired his reputation as a gentleman. See, William Osler, "The Master Word in Medicine," lecture given at Toronto University, 1903, in *Aequanimitas* (Philadelphia: P. Blakiston's Son & Co 1904), 369-371.

10 D.D. Calvin, *Queen's University at Kingston: The First Century of a Scottish Canadian Foundation 1841-1941* (Kingston: Trustees of Queen's University 1941), 190-191.

11 W. L. Herriman, "Medical Faculty Jubilee Celebrations 1903," *QMQ* new series (1903): 6.

12 Another name and chair, now illegible.

13 "Minutes of the original meeting held in John A. Macdonald's front parlour on the evening of 7 (not 3) February 1854," QUA.

14 Ibid.

15 Ibid.

16 "Report on the Founding of Queen's College Medical Department, 1 March 1862," QUA.

17 Ibid.

18 "MBT, 7 February 1854."

19 "Annual Report to the Colonial Committee of the Church of Scotland in Edinburgh from the Board of Trustees, Queen's College, 7 March 1854," QUA.

20. "MBT, 2 August 1854."

21 Professors Williamson, Smith and Mr. Drummond to all trustees, 26 August 1854, QUA.

22 "MBT, 2 August 1854."

23 Hilda Neatby, *Queen's University*, vol. 1, 1841-1917, ed. Frederick W. Gibson and Roger Graham (Montreal: McGill-Queen's University Press 1978), 104-105.

24 H. Munro Thomas, "The Makers of Queen's – Fife Fowler, M.A. F.R.C.S. (Edin.)," *Queen's Review* 3, no. 2 (1929): 39-41.

25 John Stewart, "The Penitentiary," editorial in *Argus*, 5 February 1862.

26 Munro, "Makers of Queen's" 40.

27 "MBT Executive Committee, 3 October 1854."

28 Letter written by W. J. Hamilton, 7 October 1854, QUA.

29 Michael Sullivan, *Retrospect of Fifty Years of the Medical School in Kingston* (1905), QUA.

30 Ibid., 5.
31 *Chronicle and News*, Friday, 10 November 1854. This article reported the opening ceremonies at Queen's College medical school.
32 Michael Sullivan, *Retrospect*, 5.
33 Canniff, *The Medical Profession*, 42; 226-227.
34 John Watson, "Reminiscences of Dr. John Stewart," *QR* 3 (1929): 151-153.
35 The killing by smothering of at least sixteen victims obviated the necessity for Burke and Hare to "resurrect" the bodies which they sold to Dr Knox. Hare turned "King's evidence," while Burke was hanged in Edinburgh, 28 January 1829. See Hugh Douglas, *Burke and Hare: The True Story* (London: Robert Hale 1973).
36 Years later, when his academic colleagues enumerated the causes that justified his dismissal from his university chair, they held that his preference for the plaid and bonnet over the two-tasselled cap and gown was proof of his unfitness for the groves of academe.
37 Watson, "Reminiscences of Dr John Stewart."
38 Thomas Gibson, "A Sketch of the Career of Doctor John Robinson Dickson," n.d., QUA.
39 Horatio Yates, "Trinidad de Cuba as a Climate for Invalids," *Canadian Medical Journal* 1 (1852): 198-200.
40 "MBT, 20 June 1855."
41 Thomas Gibson, "The Astonishing Career of John Palmer Litchfield, the First Professor of Forensic Medicine at Queen's University, Kingston," n.d., typewritten manuscript, QUA.
42 *Adelaide Register*, 25 May 1839.
43 John A. Macdonald to the provincial secretary, 27 February, 5 March, 6 June, and 21 July 1855 and 26 April, 5 September, 26 November, and 2 December 1856, PAC.
44 "MBT, 20 June 1855."
45 *Toronto Globe*, 22 August 1855.
46 Letter written by John Stewart, *Toronto Globe*, 24 August 1855.
47 *Globe*, 30 August 1855.
48 Ibid., 31 August 1855.
49 Ibid., 22 August 1855.

CHAPTER THREE

1 Fife Fowler, "materia medica account book," QUA. The apparent discrepancies between number of students and total fees arise from either an increase of fees (£2.10 to £3.00 in 1856) or some students holding perpetual tickets after paying the annual fee and voluntarily taking the course twice.
2 At that time, of course, most, if not all midwifery was carried out in

private homes. No one would have undergone the inconvenience and discomfort or risk the social stigma attached to going to hospital for the birth of a baby. Only unwed mothers – or worse – did that.

3 "Announcement of the Medical Faculty of Queen's College, Kingston, Canada for Session 1856/57," 8, QUA.

4 Michael Sullivan, *Retrospect of Fifty Years of the Medical School in Kingston* (1905), 4, QUA.

5 "The Late Doctor Stewart as Professor," *QCJ*, 23 February 1891.

6 John Watson, "Reminiscences of Dr. John Stewart," *QR* 3 (1929): 151-153.

7 "Announcement of the Faculty of Medicine, 1860/61," 5 QUA.

8 "Announcement of the Faculty of Medicine, 1856/57," 7-8.

9 Calendar, Queen's College, Faculty of Medicine, 1862/63, 42 QUA.

10 This is probably why John A. Macdonald called on Dr Dickson and not, as might be expected, on the Queen's professor of obstetrics to conduct the delivery of his son, Hugh.

11 J. P. Litchfield, "Memorandum to the Board of Trustees, 13 June 1857," QUA.

12 The introduction of the institutes of medicine coincided with the culmination of Dr Stewart's quarrels with his colleagues – and possibly with their recognition of his ineptness as a teacher of physiology.

13 "Announcement of Queen's College, Kingston, 1856/57," 9.

14 Calendar, Faculty of Medicine, 1862/63, 40-41.

15 "Secretary's Annual Report to the Board," QUA. The following is an example of the faculty secretary's annual report to the board:

> Number of Students 60
> Number over 16, all of them
> Number under none (of course)
> Increase 3 "Notwithstanding" (as I say in the petition) the pecuniary difficulties of the times, which have compelled many former students, and not a few others, to postpone their attendance to next session. You may state that we have *25* new students this year.
> The list of Professors you will see in the "Annual Announcement". You may state if you choose that Mr. Henry Wirtz, who was recommended by Professor Silleman lectured temporarily on Chemistry, but that chair will be filled next year by Dr. Lawson from Edinburgh.
> God Save the Queen!

16 John Stewart, "Financial Report by the Medical Faculty to the Board of Queen's College, 1856," Box 3, Folder 17, Medical Faculty Records, QUA.

17 "Minutes of the Board of the Executive Committee of the Board of Trustees," 2 January 1855, QUA.

18 John Paton to Rev. Dr Mathieson, 20 June 1857, Board of Trustees' Letter Book, 1855/58, 264-265, QUA.

19 H. Pearson Gundy, "Growing Pains: The Early History of Queen's Medical Faculty," *Historic Kingston* 10 (1974): 20.

20 John Paton to John Stewart, 5 May 1857, Board of Trustees' Letter Book, 1855/58, 257.

21 "MBT, 30 July 1858."

22 Hilda Neatby, *Queen's University*, vol. 1, 1841-1917, ed. Frederick W. Gibson and Roger Graham (Montreal: McGill-Queen's University Press 1978), 73; 312; notes 15 and 16.

23 Dickson to Hon. John Hamilton, Chairman, Trustees of Queen's College, 11 September 1857, QUA.

24 Sampson's resignation as president probably was due to the fact that he was simply worn out with his work as medical superintendent of the penitentiary; also the faculty squabbling was becoming a nuisance he could well do without at his age.

25 John Stewart, "Memorandum to the Trustees of Queen's College, September 1857," 9-10, QUA.

26 Ibid., 10.

27 "MBT, 8 December 1857."

28 Michael Sullivan, *Retrospect*, 8.

29 Neatby, *Queen's University*, 71.

30 Editorial, *Argus*, 5 November 1862.

31 Ibid., 26 November 1862.

32 George Lawson to John Paton, Esq., secretary to the board of trustees, 6 August 1860, with complete statement of purchase and sale of microscopes to students, QUA.

33 George Lawson to John Paton, 5 June 1861, QUA.

34 Jacques Rousseau and William G. Dore, "Dr. George Lawson 1827-1895 – A Forgotten Canadian Botanist," *Historic Kingston* 15 (January 1967): 19-23.

35 *Annals of the Botanical Society of Canada*, vol. 1, part 1, 7 December 1860-8 March 1861 (Kingston: James M. Creighton), 60.

36 *Argus*, 19 February 1862.

37 "MFM, 13 April 1861."

38 Rev. Professor Williamson's copy of a memorandum printed for private circulation and presented by a deputation of the medical faculty in the presence of Professor Lawson's class," 5 February 1862, QUA.

39 *Argus*, 5 November 1862.

CHAPTER FOUR

1 D.D. Calvin, *Queen's University at Kingston: The First Century of Scot-*

tish-Canadian Foundation, 1841-1941 (Kingston: Trustees of Queen's University 1941) 69.

2 Hilda Neatby, *Queen's University*, vol. 1, 1841-1917, ed. Frederick W. Gibson and Roger Graham (Montreal: McGill-Queen's University Press 1978), 85.

3 "MFM, 21 April 1862": "The Faculty agreed to recommend the substitution of the term 'Dean' for that of 'Vice President' of the Medical Faculty." This was read to and accepted by the board on 23 April 1862.

4 "The Medical Battle," *Argus*, 5 March 1862 and "Medical Department," *Argus*, 19 March 1862.

5 John Stewart, "Manuscript Memorandum Prepared for the Board to Ratify and Transmit to the Legislative Assembly," n.d., QUA.

6 *Argus*, 10 December 1862.

7 *Argus*, 19 March 1862.

8 Stewart to Principal Leitch, 6 April 1861, published in *Argus*, 5 March 1862.

9 Senate of Edinburgh University, "Minutes of the Senatus Academicus, 31 July 1860," QUA.

10 Belatedly justifying Dr Stewart, who three years earliers had almost brought the school to its knees on this very issue.

11 Personal communication to the author from Dr Ruth G. Hodgkinson, 20 January 1980.

12 Elizabeth MacNab, *A Legal History of the Health Professions in Ontario* (Toronto: The Queen's Printer 1970), 9-10.

13 "MFM, 17 December 1862 and 26 January 1863."

14 Neatby, 91.

15 "MFM, 7 February 1862."

16 Stewart to Principal Leitch, 7 March 1862, printed in *Argus*, 12 March 1862.

17 George Lawson, "Statement and Complaint," transmitted to the board of trustees on behalf of the Faculty of Medicine, 13 February 1862, QUA.

18 "MBT, 12 March 1862."

19 "MBT, 15 April 1862."

20 "Minutes of the Senate, 18 December 1862," Stewart to the Reverend Dr Williamson, 22 and 27 December 1862, and draft of Williamson's reply, 31 December 1862, QUA.

21 The Royal Charter establishing Queen's College in Kingston, 1841, QUA.

22 Statutes of Queen's University and College at Kingston, 1863. The following two general statutes give some indication of the changes that have occurred in university life over the last century:

37. Each professor in the exercise of discipline in his class, shall have the power to admonish and fine – the fine in any one case not to exceed one dollar. Fines may be inflicted for lateness, absence, attending without cap and gown and similar offences. . . . . 54. Every student at the time of his matriculation shall suscribe to the following declaration – I, ------, being now admitted a student of Queen's College, do hereby sincerely and solemnly declare and promise that at all times render due respect and obedience to the Principal, Professors, and other authorities of the University, and strictly observe the laws and statutes thereof.

23 "MFM, memorandum, dated September 1863," an extract from minutes of the medical faculty of 21 March 1863 and extract minutes of the proceedings of the senate, 3 September 1863.
24 "Minutes of the original meeting held in John A. Macdonald's front parlour on the evening of 7 February 1854," QUA.
25 "MFM, 27 and 28 October 1863."
26 "MFM, 21 January 1864."
27 Ibid.
28 Ibid.
29 Bell to the board of trustees, 9 February 1864, QUA.
30 Neatby, *Queen's University*, 135.
31 Bell to the board of trustees, 26 April 1866, QUA.
32 J. R. Dickson, Letter of resignation from the deanship of the Faculty of Medicine to the Board of Trustees, 15 February 1864, QUA.
33 "MFM, 25 February 1864."
34 "MFM, Letter of 10 March 1864."
35 "Queen's College," editorial, *Daily British American*, 31 March 1864.
36 Dr. Maclean to board of trustees, 14 April 1864, QUA.
37 "MBT, 31 May 1864."
38 Perhaps with reason – physicians have always been willing to risk being labelled as free thinkers if a scientific background can help their patients.
39 "MBT, 10 June 1865."
40 *The Oxford Dictionary of the Christian Church*, 2nd ed., s.v. "Westminster Confession." The dictionary describes the confession as "the definite statement of Presbyterian doctrine in the English-speaking world." It was proposed by the Westminster Assembly, ratified by the Edinburgh General Assembly on 27 August 1647, and approved by parliament on 20 June 1648.
41 "MFM, 19 April 1866."
42 Neatby, *Queen's University*, 128.
43 Calendar, Queen's College, Faculty of Medicine, 1862, 38.
44 K.D. Keele, "Clinical Medicine in the 1860s," in F.N.L. Poynter, *Medi-*

cine and Science in the 1860s (London: Wellcome Institute of Medicine 1968), 4-7.

45 F.F. Cartwright, "Antiseptic Surgery," in Ibid., 25-27.

46 MacNab, *A Legal History of the Health Professions*, 9ff.

47 Ibid., 10.

CHAPTER FIVE

1 "MFM, 19 April 1866," QUA.

2 Snodgrass, "Report to the Board of Trustees of Queen's College at Kingston on conference with Medical Faculty," read and adopted 27 April 1866, Queen's Letters 1865/66, QUA.

3 "MCRCPSK," undated first meeting, QUA.

4 The choice of "Royal" over "Queen's" appears to have been made by Macdonald.

5 The occasional references to "the charter" in connection with the Royal probably arise from Dr Michael Sullivan's loss of memory when recording his reminiscences in 1905. Dr Thomas Gibson, writing in 1935 to Professor Eldon Boyd, suggested that Dr Sullivan was the last to see the putative charter and may have torn it up in a fit of pique before his death so that it would not fall into the hands of his arch-enemy, Dean J.C. Connell.

6 Bill No. 214, "An Act to Incorporate the Royal College of Physicians and Surgeons of Kingston, 15 August 1866." (Ottawa: Queen's Printer), QUA.

7 Ibid.

8 Ibid.

9 This was perhaps another example of Macdonald keeping his fences in good repair.

10 Snodgrass, "Report to the Board of Trustees of Queen's College on the Affiliation of the College of Physicians and Surgeons, 24 July 1866," Queen's Letters 1865/66, QUA.

11. Ibid.

12 "Draft bylaws of the Senate with Reference to Graduation in Medicine, 29 August 1866, Queen's Letters 1865/66, QUA.

13 "MBT, 29 August 1866."

14 Surgeon 1st Class Mair (retd.) may have been named one of the original incorporators of the Royal because he was the favourite doctor of Isabella Macdonald, John A.'s first wife. He wrote widely on the biblical and medical evils of alcohol. His nephew, Charles Mair, the Confederation poet, was for a short time a medical student at Queen's.

15 "MCRCPSK, 21 August 1866."

16 Perhaps the controversial situation that had arisen from the appoint-

ment of Mr Bell to the Queen's medical faculty led to this restriction.

17 "Announcement of the Opening of the Royal College of Physicians and Surgeons, Kingston, Canada on Wednesday 3 October 1866," 2, QUA.

18 "MCRCPSK, 28 September 1882."

19 "MCRCPSK, 27 September 1889":

> Meeting of Corporation September 27, 1889 Dr. Sullivan's Office.
> Present: Drs. Fowler, Irwin, Saunders, Oliver and Sullivan acting as Secretary Dr. Fowler Pres in Chair.
>
> Dr. Fowler stated that he had received a letter from Toronto stating that the conduct of Dr. Dupuis a professor of the Royal College was on a recent occasion at Winnipeg, while attending a meeting of the Dominion Medical Association, of a most disgraceful character, which statement was corroborated from other sources. In view of this, and the continued violation of all the rules of decency by repeated acts of drunkenness and disorderly conduct, and whereas the Corporation has been repeatedly informed of the dangerous example and injurious consequences to the College of such conduct, and moreover as Dr. Dupuis while denying the alleged disgraceful conduct at Winnipeg, has admitted the charges of intoxication and the commission of other charges, it was therefore unanimously resolved that if Dr. Dupuis should again so far forget himself as to become intoxicated, he shall be de facto suspended and dismissed from the position which he now holds in the Corporation and Faculty of the Royal Coll. of Phys. and Surgeons of Kingston, and forfeit any claim to any right, privilege or emolument belonging to the said offices. Dr. Dupuis having been called in and the above statement read to him, agreed to the terms therein contained.

20 James Dunsmore, president of the Royal College of Surgeons, Edinburgh to John R. Dickson, Esq. M.D., F.R.C.P.S.(E.). Kingston, Canada West, 21 November 1866, QUA.

21 "MFRCPSK, 11 December 1866."

22 Snodgrass to Fowler, 29 January 1867, QUA.

23 Queen's Medical Faculty, II, "Minutes and Reports," 1854-1898, Folder No. 16, QUA.

24 Fife Fowler and James Neish to the trustees of Queen's University and College, Kingston, 20 December 1869, QUA.

25 Snodgrass to Fowler, 21 January 1870, QUA: "Queen's College is at present a beggar from door to door; asking favours not giving them is the rule of its existence."

26 "MCRCPSK, 26 September 1873 and 22 June 1874."

27 Excerpt from Grant's inaugural address as principal of Queen's College, *DBW*, 6 December 1877.

28 Ibid.

29 "MCRCPSK, 17 February 1881."

30 "MCRCPSK, 22 January 1885." As events proved, the Royal's and then

Queen's medical faculty and the neophyte school in London, Ontario were able to withstand Toronto's siren call.

31 "MBT, final reply of the board ordered to be sent to the minister of education, 28 April 1885."

32 "Minutes of the Corporation of Trinity College, 9 February 1885," Trinity Archives, Robarts' Library, University of Toronto.

33 In keeping with paragraph seven of its act of incorporation.

34 "Minutes of the Corporation of Trinity College," and "Report of its Executive Committee, 13 April 1887." Also, "MFRCPSK, 16 April 1887." A copy of a letter from Trinity offering affiliation signed by William Jones, M.A., Registrar.

35 "Minutes of the Corporation of Trinity College, 9 January 1889."

CHAPTER SIX

1 The Medical Council's matriculation examinations were held in Toronto and Kingston (for the convenience of the Royal's students) on the first Wednesday and Thursday of April and the last Wednesday and Thursday in September of every year. Every student had to pass these examinations satisfactorily, before graduating in medicine: English language (grammar and composition), arithmetic (vulgar and decimal fractions), algebra (including simple equations), geometry (first two books of Euclid), Latin translation and grammar; and in one of the following subjects freely chosen: Greek, French, German or natural philosophy (mechanics, hydrostatics and pneumatics). The Council appeared to frown on Greek and favour modern languages and natural philosophy. But if a student insisted on Greek, he was examined on the first chapter of St John's Gospel and the first book of Xenophon's *Anabasis*.

Professional Medical Council examinations, which effectively controlled the curriculum, were divided into two parts: "primary" and "final." The former consisted of examinations in descriptive anatomy, physiology, theoretical chemistry, toxicology, botany, *materia medica* and therapeutics. Therapeutics could be taken either as a "primary" or "final" examination along with medical diagnosis, pathology, surgical anatomy, practical chemistry, medical jurisprudence, sanitary science, operative midwifery, operative surgery and surgical anatomy, *materia medica* and therapeutics, midwifery other than operative, and theory and practice of medicine.

2 Editorial *QCJ*, 2 April 1881.

3 Elizabeth Smith, manuscript notebooks in physiology and *materia medica*, n.d., UWCS.

4 "Minutes of Cataraqui Medical Society, 4 March 1881," QUA.

5 Calendar, Women's Medical College, 1887/88, QUA.

6 Smith, physiology notebook.

7 See chapter seven for more details.

8 Smith, physiology notebook.

9 Calendar, Women's Medical College, 1887/88.

10 Ibid.

11 Ibid.

12 "MFRCPSK, 3 June 1881."

13 Extract from address at Jubilee Banquet, Tweed Park Pavilion, 9 June 1838, typescript.

14 Ibid.

15 *QCJ*, 22 November 1889.

16 "MFRCPSK, 17 November 1875," QUA.

17 "Minutes, Board of Medical Studies of Queen's University, 20 April 1891," QUA.

18 Ibid.

19 Ibid.

20 Ibid., 23 December 1891: "Dr. Fowler reported that the Medical Council of Ontario, at their last meeting, had adopted substantially the recommendations of this Board."

21 "The Medical School," *QCJ*, 25 October 1873.

22 "A Resurrection," *QCJ*, December 8 1883.

23 "Our University Court System," *QCJ*, 12 March 1914.

24 Queen's first faculty of law had closed some years earlier.

25 This was before the temperance movement had dried up the country and parched the Medical Building.

26 "Note on the *Concursus Iniquitatis*," *QCJ*, 22 November 1879.

27 "A Visit to the '*Concursus Iniquitatis*,'" *QCJ*, 8 February 1879.

28 "MFRCPSK, 15 January 1882."

29 "Medical Supper," *QCJ*, 3 November 1877.

30 "Principal Grant," *QCJ*, 22 November 1879.

31 "Principal Grant," *QCJ*, 18 December 1884.

32 "The Medical Conversazione," *QCJ*, 25 January 1887.

33 "Lectures," *QCJ*, 20 December 1879.

34 "Editorial," *QCJ*, 10 April 1880.

35 *QCJ* 5 (22 November 1879): 26.

36 "On the Old Ontario Strand," *QCJ*, 24 December 1886.

37 "Valedictories – Medicine," *QCJ*, midsummer 1884.

38 "Valedictory," *QCJ*, 1 June 1885.

39 Ibid.

40 "Valedictory," *QCJ*, 11 May 1887.

41 Ibid.

42 "The General Hospital," *QCJ*, 11 May 1887.

43 Ibid., "Letter to the chairman and governors of Kingston General Hospital, 30 April 1887," *QCJ*, 11 May 1887.

44 "Valedictory," *QCJ*, 9 May 1891.

45 "Death of Thomas Coffey," *QCJ*, 17 October 1904.

46 subject, cadaver

47 "Death of Thomas Coffey," *QCJ*, 17 October 1904.

CHAPTER SEVEN

1 MFRCPSK, 18 June 1877, QUA.

2 Carlotta Hacker, *The Indomitable Lady Doctors* (Toronto: Clarke Irwin & Co. Ltd. 1974), 17-37.

3 Ibid., 38-54.

4 Archibald MacMurchy to Miss Smith, 8 May and 8 June 1878, File no. 291 University of Waterloo Special Collections.

5 "MFRCPSK, 14 September 1879."

6 Mrs Adam Shortt, M.D., "The Women's Medical College," *QR* 3 (March 1929): 81.

7 Elizabeth Smith, *A Woman With a Purpose, The Diaries of Elizabeth Smith 1872-1894*, ed. Veronica Strong Boag (Toronto: University of Toronto Press 1980), 169.

8 According to Elizabeth's diary, Annie Dickson, the daughter of the Royal's president, was the fourth, but the university's student register shows that Annie first enrolled in the chemistry course of the arts faculty and only transferred into medicine in 1881.

9 Smith, *Diaries*, 169.

10 Shortt, "The Women's Medical College," 82.

11 Smith, *Diaries*, 172.

12 Shortt, "The Women's Medical College," 82.

13 Smith, *Diaries*, 180-181.

14 Editorial, *QCJ*, 9 December 1880.

15 Shortt, "The Women's Medical College," 83.

16 Smith, *Diaries*, 273-274.

17 Ibid., 275 and 277.

18 *DBW*, Friday, 8 December 1882.

19 Ibid.

20 Smith, *Diaries*, 277-278.

21 "College Troubles," *DBW*, Tuesday, 12 December 1882.

22 Smith, *Diaries*, 279-281, entry for Wednesday, 14 December (note error in date).

23 *DBW*, Friday, 15 December 1882.

24 "Fruitless Meetings, *DBW*, Thursday, 14 December 1882.

25 Ibid.

26 Ibid.
27 "Amicably Settled," *DBW*, Friday, 15 December 1882.
28 Ibid.
29 Editorial, *QCJ*, 21 December 1882.
30 *GRIP*, Saturday, 13 January 1883.
31 Smith, *Diaries*, 285.
32 Ibid.
33 Ibid., 288.
34 Dr Jenny K. Trout to Miss Smith, 12 May 1883, File no. 443 UWSC.
35 Hacker, *The Lady Doctors*, 17-37.
36 "Female College," *DBW*, 9 June 1883.
37 'Woman's Medical School," *Toronto Globe*, Wednesday, 13 June 1883.
38 *DBW*, 14 June 1883.
39 "MBT, WMC, 25 June 1883, QUA."
40 Ibid., 6 July 1883.
41 "Minute Book, City of Kingston Council Meeting, 8 p.m. 6 August 1883," p. 432, QUA:

A communication from Mr. A. P. Knight on behalf of the Committee of Citizens. In Re. establishment of a Medical College for women was read asking for the use of certain rooms in the City Buildings for the use of the said College. A communication from the Hon. Sir Richard J. Cartwright on the same subject was read.

Ald. McGuire moves seconded by Ald. Whiting that the prayer of the petition of Sir Richard J. Cartwright asking for a lease of Ontario Hall and a room above it for five years for the use of the Ladies Medical College be granted subject to the conditions in the recommendation annexed to the said petition.

In amendment:

Ald. McIntyre moves second by Ald. Downing that the communication of Mr. A. P. Knight be referred to the Committee on City property to report, which being put was lost.

Yeas Mayor Livingston, Aldm. Crothers, Downing, McIntyre, Quigley - 5.

Nays Aldm. Allen, John Carson, Creggan, Dunn, Gildersleeve, Irving, Law, McGuire, Redden, Whiting, J. Wilson - 11 and the original motion being put was *carried*. Yeas 11, Nays 5.

42 D.D. Calvin, *Queen's University at Kingston: The First Century of Scottish-Canadian Foundation, 1841-1941* (Kingston: Trustees of Queen's University 1941), 244.
43 "A Wail from the Lady Meds," *QCJ*, xvi, no. 7 (4 March 1889): 96.
44 Women's Medical College, Calendar 1883/84. This abstract is included in Shortt, "The Women's Medical College," part 3, *QR* 3 (1929): 153-154.

45 "MBT, WMC 26 February 1884."

46 "MBT, WMC, WMC meeting in editorial rooms of the *British Whig*, 5 October 1885."

47 "MBT, WMC, 11 April 1889."

48 Fielding H. Garrison, *History of Medicine* (Philadelphia: W. B. Saunders, 1929; 4th ed. 1960), 772-773.

49 Interestingly, Dr K.N. Fenwick, the archenemy of the women doctors, was the prime mover in the establishment of the Kingston General Hospital School of Nursing at about this time. See Margaret Angus, *Kingston General Hospital: A Social and Institutional History* (Montreal: McGill-Queen's University Press 1973), 60-63; also Katherine Connell Crothers, *With Tender Loving Care: A Short Story of the K.G.H. Nursing School*, (Kingston: Kingston General Hospital Nurses Alumnae 1973), 10. Fenwick seemed to think women were fit to be hand-maidens to the disciples of Aesculapius but not priestesses in his temples.

50 "MBT, WMC, 8 June 1889."

51 *QCJ*, 12 April 1890.

52 *QCJ*, 10 December 1890.

53 Ibid.

54 "MBT, WMC, special meeting, 31 March 1890."

55 "MBT, WMC, special meeting, 28 September 1893."

56 Hilda Neatby, *Queen's University*, vol. 1, 1841-1917, ed., Frederick W. Gibson and Roger Graham (Montreal: McGill-Queen's University Press 1978), 217.

57 "Women's Medical College of Kingston Register of Students, 1883-1894," QUA. This document records year by year the student enrolment, giving names, ages, religious affiliation, home town or village, and year of study.

58 Mrs Adam Shortt, "A Letter of Appreciation of Co-eds at Queen's, *QR* 13 (1939): 88.

CHAPTER EIGHT

1 Hilda Neatby, *Queen's University*, vol. 1, 1841-1917, ed., Frederick W. Gibson and Roger Graham (Montreal: McGill-Queen's University Press 1978), 124; 174. See also D.D. Calvin, *Queen's University at Kingston: The First Century of a Scottish-Canadian Foundation, 1841-1941* (Kingston: Trustees of Queen's University 1941), 78.

2 "MUC, 26 April 1892," QUA.

3 Ibid.

4 "MUC, 27 April 1892."

5 "MBT, 27 April 1892."

6 Ibid.

7 "MFM, 13 September 1892."

8 Principal Grant's address, "Opening of the Medical Faculty of the University," *QCJ*, 5 November 1892.

9 Principal Grant's address to a special meeting of the Aesculapian Society, "Medical Notes," *QCJ*, 10 December 1892.

10 "MFM, 5 May 1893."

11 "MBT, 26 April 1893."

12 Ibid.

13 Ibid.

14 Ibid.

15 "MBT, 27 April 1894."

16 G. M. Grant, "Open Fenwick Operating Amphitheatre," *QUJ*, 2 November 1895.

17 "MFM, 19 October 1896."

18 "MFM, 9 June 1902."

19 "MFM, 24 November 1894."

20 "MFM, 9 February 1895."

21 "MBT, 1 May 1895."

22 Announcement, *KMQ* 1 (1896): 84; often reprinted thereafter.

23 Neatby, *Queen's University*, 218; Calvin, *Queen's University at Kingston*, 111. The mining faction has managed to survive as the Faculty of Applied Science, but agriculture, as an academic discipline, had not much hope of lasting in eastern Ontario.

24 "Queen's School of Veterinary Science, 1895-1899," *QR*, 21 (1928): 256-258.

25 *QUJ*, 5 November 1895.

26 F.E. Gattinger, "Veterinary Instruction at Queen's and O.A.C.," *Canadian Veterinary Journal* 3 (1962): 174-182.

27 "MFM, 30 April 1897."

28 Ibid., 14 February 1901.

29 "MBT, 28 April 1901;" see also "MFM, 16 April 1901," and "Finance and Estate Committee Minutes, 27 April 1901," QUA.

30 "Queen's Medical College," *KMQ* 6 (1901): 29.

31 "Principal's Message to the Opening Convocation," *KMQ* 6 (1901): 30.

32 Ibid.

33 Ibid.

34 *QUJ*, 5 November 1892.

35 Ibid., 18 November 1893.

36 "MFM, 3 March 1894."

37 Ibid.

38 "MFM, Rules set out by Faculty Library Committee, 3 January 1896."

39 "Medical Dinner," *QUJ*, 17 November 1896.

40 "Medical Convocation Valedictory Address," *QUJ*, 13 April 1898.

41 "Minutes of the Kingston Medical and Surgical Society, 12 October 1896, QUA.

42 "MFM, 20 April 1908."

43 Kathryn Bindon, *Queen's Men, Canada's Men: The Military History of Queen's University* (Kingston: Kingston Trustees of Queen's University Contingent, Canadian Officers' Training Corps, 1978), p. 7.

44 General Sir Horace Smith-Dorrien said of the second regiment of the Canadian Mounted Rifles that "he would choose no other mounted troops in the world before them if he had his choice." George F. Stanley, *Canada's Soldiers*, 3rd ed. (Toronto: Macmillan of Canada 1974), 286.

45 *Gazette* (London), 29 March 1901; also quoted in Lt. Col. Rupert Stewart, M.V.D., *The Victoria Cross* (London: Hutchinson & Co., Ltd. 1928). A difference of opinion appears to have existed among the military establishment whether Lieutenant Douglas, acting professionally as a medical officer under fire, was eligible for the Victoria Cross. Eventually, on 8 March 1901, Commander-in-Chief Lord Roberts agreed that Douglas deserved it. Three weeks later, King Edward VII approved, and the award was reported as quoted in the London *Gazette*. See M. J. Crook, *The Evolution of the Victoria Cross* (Tunbridge Wells, Kent: Midas Books n.d.), 167–168.

46 "An unsigned article on Dr H. E. M. Douglas, including a copy of a letter to his parents dated Sunday 17 December 1899," *KMQ* 4 (1900): 140–145.

47 Bindon, *Queen's Men*, 7.

48 "No. 2 Field Hospital," *QUJ*, 9 November 1900.

CHAPTER NINE

1 *QMQ*, new series 1, 1 (1903): 2; "MFM, 4 August 1903."

2 *QMQ*, "College News," 37.

3 "MBT, annual general meeting," 29 April 1903."

4 "MBT, meeting 19 May 1903."

5 "MFM, 15 October 1903."

6 Ibid. The total time spent on Dr Connell's appointment appears to have been all of thirty minutes – a marked contrast to today's mandatory fifteen months, with advice sought *a mari usque ad mare*.

7 1 April 1912, 2 George V, C. 138, Section 19, An Act respecting Queen's College at Kingston, and to change its name to "Queen's University at Kingston."

8 Stuart E. Rosenberg, "The Queen's University Controversy," in *The Jewish Community in Canada A History*, vol. I (Toronto: McClelland and Stewart Ltd. 1970), 210.

9 "The Installation Address of Principal Gordon," *QUJ*, 6 November 1903.

10 "MFM, 26 February 1913."

11 "MFM, 17 April 1913."

12 The Constitution of the Medical Faculty as Amended, 1913, QUA.

13 "MFM, 17 April 1913."

14 "MFM, 28 January 1904."

15 "MFM, 13 December 1905."

16 *QMQ* III, no. 3, new series (April 1906):1.

17 "Minutes of the Finance and Estate Committee, 2 June 1906."

18 *DBW*, 14 January and 15 1908.

19 "MFM, 19 October 1895."

20 Personal communication to the author from Professor Stewart Fyfe. An entry in the faculty minutes for 7 April 193 is also of interest: "The question of the scandal in connection with the recent attempted grave robbery was discussed and the whole question of supply of anatomical material was referred to a committee consisting of Drs. Ryan and Mundell and the Demonstrators in Anatomy."

21 "MFM, 25 February 1904."

22 "MBT, 27 April 1904."

23 "MFM, 22 May 1905."

24 W. T. Connell, *A Laboratory Guide in Practical Bacteriology*, 3rd ed. (Kingston: R. Uglow & Co. 1913).

25 "MFM, 9 September 1904, 29 September 1904, 10 February 1905, and 15 November 1906."

26 R. W. Garrett, *Textbook of Medical and Surgical Gynaecology* (Kingston: R. Uglow & Co. 1897).

27 Michael Sullivan, *Retrospect of Fifty Years of the Medical School in Kingston* (1905), 25-27, QUA.

28 D. E. Mundell, *Anatomy Applied to Medicine and Surgery* (Kingston: D.E. Mundell at the Department of Agriculture, 1903).

29 "MFM, Report on Teaching in Medicine, 14 September 1905."

30 "MFM, 14 February 1906."

31 "MFM, 6 May 1903."

32 Abraham Flexner, *Medical Education in the United States and Canada* (New York: The Carnegie Foundation for the Advancement of Teaching 1910), viii.

33 "MFM, 11 December 1907."

34 "MFM, 11 December 1907."

35 Ibid.

36 "What Others Are Saying About Us," editorial, *QMQ*, v, no. 3 (April 1908): 98-100.

37 Flexner, *Medical Education*.

38 Ibid., viii.

39 Ibid., 56.

40 Ibid., 76.

41 Ibid., 150.
42 Ibid., 322.
43 Ibid., 325–326.
44 Ibid., 244.
45 Ibid.
46 J.C. Connell, "Dean's Report to the Board of Trustees, April 1910," QUA.
47 J.C. Connell, "Dean's Report to the Board of Trustees, April 1911," QUA.
48 "Report of the Aesculapian Society Lecture," *QUJ*, 24 November 1909.
49 "Dr. Eshoo," *QUJ*, 16 February 1904, 16 March 1904, and 4 May 1906.
50 "A few years hence or the facts of the final year," *QUJ*, 6 February 1903.
51 "Notes on Dean J.C. Connell's reply in *Journal of the American Medical Association*," *QUJ*, 1 March 1906.
52 "Hagen-Burger Degree Cancelled," *QMQ*, new series 4 (1906-1907): 221–224.
53 Dr Arthur E. Ross to Dr H. G. Kelly, April 1982.
54 "MFM, 14 September 1905."
55 *DBW*, 8 and 9 October 1909.

CHAPTER TEN

1 Dean W. L. Goodwin, special convocation address, 18 February 1915, "A Soldiers' Convocation," *QUJ*, 22 February 1915.
2 J. George Adami, *War Story of the Canadian Army Medical Corps*, vol. I (London: Colons Ltd. 1916), 47.
3 *QUJ*, 21 December 1914.
4 Adami, *War Story*, 42.
5 *QUJ*, 22 October 1914.
6 "Military Drill," *QUJ*, 29 October 1914.
7 "MFM, 5 March 1915."
8 *QUJ*, 5 November 1914.
9 "Dr. Kidd Addresses Medical Sophomores," *QUJ*, 19 November 1914.
10 "Faculty Notes," Aesculapian Society, 19 November 1914, QUA.
11 "MFM, 5 March 1915."
12 "MFM, 5 February 1915."
13 *QUJ*, 5 February 1915.
14 "Home from the Front," *QUJ*, 25 October 1915.
15 "MFM, 30 March 1915."
16 "MFM, 8 April 1915."
17 Colonel Etherington, *A History of No. 7 (Queen's) Canadian General Hospital, March 26, 1915-November 15, 1917* (London: C.W. Faulkner

& Co. Ltd. 1917), 4. It is probably fortunate for the outcome of the war that all the imperial recruiting officers did not require the same standards as Queen's No. 5 Stationary Hospital!

18 Ibid., 6.
19 J. C. Connell, "Faculty of Medicine Annual Report," April 1916, 3, QUA.
20 *QUJ*, 20 December 1915.
21 "No. 7 (Queen's) Canadian General Hospital," printed by C.W. Faulkner and Co. Ltd., 79 Golden Lane, E.C.1., 6.
22 *QUJ*, 18 October 1915.
23 Walter T. McCree, "News from Cairo," *QUJ*, 20 December 1915.
24 Ibid.
25 E. C. A. Crawford, "Letter from Cairo," *QUJ*, 22 October 1915.
26 "No. 7 (Queen's) Canadian General Hospital." This was probably written by Dean J. C. Connell or Dr A. R. B. Williamson, treasurer of the faculty, or both.
27 Etherington, *Canadian General Hospital*, 40.
28 Walter T. McCree, "News."
29 Etherington, *Canadian General Hospital*, 13.
30 Ibid., 15
31 Adami, *War Story*, 237-38.
32 Etherington, *Canadian General Hospital*, 22, 40.
33 J. C. Connell, "FMAR, April 1916," 3-4.
34 Kathryn M. Bindon, *Queen's Men, Canada's Men: The Military History of Queen's University* (Kingston Trustees of Queen's University Contingent, Canadian Officer's Training Corps 1978), 41.
35 "Queen's Ambulance Makes Appeal," *QUJ*, 9 February 1917.
36 J. C. Connell, "FMAR, April 1917," 5.
37 "Minutes of Finance and Estate Committee, 29 November 1916."
38 Ibid., 26 December 1916.
39 "Military Hospital," *QUJ*, 9 February 1917.
40 J. C. Connell, "FMAR, April 1919," 7.
41 "Vocational Building," *QUJ*, 19 October 1917.
42 J. C. Connell, "FMAR, April 1919," 7.

CHAPTER ELEVEN

1 "FMAR, April 1913," 3.
2 Ibid., 5.
3 "FMAR, April 1915," 32.
4 Ibid. 31. Dr James Douglas, a Presbyterian minister turned successful businessman endowed the lectureship in pharmacology. He served as chancellor of the university from 1915 to 1919 and gave an estimated $900,000 to his Alma Mater.

5 "FMAR, April 1916," 5.

6 Margaret Angus, *Kingston General Hospital: A Social and Institutional History* (Montreal: McGill-Queen's University Press 1973), 103.

7 "MFM, 11 December 1916."

8 "MFM, 5 October 1917."

9 "MBT, 20 October 1915."

10 "MFM, 29 October 1915."

11 "FMAR, April 1918," 4.

12 *DBW*, 5 October 1918.

13 Ibid., 17 October 1918.

14 *QUJ*, 18 October 1918.

15 *QUJ*, 8 November 1918.

16 "MFM, 4 January 1918."

17 "MFM, 1 February 1918."

18 "FMAR, April 1911."

19 "FMAR, April 1916."

20 "MFM, 7 April 1916."

21 "MFM, 20 April 1916."

22 "FMAR, April 1918."

23 Had this recommendation been pursued more vigorously, the pressure generated across the province by the drugless practitioners might have been relieved.

24 "MFM, 3 November 1916."

25 "FMAR, April 1917."

26 "FMAR, April 1919."

27 *QUJ*, 16 November 1899.

28 "FMAR, April 1917."

29 "MBT, 25 April 1917."

30 "FMAR, April 1919."

31 "MFM, 30 October 1918."

32 Etherington to Principal Taylor, 13 January 1919, QUA.

33 Taylor to Etherington, 6 February 1919, QUA.

34 Connell to Etherington, 17 March 1919, QUA.

35 Connell to Taylor, 14 September 1919, QUA.

36 "MFM, 26 September 1919."

37 D. M. Finnie, chairman of the Ottawa Civic Hospital board, to Principal Taylor with appended draft agreement between Ottawa Civic Hospital and Queens, 14 November 1919, QUA.

38 J.C. Connell to Board of Trustees of Queen's University, November 1919.

39 Kingston Board of Trade to Principal Taylor, 17 December 1919, QUA.

40 "MBT, 3 February 1920."

Index